C

5

*Jennifer Szumilas*
*104 MANASSAS CT.*
*Simpsonville, 29681*

*Solving Problems in Chemistry*

*7.00*

Robert C. Smoot
McDonogh School
McDonogh, Maryland

# MERRILL
## PUBLISHING COMPANY
A Bell & Howell Information Company
Columbus, Ohio
Toronto • London • Sydney

# A MERRILL SCIENCE PROGRAM

*Chemistry: A Modern Course*
*Chemistry: A Modern Course,* Teacher Annotated Edition
*Chemistry: A Modern Course,* Teacher Resource Book
*Chemistry: A Modern Course,* Spirit Duplicating Evaluation Program
*Chemistry: A Modern Course,* Reproducible Masters Evaluation Program
*Laboratory Chemistry*
*Laboratory Chemistry,* Teacher Annotated Edition
*Laboratory Chemistry,* Computer-Assisted Data-Checking Programs and
    Teacher Guide
*Solving Problems in Chemistry*

*Project Editor:* Mary E. Gallant; *Editor:* Teresa Anne McCowen;
*Project Artist and Designer:* Kip M. Frankenberry; *Artist:* Lucia Condo;
*Production Editor:* Joy E. Dickerson; *Cover Design:* Jim Shough

**ISBN 0-675-06412-0**

Published by

**MERRILL PUBLISHING COMPANY**
**A Bell & Howell Information Company**
Columbus, Ohio 43216
Toronto • London • Sydney

# PREFACE

*Solving Problems in Chemistry* helps to develop problem-solving skills essential to the study of chemistry, through the use of Example and practice problems. The chapters contain brief explanations of basic chemistry principles. A variety of Example problems are provided to illustrate these principles. The factor-label method of problem-solving is used as part of the step-by-step process in solving the Example problems. Answers to all practice problems are provided at the end of the book, enabling students to check their own progress.

The authors offer a wide range of expertise in the field of chemistry. The sixth edition of **Solving Problems in Chemistry** reflects a blend of their experiences in the high school and college classroom as well as in industry. Emphasis has been placed on practical applications. Environmental concerns, career information, and everyday uses of chemicals have been integrated into the problems where appropriate. In using this book, it is hoped that today's chemistry students will become familiar with ways in which the principles and concepts of chemistry affect their daily lives.

**Solving Problems in Chemistry** is designed for use with the text **Chemistry: A Modern Course.** This problems book can also be used as a supplement to standard first-year textbooks, as a guide to independent study, or as a reference in reviewing basic chemistry principles. Students will find **Solving Problems in Chemistry** a valuable aid in achieving a better understanding of chemistry. Teachers will find it a time-saving resource for planning an introductory chemistry course for today's students.

# CONTENTS

# CHEMISTRY SKILLS

# 1

The factual style of writing in science textbooks is different from the narrative style of most other books you read. Thus, reading science requires special skills. In order to be successful in chemistry, you must adjust to the amount of factual information presented. You must read critically and sense relationships among ideas, as well as build on previous knowledge. You must master a new, technical vocabulary. Skills are needed to use supplementary materials, like this problems book, to enhance understanding. You must learn to interpret information presented in tables, graphs, and diagrams. Laboratory experimentation also requires special skills to interpret and apply scientific knowledge. In this chapter you will learn some techniques that can help you master these skills.

## 1:1 READING SCIENTIFIC MATERIALS

Reading for meaning, or comprehension, is one of the most important skills to master. Once the foundation is laid for strong comprehension the other skill areas will be facilitated. For example, if you have a basic understanding of the concepts presented in a particular chapter, new vocabulary words will be grasped more quickly from context clues. Problems and laboratory activities will also gain perspective.

When previewing or reading you should identify the main ideas in the material. The **main idea** is the most important concept described in a passage. The main idea can be located at any point in a paragraph and may not be a single sentence. The main ideas in a sequence of paragraphs can serve as a summary of the material.

You should always try to understand what you read and avoid rote memorization. One way to broaden your understanding is to look for statements that support the main idea. Some of these statements may be real world examples of the main idea; others may be conclusive research data. Supporting statements often explain the "how" or "why" questions you may have about the main idea. You should associate these supporting statements with the main idea. These associations will help you increase your knowledge from factual repetition of main ideas to broader understanding of the concept described.

One additional type of statement you should look for as you read is linking sentences. Linking sentences provide perspective on the material. The linking sentences tie the main idea to previously learned material or to material to be presented later. Use linking sentences to determine where to store new information in your mind. As you add new information to various compartments of information your knowledge base will expand. You will also avoid trying to remember lots of unrelated concepts.

Let's practice some of these suggestions with a paragraph from your textbook.

> Carbon atoms may bond to each other by the overlap of an orbital of one carbon atom with an orbital of another carbon atom. *The carbon-carbon single bond is a sigma type bond.* Many carbon atoms may bond in this manner to form a chain or ring. Recall from Chapter 11 that carbon exhibits catenation. Plastics, synthetic fibers, and synthetic rubber all contain molecules with hundreds or thousands of carbon atoms joined in chains and rings.

The main idea is italicized. This information alone is not very helpful to our general understanding of carbon bonding. However, if you remember that carbon atoms may bond by orbital overlap and they bond in chains or rings, two "how" questions are answered. The fourth sentence serves as a link with previous information. The last sentence provides real world application of the main idea.

# 1:2   DRAWING CONCLUSIONS

You may be asked to draw conclusions concerning a passage you have read. The answer to the question may not be stated directly in the passage. However, by understanding the main idea and some supporting details you can make an educated guess. For example, you know that pressure is caused by the collisions of particles with the walls of their container. You also know that temperature increases the speed of particles. You conclude that pressure increases with an increase in temperature because the particles would have more collisions.

When you make conclusions you may use inductive reasoning. **Inductive reasoning** involves applying specific concepts to general situations to form a conclusion. For example, consider the following.

> Hans Geiger and Ernest Marsden subjected a very thin sheet of gold foil to a stream of subatomic particles. They found that most of the particles passed right through the sheet. From this observation Rutherford concluded that the atom is mostly empty space. They also found that a few particles (about 1 in 8000) bounced back in almost the opposite direction from which they started. Rutherford explained this observation as meaning that there was a very small "core" to the atom. The core contained all the positive charge and almost all the mass of the atom. This core is now called the nucleus.

Rutherford used inductive reasoning to develop this theory of atomic structure. He used specific data from the Geiger-Marsden experiment to develop a general description of atomic structure.

**Deductive reasoning** involves applying general concepts to answer specific problems. Following is an example of how deductive reasoning is used.

> Every system has some internal energy which is designated by U. The internal energy is a state function. Since we will be interested only in ΔU, changes in the internal energy of a system, we do not have to know absolute values of U for systems.

General information about the change in internal energy is used to find specific answers to the problems in Chapter 20.

## PROBLEMS

*Read the following paragraph and answer the questions that follow.*
The density of gases and vapors is most often expressed in grams per cubic decimeter. We express it in these units because the usual density units, $g/cm^3$, lead to very small numbers for gases. It is possible to calculate the density of a gas at any temperature and pressure from data collected at any other temperature and pressure. Assuming that the number of particles remains the same, a decrease in temperature would decrease the volume and increase the density. An increase of pressure would decrease the volume and increase the density. The following problem illustrates this calculation. (Remember 1000 $cm^3$ equals 1 $dm^3$.)

1. The purpose of this passage is to describe
   **a.** how many $cm^3$ are in 1 $dm^3$
   **b.** the units used for gas density
   **c.** typical density units
   **d.** the effects of temperature and pressure on gas density

2. In what units is gas density measured?
   **a.** $g/cm^3$      **c.** $g/dm^3$
   **b.** 1000 $cm^3$      **d.** 1 $dm^3$

3. What value must remain constant in order to determine gas density?
   **a.** number of particles      **c.** pressure
   **b.** temperature      **d.** volume

4. Which of the following is not mentioned in the paragraph?
   **a.** effects of temperature      **c.** usual density units
      decrease      **d.** gas density units
   **b.** effects of pressure decrease

5. What can you expect to learn in the text that would follow this paragraph?
   a. effects of temperature on volume
   b. effects of pressure on volume
   c. how to calculate gas density
   d. conversion units for density

6. Compare gas density units with usual density units. You would conclude that
   a. gases are less dense than other forms of matter
   b. gases are more dense than other forms of matter
   c. gases have the same density as other forms of matter

7. In order to answer question 6 you must use
   a. deductive reasoning          b. inductive reasoning

8. If the temperature of a sample of gas changed from 52°C to 23°C, the volume of the gas would
   a. increase          b. decrease          c. remain the same

9. In order to answer question 8 you must use
   a. deductive reasoning          b. inductive reasoning

## 1:3 GRAPHING

Throughout your study of chemistry you will be required to prepare graphs or interpret graphs of experimental data. Thus you should be familiar with the composition of a graph.

The data that you will be using involves two variables, dependent and independent. The quantity that is deliberately varied is the **independent variable.** The quantity that changes due to variation in the independent variable is the **dependent variable.** The independent variable is plotted on the horizontal axis. This axis is referred to as the **abscissa** or *x* axis. The dependent variable is plotted on the vertical axis. The vertical axis is referred to as the **ordinate** or *y* axis.

Graph titles should clearly state the purpose of the graph and include the dependent and independent variables. For example, Figure 1-1 is titled

**FIGURE 1-1.** The effect of temperature on the volume of a gas

volume vs. temperature of a gas. Each axis should be labeled with the appropriate variable and units of measurement. For Figure 1-1 the abscissa is labeled Temperature (K, C°), indicating that the scale is marked in both kelvins and Celsius degrees. The ordinate is labeled Volume (dm³), with the scale marked in cubic decimeters. Each axis has equal intervals. The intervals are 0.5 dm³ for the ordinate and 100°C or K for the abscissa.

## 1:4  INTERPRETING GRAPHS

Sometimes it is necessary to find a value for a variable at a point along the graph that is not one of the original data points. For example, on Figure 1-1 assume that we want to know the volume of a gas when the temperature is 75°C. The original data was not recorded at 75°C. In order to determine the volume of the gas at 75°C you must **interpolate,** or read from the graph between data points. By interpolating we can see that the volume of the gas is 2.3 dm³ at 75°C.

If a value is needed that is beyond the limits of the graph you must extrapolate. Reading a graph beyond the limits of the experimentally determined data points is **extrapolation.** To determine the theoretical volume of a gas at −273°C we must extrapolate to find the answer, 0 dm³. You should be cautious when extrapolating data. The relationship between the variables may not remain the same beyond the limits of your investigation.

## CHAPTER REVIEW PROBLEMS

*Read the following paragraph and answer the questions that follow.*

An immediate application of electrochemistry is its use in quantitative analysis. For example, suppose that it is necessary for you to determine the percentage of copper in a given water soluble copper compound. A sample of the compound of known mass could be dissolved in water and inert electrodes inserted. The mass of the cathode should be measured before the current is applied. As the current is passed through the cell, metallic copper plates onto the electrode of known mass. When the action is complete and current no longer flows, all the copper is plated. The mass of the electrode is again measured. The difference in mass (due to the copper) is compared to the mass of the sample to find the percentage of copper in the sample. Electroanalysis is a useful tool of the chemist.

1. The best title for this passage is
   a. Electroanalysis              c. Copper Analysis
   b. Electrochemistry             d. Chemistry Tools
2. All the copper has been plated when
   a. the copper compound dissolves in water
   b. the percentage of copper in the sample is determined
   c. current no longer flows
   d. the mass of the electrode is measured

3. Which of the following is not mentioned as a step in plating copper?
   a. a sample of copper compound is dissolved in water
   b. the electrodes are attached to a power source
   c. the mass of the cathode is measured
   d. electrodes are inserted into the copper solution

4. With what topic is this passage most closely associated?
   a. finding mass of substances    c. electrochemistry
   b. electricity                   d. chemistry of copper

5. Electroanalysis is
   a. an application of electrochemistry
   b. a useful tool of the chemist
   c. a form of quantitative analysis
   d. all of the above

6. You should conclude that the mass of the cathode
   a. increases with plating        c. remains the same with plating
   b. decreases with plating

7. In order to answer question 6 you must use
   a. deductive reasoning           b. inductive reasoning

**The effects of temperature and pressure on the percent yield of NH₃**

**FIGURE 1-2.**

8. What is the title of the graph?
9. What variable is plotted along the abscissa?
10. What variable is plotted along the ordinate?
11. In what units is pressure measured?
12. What is the interval for each block along the $y$ axis?
13. At 70 kPa and 600°C, what is the percent yield of $NH_3$?
14. Predict the percent yield of $NH_3$ at 120 kPa and 200°C.
15. Considering the usual range of industrial processes, what is the maximum yield that can be expected?
16. In order to obtain at least a 90% yield, in what temperature range would $NH_3$ be produced (pressure not to exceed 100 kPa)?

# MEASURING AND CALCULATING 2

Chemistry is a physical science based on measurements. A chemist uses these measurements to form conclusions about the behavior of matter. The units of the measurement designate the quantity being measured. If scientists are to understand one another, units that are familiar to all scientists must be used. Standard units have been adopted so that scientists everywhere can communicate their findings.

## 2:1 THE INTERNATIONAL SYSTEM (SI)

During the past two centuries, many versions of the metric system have been used. One system, called the **International System of Units (SI),** was established by international agreement. SI is used commonly by scientists in all countries. The most common SI units used in chemistry are listed in Table A-1 of the Appendix.

In the SI system there is one base unit for each category of measurement—mass, length, time, and so on. These base units are multiplied by factors of ten to form larger and smaller units. The factors are indicated by prefixes attached to the base units. Table A-2 of the Appendix lists the SI prefixes. A kilometer, for example, is 1000 meters; a microgram is one millionth of a gram; a nanomole is one billionth of a mole.

Two situations that often confuse students are the measurements for mass and weight and temperature and heat. Mass and weight are different quantities and are not interchangeable in usage. **Mass** is a measure of the quantity of matter in an object and is measured in grams. **Weight** is a measure of gravitational attraction on an object and is measured in Newtons. Only mass will be used in this book. **Temperature** is a measure of the kinetic energy of particles. While the standard unit of temperature is the kelvin (K), the size of the Celsius degree (C°) is equal to the kelvin.

$$°C = K + 273$$

**Heat** is a means of energy transfer and is measured in joules.

## 2:2 SIGNIFICANT DIGITS

The accuracy of the answer to a problem depends upon the accuracy of the numbers used to express each measurement. The **accuracy** of any measurement depends upon the instrument that is used and upon the observer. The digits in an answer that imply more accuracy than the measurements justify are not significant and should be dropped. The digits that remain truly indicate the accuracy of the original measurements. These remaining numerals are called significant digits. **Significant digits** consist of the definitely known digits plus one estimated digit.

Imagine that you have measured the length of a page in this book with a small ruler that is calibrated in tenths of a centimeter. You find that the edge of the page is between 22.6 and 22.7 cm. You estimate that the last digit is closer to 0.7. You record the measurement as 22.7 cm. You did not record the length as 22.6895 cm because you would be exceeding the accuracy of the ruler and your ability to estimate that number of decimal places. Since the last digit is estimated, it is said to be uncertain. Unless otherwise stated, the uncertainty in a measurement is assumed to be within ±1 in the last indicated digit. Therefore, the uncertainty of your measurement can be expressed as 22.7 ±0.1 cm. The last digit is uncertain but it is part of the measurement and is a significant digit. The significant digits of a measurement consist of all known digits plus one estimated digit.

If five people measured the same page in this book using the same ruler and recorded the length as 22.7 cm, we would say that the measurement is precise. Precision refers to the reproducibility of identical measurements of a quantity on the same instrument. The accuracy is determined by comparison of the measured value to an accepted or true value. The ruler, if poorly made, may give precise measurements that are not accurate. Measurements are written using the correct number of significant digits in order to indicate precision.

The following rules are used to determine the number of significant digits in a recorded measurement.

**1.** Digits other than zero are always significant.

    56.1                3 significant digits

**2.** Zeros between nonzero digits are always significant.

    3.108               4 significant digits

**3.** Any final zero used after a decimal point is significant.

    4.320               4 significant digits

**4.** Zeros used solely for spacing the decimal point (place holders) are not significant.

    400                 1 significant digit
    0.0026              2 significant digits

Not all numbers used in a calculation are measurements. Exact numbers, such as counted numbers or defined numbers, may be part of the calculation. How many students are present in your chemistry class? The answer is an exact number. It contains no uncertainty. Exact numbers are sometimes said to have an infinite number of significant digits. Definitions, such as 1 minute = 60 seconds, contain exact numbers and do not limit the number of significant digits used in a calculation.

## Example 1

Determine the number of significant digits and the uncertainty in the measurement 20.17 grams.

**Solving Process:**

Rules 1 and 2 indicate that there are 4 significant digits. The last digit is estimated and is uncertain. It occurs in the hundredth's place. The uncertainty is ±0.01 gram.

## PROBLEM

1. Determine the number of significant digits and the uncertainty in each of the following.

| | | |
|---|---|---|
| **a.** 6.751 g | **f.** 30.07 g | **k.** 54.52 cm$^3$ |
| **b.** 0.157 kg | **g.** 0.106 cm | **l.** 0.1209 m |
| **c.** 28.0 mL | **h.** 0.0067 g | **m.** 2.690 g |
| **d.** 2500 m | **i.** 0.0230 cm$^3$ | **n.** 43.07 cm |
| **e.** 0.070 g | **j.** 26.509 cm | **o.** 6 352 001 g |

# 2:3  HANDLING NUMBERS IN SCIENCE

The least accurate measurement determines the accuracy of an answer in an addition or subtraction problem. The answer must be rounded off to the highest decimal place containing uncertainty. Use the following guidelines when rounding measurements.

1. If the eliminated digit is less than 5, do not change the preceding digit.

| *Rounded to 3 digits* | *Rounded to 2 digits* |
|---|---|
| 2.473 becomes 2.47 | 3.64 becomes 3.6 |

2. If the eliminated digit is 5 or more, add 1 to the preceding digit.

| *Rounded to 3 digits* | *Rounded to 2 digits* |
|---|---|
| 8.276 becomes 8.28 | 0.478 becomes 0.48 |

In the addition and subtraction examples below the answers must be rounded to the tenth's place. In each case the least accurate measurement is expressed to tenths.

| **Add** | | **Subtract** |
|---|---|---|
| 50.23 g | | 28.75 cm |
| 23.7 g | | 17.5  cm |
| 14.678 g | | 11.25 cm |
| 88.608 g | | |
| 88.6 g | **Answer** | 11.3 cm |

In multiplication and division, the answer should have the same number of significant digits as the factor having the least number of significant digits (the least precise measurement) in the problem.

If you are using a calculator to obtain your numerical answer, you must be very careful to observe significant digits. The calculator may give you an answer of eight or more digits. All of these digits may not be justified by your data. For example, in the problem 4.8070/1.23 the number of significant digits is five and three, respectively. The calculator answer may appear as 3.908 130 081, but rounding the calculator answer to the smaller number of significant digits (three) gives a final answer of 3.91.

## PROBLEMS

*Express each answer in the correct significant digits.*

2. Add.
   a. 16.5 cm + 8 cm + 4.37 cm
   b. 13.25 g + 10.00 g + 9.6 g
   c. 2.36 m + 3.38 m + 0.355 m + 1.06 m
   d. 0.0853 g + 0.0547 g + 0.037 g + 0.00387 g

3. Subtract.
   a. 23.27 km − 12.058 km      c. 350.0 m − 200 m
   b. 13.57 g − 6.3 g            d. 27.68 cm − 14.369 cm

4. Multiply.
   a. 2.6 cm × 3.78 cm          d. 3.08 km × 5.2 km
   b. 6.54 m × 0.37 m           e. 3.15 dm × 2.5 dm × 4.00 dm
   c. 0.036 m × 0.02 m          f. 35.7 cm × 0.78 cm × 2.3 cm

5. Divide.
   a. 35 cm$^2$ ÷ 0.62 cm       d. 40.8 m$^2$ ÷ 5.050 m
   b. 39 g ÷ 24.2 g             e. 3.76 km ÷ 1.62 km
   c. 0.58 dm$^3$ ÷ 2.15 dm     f. 0.075 g ÷ 0.003 cm$^3$

## 2:4  DERIVED UNITS

By combining basic SI units, we obtain measurement units used to express other quantities. Distance divided by time equals speed, m/s. If we multiply length by length, we get area, cm$^2$. Length cubed equals volume, dm$^3$.

Other derived units are given special names. The force that will cause a 1.00-kg mass to accelerate at 1.00 m/s$^2$ is defined as one newton, N. One pascal, Pa, is a pressure of one newton per square meter, N/m$^2$. Gas pressure is measured in pascals. Derived units are also used as labels in the factor label method of problem solving, Section 2:6.

# 2:5  CONVERSION FACTORS

In Table A-2 the values of the SI prefixes are described. Using these definitions and SI base units we can form conversion ratios to convert a given unit to any other related unit.

**Example 2**

How many meters are in 175 cm?

**Solving Process:**

Table A-2 defines centi- as 1/100. Therefore there are 100 cm in 1 m. Since 100 cm = 1 m, two ratios equal to 1 are possible.

$$\frac{100 \text{ cm}}{1 \text{ m}} \quad \text{or} \quad \frac{1 \text{ m}}{100 \text{ cm}} = 1$$

Since we wish to convert cm to m, we use the second ratio.

$$\text{number of meters} = \frac{175 \text{ cm}}{} \left| \frac{1 \text{ m}}{100 \text{ cm}} \right. = 1.75 \text{ m}$$

The centimeters divide out and the answer is given in meters. Since the multiplying ratio equals one, the quantity has not changed, merely the units in which it is expressed.

**PROBLEM**

6. Convert.
   a. 0.75 kg to mg
   b. 1500 mm to km
   c. 1.00 day to seconds
   d. 0.52 kilometer to meters
   e. 65 grams to kilograms
   f. 750 micrograms to grams

# 2:6  PROBLEM SOLVING—FACTOR LABEL METHOD

The study of chemistry requires skill in handling units and solving problems. You can develop this skill in problem solving by practice. Essentially, successful problem solving requires that you look for a pattern.

Problems consist of three parts: a known beginning, a desired end, and a connecting path or conversion method. For any word problem, first select the information that is given or known. Then decide what information you must find. The connecting path comes from your general knowledge and the chemistry knowledge you acquire on a regular basis through study. This connecting path involves the use of conversion factors.

Consider the following problem. Ask yourself what is known, what is desired, and what is the connecting path.

## Example 3

An object is traveling at a speed of 7500 centimeters per second. Convert the value to kilometers per day.

**Solving Process:**

From the problem, the known value and the desired value can be written as ratios.

$$\frac{7500 \text{ centimeters}}{\text{second}} \quad \text{and} \quad \frac{? \text{ kilometers}}{\text{day}}$$

What relationships are known between centimeters and kilometers? Between second and day? Write them down.

$$100 \text{ cm} = 1 \text{ m} \quad 1000 \text{ m} = 1 \text{ km} \quad 60 \text{ s} = 1 \text{ min}$$
$$60 \text{ min} = 1 \text{ h} \qquad 24 \text{ h} = 1 \text{ day}$$

Use these relationships as ratios in such a way that seconds, minutes, hours, centimeters, and meters divide out. If the units don't divide out, your answer will have unusual units such as second squared.

$$\frac{\text{km}}{\text{day}} = \frac{7500 \text{ cm}}{s} \left| \frac{60 \text{ s}}{1 \text{ min}} \right| \frac{60 \text{ min}}{h} \left| \frac{24 \text{ h}}{\text{day}} \right| \frac{1 \text{ m}}{100 \text{ cm}}$$

$$\left| \frac{1 \text{ km}}{1000 \text{ m}} \right. = 6480 \frac{\text{km}}{\text{day}} = 6500 \frac{\text{km}}{\text{day}}$$

Note that this example is for one chain of operations. Lengthy operations that require the use of more than one line will use the above format.

## Example 4

One edge of a copper cube is carefully measured and found to be 2.162 cm. An atom of copper is 0.2560 nm in diameter. How many atoms of copper are contained in the cube?

**Solving Process:**

To develop your skill in solving problems, it is good practice to write down the given values, the desired quantity, and the relationships used to construct conversion factors.

*Given:* edge of cube = 2.162 centimeters (cm)
diameter of copper atom = 0.2560 nanometer (nm)

*Desired quantity:* number of copper atoms in cube

*Relationships:* $10^9$ nm = 1 m
$10^2$ cm = 1 m
Volume of cube = $edge^3$
Volume of atom = $\frac{4}{3}\pi r^3 = \frac{\pi d^3}{6}$

To relate the volume of a copper atom to the volume of the cube, length values must be in the same units.

$$\text{edge of cube} = \frac{2.162\ \cancel{cm}}{\phantom{x}}\ \left|\ \frac{1\ \cancel{m}}{1 \times 10^2\ \cancel{cm}}\ \right|\ \frac{1 \times 10^9\ nm}{1\ \cancel{m}}$$

$$= 2.162 \times 10^7\ nm$$

$$\text{volume of cube} = edge^3 = (2.162 \times 10^7\ nm)^3 = 1.011 \times 10^{22}\ nm^3$$

$$\text{volume of copper atom} = \frac{\pi\, d^3}{6}$$

$$= \frac{\pi\, (0.2560\ nm)^3}{6} = 8.785 \times 10^{-3}\ nm^3$$

$$\text{number of atoms in cube} = \frac{1.011 \times 10^{22}\ \cancel{nm^3}}{\text{cube}}\ \left|\ \frac{1\ \text{atom}}{8.785 \times 10^{-3}\ \cancel{nm^3}}\right.$$

$$= 1.151 \times 10^{24}\ atoms/cube$$

## PROBLEMS

7.  The following information is given in a science supply catalog:

    60 rubber stoppers = 500.0 grams = $4.89

    Each student in a class will need 4 stoppers. There are 24 students in the class. What mass of stoppers must be ordered and what will be the cost?

8.  The speed of a skyrocket is measured and found to be 145.3 m/s. What is the rocket's speed in km/h?

9.  The dimensions of an aquarium are found to be 76.7 cm, 114.5 cm, and 104.2 cm. What is its volume in $m^3$?

10. An aquarium filter will clean 275 $cm^3$ of water per minute. How long will it take to filter 125 $dm^3$ of dirty water?

11. A light-year is the distance light can travel in one year. If the sun is 150 000 000 kilometers away, how many light years is the sun from the earth? Assume that light travels at a speed of $3.00 \times 10^{10}$ cm/s.

## 2:7  SCIENTIFIC NOTATION

The average distance between the earth and the sun is 150 000 000 kilometers. This large number can be written as $1.5 \times 10^8$ kilometers. The diameter of atoms is about 0.000 000 02 centimeter. This small number can be written as $2 \times 10^{-8}$ centimeter.

Both large and small numbers can be manipulated with ease in multiplication and division problems by putting them in scientific notation. In **scientific notation** the number is expressed in the form $M \times 10^n$, where $1 \le M < 10$ and $n$ is an integer.

Numbers written as powers of 10 can be used to indicate the number of significant digits. The total number of digits in the first portion of a value (*M* above) in scientific notation indicates the number of significant digits.

| Number of Significant Digits Required in Answer | | Power of Ten |
|---|---|---|
| 2 | | $1.5 \times 10^5$ |
| 3 | (Answer) | $1.50 \times 10^5$ |
| 4 | 150 000 | $1.500 \times 10^5$ |
| 5 | | $1.5000 \times 10^5$ |

Let us review the addition, subtraction, multiplication, and division of values expressed in scientific notation.

To add or subtract numbers with exponents ($M \times 10^n$), all exponents must be the same.

## Example 5

Find the sum of $(6.5 \times 10^2 \text{ g}) + (2.0 \times 10^3 \text{ g}) + (30.0 \times 10^3 \text{ g})$.

**Solving Process:**

*Method 1:* Using longhand calculations

Change $6.5 \times 10^2$ to $M \times 10^3$

$$6.5 \times 10^2 = 0.65 \times 10^3$$
$$(0.65 \times 10^3) + (2.0 \times 10^3) + (30.0 \times 10^3) = (0.65 + 2.0 + 30.0) \times 10^3$$
$$= 32.7 \times 10^3$$
$$= 3.27 \times 10^4 \text{ g}$$

*Method 2:* Using a calculator

Enter the *M* part of the numer (6.5) into the calculator. Then instead of multiplying by $10^2$, press the $\boxed{\text{EE}}$ or $\boxed{\text{EXP}}$ key followed by the value of the exponent. If the exponent is negative, change its sign by using the $\boxed{+/-}$ key.

The key stroke sequence for the above problem is

6.5 $\boxed{\text{EE}}$ 2 + 2.0 $\boxed{\text{EE}}$ 3 + 30.0 $\boxed{\text{EE}}$ 3 = $3.27 \times 10^4$ g

For multiplication problems involving numbers with exponents ($M \times 10^n$), multiply the values of *M* and add the exponents. The exponents do not need to be alike as they do in addition and subtraction in order to do longhand calculations.

## Example 6

Find the product of $(4.0 \times 10^{-2} \text{ cm})(3.0 \times 10^{-4} \text{ cm})(2.0 \times 10^1 \text{ cm})$.

**Solving Process:**
Add the exponents: $-2 + (-4) + 1 = -5$
Multiply the values of $M$: $4.0 \times 3.0 \times 2.0 = 24$

$$(4.0 \times 10^{-2})(3.0 \times 10^{-4})(2.0 \times 10^{1}) = (4.0 \times 3.0 \times 2.0) \times 10^{-2-4+1}$$
$$= 24 \times 10^{-5} = 2.4 \times 10^{-4} \text{ cm}^3$$

Division is similar to multiplication except the exponents are subtracted instead of added. The exponents do not need to be the same. To divide exponential numbers ($M \times 10^n$), divide the values of $M$ and subtract the exponent of the denominator from the exponent of the numerator.

## Example 7

Divide $(12.73 \times 10^{-6} \text{ g})$ by $(4.6 \times 10^2 \text{ cm}^3)$
**Solving Process:**
Subtract the exponents: $-6 - (2) = -8$
Divide the values of $M$: $\dfrac{12.73}{4.6} = 2.8$

$$\frac{12.73 \times 10^{-6} \text{ g}}{4.6 \times 10^2 \text{ cm}^3} = \frac{12.73}{4.6} \times 10^{-6-2} = 2.8 \times 10^{-8} \text{ g/cm}^3$$

## Example 8

$$\frac{(8.0 \times 10^6 \text{ cm}^3)(4.0 \times 10^3 \text{ kPa})(3.0 \times 10^2 \text{ K})}{(3.0 \times 10^4 \text{ kPa})(2.0 \times 10^2 \text{ K})}$$

**Solving Process:**

$$= \frac{(8.0 \times 4.0 \times 3.0) \times 10^{6+3+2} \text{ cm}^3}{(3.0 \times 2.0) \times 10^{4+2}}$$

$$= \frac{96}{6.0} \times \frac{10^{11}}{10^6} = 16 \times 10^{11-6} \text{ cm}^3$$

$$= 16 \times 10^5 = 1.6 \times 10^6 \text{ cm}^3$$

## PROBLEMS

**12.** Express the following in scientific notation.
  **a.** 0.000 03 cm        **c.** 55 000 000 m        **e.** 0.000 007 m
  **b.** 8 000 000 g        **d.** 0.002 g        **f.** 65 000 km
**13.** Do the following calculations using scientific notation.
  **a.** $(5.1 \times 10^{-4} \text{ cm})(2.8 \times 10^{-3} \text{ cm})$
  **b.** $(6.5 \times 10^4 \text{ m})(3.27 \times 10^{-5} \text{ m})$

c. $(4.00 \times 10^2 \text{ g}) \div (2.000 \times 10^2 \text{ cm}^3)$

d. $\dfrac{(6.33 \times 10^{-7} \text{ km})(2.189 \times 10^{-3} \text{ km})}{(3.007 \times 10^{-8} \text{ km})}$

e. $(7.072 \times 10^5 \text{ cm})(5.77 \times 10^{-3} \text{ cm})(2.0 \times 10^2 \text{ cm})$

f. $(7.5 \times 10^5 \text{ g}) \div (2.5 \times 10^2 \text{ g})$

g. $(9.000\ 00 \times 10^7 \text{ m}) \div (3.0000 \times 10^3 \text{ s})$

h. $\dfrac{(4 \times 10^5 \text{ m}^3)(345 \text{ K})(2.008 \times 10^2 \text{ kPa})}{(273 \text{ K})(1.013\ 25 \times 10^2 \text{ kPa})}$

## 2:8  DENSITY

One quantity used to characterize substances is density. **Density*** is the mass of a substance that occupies a given volume. Though the SI standard unit of volume is the cubic meter ($\text{m}^3$), it is more practical to express the density of solids and liquids in $\text{g/cm}^3$. Gases are much less dense than solids or liquids. Their densities are usually given in $\text{g/dm}^3$. The densities of gases will be discussed in detail in Chapter 18.

**Table 2-1**

| Densities of Some Materials at 25°C (g/cm³) | | | |
|---|---|---|---|
| aluminum | 2.70 | mercury | 13.534 |
| carbon (diamond) | 3.614 | platinum | 21.410 |
| gold | 19.3 | potassium | 0.856 |
| iron | 7.874 | sodium | 0.968 |
| lead | 11.34 | water | 1.00 |
| magnesium | 1.738 | | |

### Example 9

What is the density of a hydrochloric acid solution that has a mass of 17.84 g and occupies 15.00 cm³?

**Solving Process:**

$$density = \frac{mass}{volume}$$
$$= \frac{17.84 \text{ g}}{15.00 \text{ cm}^3}$$
$$= 1.189 \text{ g/cm}^3$$

The equation for density may be solved for volume or mass as well.

*Density varies with temperature. For convenience, we will assume that the density of solids and liquids does not vary significantly.

## PROBLEMS

*Calculate the density of the following materials.*

**14.** 35.0 g of a substance that occupies 25.0 cm³

**15.** 2.75 kg of a substance that occupies 250 cm³

**16.** 2.80 g of a substance that occupies 2.00 dm³

**17.** Determine the volume that 35.2 g of carbon tetrachloride will occupy if it has a density of 1.60 g/cm³.

**18.** The density of ethanol is 0.789 g/cm³ at 20°C. What is the mass of 150 cm³ of this alcohol?

**19.** A block of lead measures 20.00 mm × 30.00 mm × 45.00 mm. Calculate the mass of this block, if the density of lead is 11.34 g/cm³.

## CHAPTER REVIEW PROBLEMS

**1.** A sign in a town gives the speed limit at 50 km/h. What is this speed in centimeters per second?

**2.** Convert.

    **a.** 3.50 m to cm           **c.** 0.52 km to mm

    **b.** 65 g to kg              **d.** 8.14 dm³ to cm³

**3.** Write the correct units to the answer for the following problem.

| lab | lump | bang | bam | bog² | mess |
|-----|------|------|-----|------|------|
|     | bog  | lump | bog | bang | bam  |

**4.** Determine the number of significant digits in each of the following.

    **a.** 35 g              **f.** 0.004 m³

    **b.** 3.57 m           **g.** 24.068 kPa

    **c.** 3.507 km        **h.** 268 K

    **d.** 0.035 kg        **i.** 20.040 80 g

    **e.** 0.246 cm       **j.** 730 000 kg

*Perform the following calculations and express your answer to the proper number of significant digits.*

**5.** (5.14 cm) (6.742 × 10² cm)

**6.** 2.8 × 10³ g ÷ 6.86 × 10² cm³

**7.** $\dfrac{(6.88 \times 10^2 \text{ m}^3)(2.14 \times 10^2 \text{ K})}{(3.8 \times 10^2 \text{ K})}$

**8.** (7.500 00 cm) (2.040 × 10³ cm) (3.0 × 10² cm)

**9.** 6.0 × 10⁻³ m ÷ 3 × 10⁻⁴ s

**10.** $\dfrac{(5 \times 10^3 \text{ cm}^3)(8 \times 10^2 \text{ kPa})}{(4.5 \times 10^2 \text{ kPa})}$

11. 30.0 g of each of the following acids are needed. What volume of each should be measured out?

| Acid | Density (g/cm³) |
|------|-----------------|
| a. hydrochloric acid, HCl | 1.1639 |
| b. sulfuric acid, $H_2SO_4$ | 1.834 |
| c. nitric acid, $HNO_3$ | 1.251 |

12. Use the densities given in Table 2-1 to determine which would be heavier—a ball of lead with a diameter of 2.00 cm or a cylinder of iron with a diameter of 3.00 cm and a height of 8.00 cm.

(Volume of a sphere $= \dfrac{1}{6} \pi d^3$. Volume of a cylinder $= \pi r^2 h$.)

# MATTER

3

Matter is anything that has the property of inertia. It can also be defined as anything that has mass and volume. Matter can be classified in a variety of ways. When matter is classified according to physical state, it can be solid, liquid, or gas. We may also classify matter according to composition as homogeneous or heterogeneous, substance or mixture, element or compound.

## 3:1 HETEROGENEOUS AND HOMOGENEOUS MATERIALS

Most of the things around us contain two or more different materials. Concrete, for example, contains sand, gravel, lime, and clay. Air is a mixture of oxygen, nitrogen, carbon dioxide, and other gases. If we look closely at a piece of concrete, we see it is not uniform throughout. Such nonuniform materials are called **heterogeneous mixtures.** The physically separate parts, such as sand, gravel, lime, and clay, are called phases. A **phase** is any region of a material with a uniform set of properties. The phase boundaries in heterogeneous materials are called **interfaces.**

Materials such as air, which consist of only one phase, are **homogeneous.** Within these materials there is a uniform distribution of particles. Homogeneous mixtures are called **solutions.** They contain a dissolved material called a **solute,** and a dissolving material called a **solvent.** As in all mixtures, the components of a solution may be present in varying amounts or concentrations.

## 3:2 ELEMENTS AND COMPOUNDS

Homogeneous materials that contain one kind of matter are called substances. A **substance** is a material with definite composition and properties. Substances composed of only one kind of atom are **elements.** Substances composed of atoms of two or more elements are **compounds.**

### PROBLEM

1. Indicate which of the following is an element, compound, heterogeneous mixture, or solution.

   **a.** ocean water     **e.** copper     **i.** aluminum foil
   **b.** calcium     **f.** grain alcohol     **j.** milk
   **c.** vitamin C     **g.** after-shave lotion     **k.** table salt
   **d.** dry ice (solid $CO_2$)     **h.** hamburger     **l.** iron nail

## 3:3   PHYSICAL PROPERTIES AND CHANGES

A **physical property** is a characteristic that can be specified without reference to another substance. Physical properties are divided into two types, extensive and intensive. **Extensive properties** depend upon the amount of matter present. Mass, length, and volume are examples. **Intensive properties** do not depend upon the amount, but upon the nature of the substance. Density, solubility, boiling point, and conductivity are examples.

When a material changes form, but not chemical composition, a **physical change** has occurred. Grinding into powder, melting, boiling, and dissolving are examples. Physical changes are often used to separate mixtures. Salt may be separated from a saltwater solution by boiling off the water. Distillation, fractional crystallization, filtration, and precipitation are laboratory techniques that are used to separate the components of mixtures.

## 3:4   CHEMICAL PROPERTIES AND CHANGES

A familiar chemical reaction is burning. The color, density, and other characteristics of the ashes are different from the material before it was burned. A **chemical change** occurs when a substance burns because new substances with different properties are formed. **Chemical properties** relate to the ability of a substance to change to a different substance. For example, does it burn? Does it react with acids? Such questions help to determine the chemical properties of a substance.

### PROBLEMS

2. Classify each of the following as a chemical or physical property.

   a. reacts with $H_2O$
   b. is red
   c. conducts electricity
   d. resists corrosion
   e. boils at 88°C
   f. dissolves in gasoline
   g. is ductile
   h. is flammable
   i. is 1.5 m long
   j. is malleable
   k. is corrosive
   l. freezes at $-17°C$

3. Classify each of the following as a chemical or physical change.

   a. alcohol evaporating
   b. a firefly lighting up
   c. a battery charging
   d. ice melting
   e. an explosion
   f. salt dissolving in $H_2O$
   g. digesting food
   h. hammering hot iron into a sheet

## 3:5   MEASURING ENERGY CHANGES

The heat required to change the temperature of a substance depends upon the amount and nature of the substance as well as the extent of the temperature change. For example, one gram of water requires 4.18 joules of energy to cause a temperature change of one Celsius degree. It takes only 0.987 J to raise the temperature of 1 g of $AlF_3$ one Celsius degree.

Energy can be transferred between a system and its surroundings. The amount of energy transferred can be calculated from the relationship

$$\begin{pmatrix} heat\ gained \\ or\ lost \end{pmatrix} = \begin{pmatrix} mass \\ in\ grams \end{pmatrix} \begin{pmatrix} change\ in \\ temperature \end{pmatrix} \begin{pmatrix} specific \\ heat \end{pmatrix}$$

$$q = (m)(\Delta T)(C_p)$$

where $q$ is the heat added (or removed), $m$ is the mass of the substance, $T$ is the change in temperature, and $C_p$ is a property of the substance called its **specific heat.** The specific heat of a substance varies with the temperature. Specific heat values are given in Table A-8.

## Example 1

How much heat is required to raise the temperature of 68.0 g of $AlF_3$ from 25.0°C to 80.0°C?

**Solving Process:**

In addition to the temperature change and mass given in the statement of the problem we must consult Table A-8 in the Appendix to obtain the specific heat of $AlF_3$, 0.987 J/g·C°.

$$q = m(\Delta T)C_p$$

$$= \frac{68.0\ g}{} \left| \frac{(80.0 - 25.0)\ °C}{} \right| \frac{0.987\ J}{g \cdot C°} = 3690\ J$$

A calorimeter containing water is often used to measure the heat absorbed or released in a chemical reaction. The temperature change of the water is used to measure the amount of heat absorbed or released by the reaction. According to the law of conservation of energy, in an insulated system, any heat lost by one quantity of matter must be gained by another. Energy flows from the warmer material to the cooler material until the two reach the same temperature.

$$heat\ lost = heat\ gained$$
$$m(\Delta T)C_p = m(\Delta T)C_p$$

## Example 2

Suppose a piece of lead with a mass of 14.9 g at a temperature of 92.5°C is dropped into an insulated container of water. The mass of water is 165 g and its temperature before adding the lead is 20.0°C. What is the final temperature of the system? $C_p$ lead = 0.138 J/g·C°

**Solving Process:**

We know the heat lost equals the heat gained. Since the lead is at a higher temperature than the water, the lead will lose energy. The water will gain an equivalent amount of energy.

**(a)** The heat lost by the lead is

$$q = (m)(\Delta T)(C_p) = \frac{14.9\,\cancel{g} \mid (92.5\,\cancel{°C} - T_f) \mid 0.138\,J}{\cancel{g}\cdot\cancel{C°}}$$

**(b)** The heat gained by the water is

$$q = (m)(\Delta T)(C_p) = \frac{165\,\cancel{g} \mid (T_f - 20.0\,\cancel{°C}) \mid 4.18\,J}{\cancel{g}\cdot\cancel{C°}}$$

**(c)** The heat gained must equal the heat lost

$$\frac{165\,\cancel{g} \mid (T_f - 20.0°C) \mid 4.18\,\cancel{J}}{\cancel{g}\cdot\cancel{C°}} = \frac{14.9\,\cancel{g} \mid (92.5°C - T_f) \mid 0.138\,\cancel{J}}{\cancel{g}\cdot\cancel{C°}}$$

$$T_f = 20.2°C$$

## PROBLEMS

4. How much heat is required to raise the temperature of 789 g of acetic acid, $CH_3COOH$, from 25.0°C to 82.7°C?

5. How much heat is released when 432 g of water cools from 71.0°C to 18.0°C?

6. Compute the heat released when 42.8 g of calcium carbide, $CaC_2$, cools from 74.2°C to 11.5°C.

7. If a piece of gold ($C_p = 0.128\ J/g\cdot C°$) with mass 45.5 g and a temperature of 80.5°C is dropped into 192 g of water at 15.0°C, what is the final temperature of the system?

8. A piece of unknown metal with mass 14.9 is heated to 100.0°C and dropped into 75.0 g of water at 20.0°C. The final temperature of the system is 28.5°C. What is the specific heat of the metal?

## CHAPTER REVIEW PROBLEMS

*Compute the energy changes associated with the following transitions using Table A-8.*

1. 49.2 g acetic acid, $CH_3COOH$, is heated from 24.1°C to 67.3°C

2. 9.61 g ethanol, $CH_3CH_2OH$, is heated from 19.6°C to 75.0°C

3. 2.47 g sand, $SiO_2$, is heated from 17.1°C to 46.7°C

4. 31.9 g calcium sulfate, $CaSO_4$, is cooled from 83.2°C to 55.5°C

5. 63.6 g zinc sulfide, $ZnS$, is cooled from 95.5°C to 42.3°C

6. If a piece of silver ($C_p = 0.2360\ J/g \cdot C°$) with mass 14.16 g and a temperature of 133.5°C is dropped into 250.0 g of water at 17.20°C, what will be the final temperature of the system?

7. A piece of unknown metal with mass 17.19 g is heated to 100.00°C and dropped into 25.00 g of water at 24.50°C. The final temperature of the system is 30.05°C. What is the specific heat of the metal?

8. In order to make 4 cups of tea, 1.00 kg of water is heated from 22.0°C to 99.0°C. How much energy is required?

# CHEMICAL FORMULAS

# 4

## 4:1 SYMBOLS

The chemical name for an element can be abbreviated to form a **chemical symbol.** Usually the chemical symbol contains the first letter of the element's name. If the names of two elements begin with the same letter, another letter from one name is added. For instance, B is boron, Br is bromine. The first letter is always uppercase, the second letter is always lowercase: Na is sodium, O is oxygen, and He is helium.

The use of upper and lowercase letters is important. For instance, the following elements and compounds are represented by the same letters.

| Elements | Compounds |
|---|---|
| Co, cobalt | CO, carbon monoxide |
| No, nobelium | NO, nitrogen(II) oxide |

For elements with atomic numbers greater than 103, the chemical symbols contain three letters. This system of naming will not be discussed here. See the Table of International Atomic Masses and the Periodic Table on the inside back cover of this book for names and symbols for these elements.

## 4:2 CHEMICAL FORMULAS

A **chemical formula** provides the clearest and simplest method of designating compounds. The chemical formula for a compound indicates the number and kind of elements in a compound. The chemical formula for vitamin A is $C_{20}H_{30}O$. Thus, in one molecule of vitamin A there are twenty carbon atoms, thirty hydrogen atoms, and one oxygen atom.

Compounds that consist of two elements are called binary compounds ($HCl$, $H_2O$, $C_2H_6$). The formula of a compound composed of a metal and a nonmetal is written with the symbol of the metal first, as in $NaCl$ and $Al_2S_3$. Generally, you can determine whether an element is a metal or a nonmetal by its position in the periodic table. Metals are listed at the left and center in the standard periodic table. Nonmetals are listed at the extreme right. Notice the diagonal line that divides the table into metallic and nonmetallic elements.

## PROBLEMS

1. Which symbol would be written first in the formula for the compound formed from each of the following pairs of elements? Use the periodic table.

   **a.** S and Cu
   **b.** Bi and S
   **c.** N and Nb

   **d.** C and Mg
   **e.** Ta and Cl
   **f.** Al and As

2. Which element would be placed first in the formula for the compound formed from each of the following pairs of elements?

   **a.** oxygen, copper
   **b.** sulfur, potassium
   **c.** lithium, fluorine

   **d.** calcium, nitrogen
   **e.** sodium, chlorine
   **f.** magnesium, bromine

## 4:3   OXIDATION NUMBER

An atom or group of atoms that is positively or negatively charged is known as an **ion.** The charge that the atom or group of atoms has is called its **oxidation number.** For example, Mg represents the metallic element magnesium, while $Mg^{2+}$ represents the magnesium ion. The oxidation number of the magnesium ion is $2+$. The nonmetallic element fluorine is represented by the symbol F, while $F^-$ represents the fluoride ion. The oxidation number of the fluoride is $1-$.

Some metals have the same positive charge in all compounds. The elements in Group IA (1), such as lithium, sodium, and potassium, always have an oxidation number of $1+$. Group IIA (2) metals, such as magnesium, calcium, strontium, and barium, always have an oxidation number of $2+$. Aluminum always has a charge of $3+$.

In ionic compounds, the total positive charge is equal to the total negative charge. One $Mg^{2+}$ ion with a charge of $2+$ will combine with two $Cl^-$ ions to form $MgCl_2$. For $MgCl_2$ the total positive charge is $2+$ and the total negative charge is $2(1-)$ or $2-$. In a correctly written formula, the sum of the total positive charge and total negative charge is zero.

## 4:4   POLYATOMIC IONS

The term **polyatomic ion** is used to designate a group of atoms that act as a unit in a wide variety of chemical reactions. A common positive polyatomic ion is $NH_4^+$, the ammonium ion. A common negative polyatomic ion is hydroxide, $OH^-$.

Two common negative polyatomic ions are $SO_4^{2-}$ and $SO_3^{2-}$. Prefixes and suffixes are used in the names of these ions to indicate the oxygen content of the polyatomic ion in relation to other ions in a series of similar ions.

| | Prefix | Suffix | Example |
|---|---|---|---|
| | per | -ate | $ClO_4^-$ perchlorate |
| *Increasing* | | -ate | $ClO_3^-$ chlorate |
| *oxygen content* | | -ite | $ClO_2^-$ chlorite |
| | hypo | -ite | $ClO^-$ hypochlorite |

**Table 4-1**

| Some Common Oxyanions | | | |
|---|---|---|---|
| | $IO_6^{5-}$ periodate | | |
| $BrO_3^-$ bromate | $IO_3^-$ iodate | $SO_4^{2-}$ sulfate | $NO_3^-$ nitrate |
| | | $SO_3^{2-}$ sulfite | $NO_2^-$ nitrite |
| $BrO^-$ hypobromite | $IO^-$ hypoiodite | | |

When more than one polyatomic ion is included in a chemical formula, the ion must be enclosed in parentheses to avoid confusion. For example, $Ca(OH)_2$ is not the same thing as $CaOH_2$. The subscript located to the right of the parenthesis indicates the number of polyatomic ions present. The formula for magnesium hydroxide, $Mg(OH)_2$, contains two hydroxide ions. There are three ammonium ions in $(NH_4)_3N$.

In more complex compounds the metallic ions are still written first. Hydrogen is indicated by adding the word "hydrogen" immediately in front of the name of the negative ion. For example, $NaHCO_3$ is sodium hydrogen carbonate. (Table A-7 lists additional polyatomic ions.)

## Example 1

Write the formula for the compound made from calcium and the phosphate ion.

**Solving Process:**

Using Tables A-6 and A-7, we see the oxidation states of calcium and the phosphate ion are as follows

$$Ca^{2+} \qquad PO_4^{3-}$$

It is necessary to have three $Ca^{2+}$ and two $PO_4^{3-}$ in the compound to maintain neutrality. Writing calcium ions in the formula is simple, $Ca_3$. For the phosphate ion, the entire polyatomic ion must be placed in parentheses to indicate that two phosphate ions are required.

$$Ca_3(PO_4)_2$$

## PROBLEMS

**3.** Write formulas for the following compounds.

| | |
|---|---|
| **a.** lithium fluoride | **g.** calcium fluoride |
| **b.** lithium chloride | **h.** calcium chloride |
| **c.** lithium bromide | **i.** calcium bromide |
| **d.** lithium iodide | **j.** calcium hydroxide |
| **e.** lithium oxide | **k.** calcium oxide |
| **f.** lithium sulfide | **l.** calcium sulfide |

**4.** Write formulas for the following compounds.

| | |
|---|---|
| **a.** sodium cyanide | **e.** barium cyanide |
| **b.** sodium hydroxide | **f.** barium hydroxide |
| **c.** sodium bromate | **g.** barium oxide |
| **d.** sodium acetate | **h.** barium sulfate |

**5.** Write formulas for the following compounds.

| | |
|---|---|
| **a.** barium azide | **f.** silver nitride |
| **b.** zinc molybdate | **g.** cadmium oxalate |
| **c.** cesium perchlorate | **h.** potassium thiocyanate |
| **d.** aluminum silicate | **i.** calcium hypophosphite |
| **e.** boron phosphide | **j.** aluminum hexafluorosilicate |

**6.** Write formulas for the following compounds.

| | |
|---|---|
| **a.** calcium sulfate | **f.** magnesium sulfite |
| **b.** sodium nitrate | **g.** lithium nitrite |
| **c.** potassium perchlorate | **h.** sodium chlorite |
| **d.** aluminum sulfate | **i.** ammonium dichromate |
| **e.** potassium chlorate | **j.** sodium nitrite |

## 4:5 NAMING COMPOUNDS

There is a systematic method of naming practically all compounds. The names of only a few compounds, particularly acids, will not be included in our discussion of this system.

Compounds containing only two elements are called binary compounds. To name a binary compound, first write the name of the element having a positive charge. Then add the name of the negative element. The name of the negative element must be modified to end in -ide.

### Example 2

Name the compound with the formula ZnO.

**Solving Process:**

The compound is formed by $Zn^{2+}$ (zinc) and $O^{2-}$ (oxide). It is named zinc oxide.

The binary compounds containing hydrogen and a nonmetal, called hydrides, often have common names, such as ammonia, $NH_3$; methane, $CH_4$; and water. These compounds will be discussed later.

**Table 4-2**

| Names for Nonmetals in Binary Compounds | | | | |
|---|---|---|---|---|
| $B^{5-}$ | $C^{4-}$ | $N^{3-}$ | $O^{2-}$ | $F^-$ |
| boride | carbide | nitride | oxide | fluoride |
| | $Si^{4-}$ | $P^{3-}$ | $S^{2-}$ | $Cl^-$ |
| | silicide | phosphide | sulfide | chloride |
| | | $As^{3-}$ | $Se^{2-}$ | $Br^-$ |
| | | arsenide | selenide | bromide |
| | | $Sb^{3-}$ | $Te^{2-}$ | $I^-$ |
| | | antimonide | telluride | iodide |
| | | | | $At^-$ |
| | | | | astatide |

Compounds containing the ammonium ion are named by using the name "ammonium" followed by the appropriate name for the negative ion.

| ammonium bromide | ammonium sulfide | ammonium nitride |
|---|---|---|
| $NH_4Br$ | $(NH_4)_2S$ | $(NH_4)_3N$ |

To name a compound containing a negative polyatomic ion, the appropriate positive ion name is followed by the name of the polyatomic ion.

| sodium sulfate | magnesium carbonate | aluminum nitrate |
|---|---|---|
| $Na_2SO_4$ | $MgCO_3$ | $Al(NO_3)_3$ |

A number of metallic elements can form compounds in which the metal ions have different charges. For example, iron forms one series of compounds in which the iron is $Fe^{2+}$, and another series in which iron is $Fe^{3+}$. In naming these compounds, the charge (or oxidation number) of the metal is written in Roman numerals enclosed in parentheses following the metal. The Roman numeral system is thus used to differentiate between ions that have two or more possible charges. For example, $FeBr_2$ is iron(II) bromide, and $FeBr_3$ is iron(III) bromide. To name these compounds we must know the oxidation number of iron.

The following rules will enable you to determine the oxidation numbers of metal ions from the formulas of their compounds.

1. *In metallic halides and other binary metallic compounds, the halogen (F, Cl, Br, and I) always has an oxidation number of 1−.* $AuCl_3$ is gold(III) chloride (read as "gold three chloride"). The three Cl atoms have a combined oxidation number of 3−. Since the compound has no charge, the oxidation number of the gold atom must be 3+.

2. *In binary compounds that contain oxygen combined with a metal, the oxygen can usually be assumed to have an oxidation number of 2−.* $FeO$ is iron(II) oxide.

3. *The sum of the charges of the atoms composing a polyatomic ion is the charge on the ion.* This charge is indicated as a superscript. The perchlorate ion, $ClO_4^-$, has a charge of $1-$ (the sum of the charges of one Cl atom and four O atoms). Since the sum of all the oxidation numbers in a compound is zero, in $Fe(ClO_4)_2$ the Fe must have an oxidation number of $2+$. This compound is named iron(II) perchlorate.

## Example 3

Write the names of the compounds $Cu_2O$ and $CuO$.
**Solving Process:**
From Rule 2 we know that O in these compounds has a $2-$ charge. Since the sum of all the oxidation numbers in a compound is zero, in $Cu_2O$ the Cu must have a charge of $1+$. In CuO, the charge on Cu must be $2+$. The compounds are named

| $Cu_2O$ | $CuO$ |
|---------|-------|
| copper(I) oxide | Copper(II) oxide |

Some binary compounds composed of nonmetals form a series of two or more compounds such as CO and $CO_2$. The number of atoms of a given kind is indicated by the use of a Greek prefix preceding the name of the element to which it refers. The prefixes are *mono*-(1), *di*-(2), *tri*-(3), *tetra*-(4), *penta*-(5), *hexa*-(6), *hepta*-(7), and *octa*-(8). The prefix mono- is usually omitted except when it is used for emphasis, as in carbon monoxide. Common usage omits the double vowel. That is, CO is named carbon monoxide, not mono-oxide. $CO_2$ is carbon dioxide.

The names of the common acids do not follow the rules for naming other compounds. The rules for naming acids will be presented in Chapter 24. Table 4-3 lists names and formulas of acids commonly used in the laboratory. They should be memorized.

**Table 4-3**

| Common Acids | | | |
|---|---|---|---|
| **Formula** | **Name** | **Formula** | **Name** |
| $CH_3COOH$ | acetic | $HNO_3$ | nitric |
| $H_2CO_3$ | carbonic | $H_3PO_4$ | phosphoric |
| HCl | hydrochloric | $H_2SO_4$ | sulfuric |

## PROBLEMS

7. Name the following compounds.
   a. $Na_2S$
   b. $Li_2O$
   c. $MgBr_2$
   d. AlN
   e. $CaF_2$
   f. KI
   g. $MgSO_4$
   h. $Ca(ClO)_2$
   i. $Ba(NO_2)_2$

8. Name the following compounds.
   - **a.** $Mg(OH)_2$
   - **b.** $CaO$
   - **c.** $LiCH_3COO$
   - **d.** $ZnCl_2$
   - **e.** $Na_3P$
   - **f.** $K_2Se$
   - **g.** $NH_4MgPO_4$
   - **h.** $KNO_2$
   - **i.** $KNaCO_3$

9. Name the following compounds.
   - **a.** $Na_2SO_4$
   - **b.** $AgNO_3$
   - **c.** $ZnCr_2O_7$
   - **d.** $NH_4CH_3COO$
   - **e.** $KClO_4$
   - **f.** $NH_4ClO_3$
   - **g.** $CaC_2O_4$
   - **h.** $BaCO_3$
   - **i.** $NaH_2PO_4$

10. Write formulas for the following compounds.
    - **a.** manganese(III) chloride
    - **b.** iron(III) bromide
    - **c.** chromium(III) bromide
    - **d.** tin(IV) chloride
    - **e.** manganese(II) bromide
    - **f.** tin(IV) oxide
    - **g.** chromium(III) oxide
    - **h.** lead(II) oxide
    - **i.** manganese(VII) oxide
    - **j.** mercury(I) oxide

11. Name the following compounds. (Roman numeral system)
    - **a.** $TiCl_2$
    - **b.** $TiBr_4$
    - **c.** $CuCl$
    - **d.** $PbI_2$
    - **e.** $SnCl_4$
    - **f.** $Sb_2O_5$
    - **g.** $CrO_3$
    - **h.** $Mn_3O_4$
    - **i.** $TiO_2$
    - **j.** $PbO$
    - **k.** $BiF_5$
    - **l.** $NiBr_2$
    - **m.** $CuBr_2$
    - **n.** $PbCl_2$
    - **o.** $CrF_3$

12. Name the following compounds. (Roman numeral system)
    - **a.** $Fe_2(SO_4)_3$
    - **b.** $Cr(OH)_2$
    - **c.** $Hg_2(ClO_3)_2$*
    - **d.** $Fe(ClO_4)_2$
    - **e.** $MnSO_4$
    - **f.** $Hg(IO_3)_2$
    - **g.** $Pb(ClO_2)_2$
    - **h.** $Cu(CH_3COO)_2$
    - **i.** $Cu_2SO_4$
    - **j.** $CoSO_4$

13. Write formulas for the following compounds.
    - **a.** copper(II) chlorate
    - **b.** bismuth(III) telluride
    - **c.** manganese(III) sulfate
    - **d.** iron(III) nitrate
    - **e.** tin(IV) nitrate
    - **f.** chromium(III) sulfate
    - **g.** iron(II) hydroxide
    - **h.** copper(II) phosphate
    - **i.** mercury(I) nitrite
    - **j.** lead(II) nitrate

14. Write formulas for the following compounds.
    - **a.** dichlorine oxide
    - **b.** chlorine dioxide
    - **c.** carbon disulfide
    - **d.** chlorine trifluoride
    - **e.** dichlorine heptoxide
    - **f.** sulfur hexafluoride

15. Name the following compounds. (Greek prefixes)
    - **a.** $CO_2$
    - **b.** $NO_2$
    - **c.** $SO_3$
    - **d.** $PCl_3$
    - **e.** $NO$
    - **f.** $P_2O_5$

*Mercury exists as $Hg_2^{2+}$, mercury (I), in which two mercury atoms are bound together. It also exists as $Hg^{2+}$, mercury(II).

## 4:6  MOLECULAR AND EMPIRICAL FORMULAS

The **empirical formula** of a compound is the smallest whole number ratio of the number of atoms of each element in the substance. The **molecular formula** gives the actual number of atoms in the molecule. For instance, $CH_2$ is the empirical formula for the series of molecular compounds $C_2H_4$, $C_3H_6$, $C_4H_8$, and so on.

There is a definite relationship between the empirical and the molecular formula. Note that the molecular formula is always a whole number multiple of the empirical formula. As can be seen in Table 4-4 the empirical formula and the molecular formula are not always the same.

**Table 4-4**

| Empirical and Molecular Formulas | | |
|---|---|---|
| **Compound** | **Empirical Formula** | **Molecular Formula** |
| water | $H_2O$ | $H_2O$ |
| hydrogen peroxide | $HO$ | $H_2O_2$ |
| mercury(I) bromide | $HgBr$ | $Hg_2Br_2$ |
| methane | $CH_4$ | $CH_4$ |
| butane | $C_2H_5$ | $C_4H_{10}$ |
| ethene | $CH_2$ | $C_2H_4$ |
| butene | $CH_2$ | $C_4H_8$ |

### PROBLEM

16. Write the empirical formula for each of the following.
    **a.** $C_6H_6$ (benzene)          **f.** $SO_3$
    **b.** $C_2H_2$ (ethyne)           **g.** $N_2O_4$
    **c.** $C_6H_{12}O_6$ (glucose)    **h.** $NO_2$
    **d.** $C_4H_{10}$ (butane)        **i.** $Ag_2C_4H_4O_6$
    **e.** $P_4O_{10}$                 **j.** $K_2S_4$

## 4:7  COEFFICIENTS

The formula of a compound represents a definite amount of that compound. This amount is called a formula unit. It may be one molecule or the smallest number of particles giving the true proportions of the elements in the compound.

When we wish to represent two molecules of water we write $2H_2O$. The number prefixed as a multiplier is called the **coefficient.** For example, when the coefficient 3 is written before the formula unit $Fe_2O_3$, it means three times everything in the formula. In $3Fe_2O_3$ there are 6 iron atoms and 9 oxygen atoms.

## PROBLEMS

**17.** Write the number of formula units represented by the following.
   **a.** $5NaCl$
   **b.** $H_2O$
   **c.** $6MgCl_2$
   **d.** $ZnSO_4$
   **e.** $2CuSO_4$
   **f.** $12Pb(NO_3)_2$

**18.** Determine the number of atoms of each element in the following.
   **a.** $7H_2O$
   **b.** $2(NH_4)_3PO_4$
   **c.** $4Al_2O_3$
   **d.** $3CuSO_4$

## CHAPTER REVIEW PROBLEMS

*Write the formula for each of the following compounds.*

**1. a.** sodium nitrite
   **b.** sodium carbonate
   **c.** sodium sulfate
   **d.** potassium hydroxide
   **e.** potassium nitrate
   **f.** potassium sulfite
   **g.** potassium phosphate
   **h.** cadmium oxalate
   **i.** cadmium carbonate
   **j.** cadmium sulfate
   **k.** cadmium phosphate
   **l.** aluminum bromide
   **m.** aluminum nitrate
   **n.** aluminum sulfide

**2. a.** magnesium nitrate
   **b.** magnesium sulfate
   **c.** magnesium carbonate
   **d.** barium bromide
   **e.** barium nitrate
   **f.** barium sulfate
   **g.** iron(II) oxide
   **h.** iron(II) hydroxide
   **i.** iron(II) carbonate
   **j.** iron(II) sulfate
   **k.** iron(III) phosphate
   **l.** iron(III) bromide

**3. a.** strontium chloride
   **b.** strontium hydroxide
   **c.** strontium nitrate
   **d.** strontium sulfite
   **e.** strontium sulfide
   **f.** iron(III) sulfate
   **g.** iron(III) phosphate
   **h.** mercury(II) bromide
   **i.** mercury(II) carbonate
   **j.** mercury(II) sulfide

*Write the name for each of the following compounds.*

**4. a.** $NaNO_3$
   **b.** $Na_2SO_3$
   **c.** $Na_3PO_4$
   **d.** $KNO_2$
   **e.** $K_2CO_3$
   **f.** $K_2SO_4$
   **g.** $CdBr_2$
   **h.** $Cd(NO_3)_2$
   **i.** $CdSO_3$
   **j.** $CdS$
   **k.** $AlCl_3$
   **l.** $Al(OH)_3$

**5. a.** $Mg(NO_2)_2$
   **b.** $MgSO_3$
   **c.** $Mg_3(PO_4)_2$
   **d.** $Ba(NO_2)_2$
   **e.** $BaSO_3$
   **f.** $BaCO_3$
   **g.** $Al_2(SO_4)_3$
   **h.** $AlPO_4$
   **i.** $FeBr_2$
   **j.** $Fe(NO_3)_2$
   **k.** $FeSO_3$
   **l.** $FeS$

**6. a.** $Ba_3(PO_4)_2$
   **b.** $SrBr_2$
   **c.** $Sr(NO_3)_2$
   **d.** $SrCO_3$
   **e.** $SrSO_4$
   **f.** $Sr_3(PO_4)_2$
   **g.** $FeCl_3$
   **h.** $Fe(NO_3)_3$
   **i.** $Fe_2S_3$
   **j.** $HgCl_2$
   **k.** $Hg(NO_3)_2$
   **l.** $HgSO_4$

7. Write the formula for each of the following compounds.
   a. sodium hydroxide
   b. mercury(II) sulfate
   c. calcium hypochlorite
   d. lead(II) phosphate
   e. aluminum chlorate
   f. ammonium sulfide
   g. copper(I) carbonate
   h. mercury(I) sulfide
   i. lead(II) acetate
   j. manganese(IV) oxide
   k. manganese(II) sulfate
   l. silver oxide
   m. zinc nitrate
   n. chromium(III) sulfite
   o. ammonium dichromate
   p. iron(III) oxide

8. Write the names for each of the following compounds.
   a. $NaCH_3COO$
   b. $Ni(NO_3)_2$
   c. $Hg_2Cl_2$
   d. $Sn_3(PO_4)_2$
   e. $Cr(OH)_2$
   f. $Zn(ClO_3)_2$
   g. $MgBr_2$
   h. $CuN_3$
   i. $CaH_2$
   j. $Ba(NO_2)_2$
   k. $MnS$
   l. $Sn(NO_3)_4$
   m. $(NH_4)_2SO_4$
   n. $PbO$
   o. $KCN$

9. Write the formula for each of the following compounds.
   a. magnesium nitrate
   b. silver acetate
   c. barium perchlorate
   d. potassium nitrite
   e. ammonium sulfate
   f. ammonium dichromate
   g. barium molybdate
   h. zinc thiocyanate

10. Write the name for each of the following compounds.
    a. $FeSO_4$
    b. $NH_4ClO_3$
    c. $Fe(CH_3COO)_2$
    d. $CuCrO_4$
    e. $Mg(NO_3)_2$
    f. $AlPO_4$
    g. $Na_2SO_3$
    h. $Ca(ClO_2)_2$
    i. $(NH_4)_2CO_3$
    j. $Ag_2CrO_4$
    k. $Ba_3(PO_4)_2$
    l. $KClO_4$

11. Write the formula for each of the following compounds.
    a. zinc hexafluorosilicate
    b. antimony(V) sulfide
    c. bismuth(III) telluride
    d. titanium(IV) iodide
    e. nickel(II) fluoride
    f. manganese(IV) oxide
    g. lead(IV) oxide
    h. calcium tartrate
    i. mercury(II) oxide
    j. cobalt(III) oxide

12. Write the name for each of the following compounds
    a. $Zn(SCN)_2$
    b. $Sb_2O_5$
    c. $TiO$
    d. $InP$
    e. $Mn_2O_3$
    f. $Cr(CH_3COO)_3$

13. Write the empirical formula for each of the following.
    a. $C_6H_{14}$
    b. $CO_2$
    c. $N_2F_4$
    d. $C_3H_6Cl_2$
    e. $C_5H_{10}O_2$
    f. $P_3N_3Cl_6$

14. Write the number of formula units expressed by each of the following.
    a. $5H_2O$
    b. $9O_2$
    c. $3(NH_4)_2SO_4$
    d. $6NF_3$
    e. $C_{12}H_{22}O_{11}$
    f. $4Fe_2O_3$

# THE MOLE

5

## 5:1  ATOMIC MASS

The actual mass of an atom is extremely small. One type of hydrogen atom has a mass of $1.67 \times 10^{-24}$ g and one type of oxygen atom has a mass of $2.66 \times 10^{-23}$ g. Because these masses are impractical to use, chemists have defined an average **atomic mass scale** based on the mass of a carbon-12 atom. **Atomic mass** is the relative mass of an average atom of an element with carbon-12 atoms used as reference. For convenience, the carbon-12 atom has been arbitrarily assigned the atomic mass of 12 atomic mass units (u). An atomic mass unit is defined as 1/12 the mass of a carbon-12 atom. The mass of an average hydrogen atom is approximately 1/12 the mass of a carbon-12 atom. See the table of International Atomic Masses on the inside back cover.

This relationship between the masses of different elements is important because it enables the chemist to predict the amount of one element that will react with a given amount of a second element to yield a certain amount of product.

## 5:2  MOLECULAR MASS

**Molecular mass** is the sum of the atomic masses of the atoms in a molecule. Generally atomic masses will be rounded to tenths. For those elements with masses less than ten, masses will be rounded to hundredths unless more significant digits are suggested by the data of the problem.

### Example 1

Find the molecular mass of vitamin A, one of the fat-soluble vitamins. Its molecular formula is $C_{20}H_{30}O$.

**Solving Process:**

$$
\begin{array}{lrl}
\text{carbon} & 20 \times 12.0 \ \text{u} = & 240 \quad \text{u} \\
\text{hydrogen} & 30 \times \phantom{0}1.01 \ \text{u} = & \phantom{0}30.3 \ \text{u} \\
\text{oxygen} & \phantom{0}1 \times 16.0 \ \text{u} = & \underline{\phantom{0}16.0 \ \text{u}} \\
& \text{Molecular Mass} = & 286 \quad \text{u}
\end{array}
$$

## 5:3  FORMULA MASS

Ionic compounds do not exist in the form of molecules. The **formula mass** is the sum of the atomic masses of the ions present in the simplest or formula unit of an ionic compound. Both the molecular and formula masses are calculated in the same manner. It is possible to calculate masses without first determining whether the substance is ionic or molecular.

Formula mass is a more general term than molecular mass. Formula mass may be used in referrring to all compounds. Molecular mass should be used only to refer to molecular compounds.

### Example 2

Determine the formula mass of calcium phosphate, $Ca_3(PO_4)_2$.
**Solving Process:**

$$
\begin{array}{llr}
\text{calcium} & 3 \times 40.1 \text{ u} = & 120.3 \text{ u} \\
\text{phosphorus} & 2 \times 31.0 \text{ u} = & 62.0 \text{ u} \\
\text{oxygen} & 8 \times 16.0 \text{ u} = & \underline{128.0 \text{ u}} \\
& \text{Formula Mass} = & 310.3 \text{ u}
\end{array}
$$

### PROBLEMS

1. Calculate the formula or molecular mass of each of the following compounds.

   a. $H_2SO_4$
   b. $NaOH$
   c. $NH_4NO_3$
   d. $Fe(CH_3COO)_3$

   e. $C_3H_5N_3O_3$, nitroglycerin
   f. $Al(NO_3)_3$
   g. $C_{63}H_{84}N_{14}O_{14}PCo$, vitamin $B_{12}$
   h. $SO_2$

2. Aspirin is used universally to decrease pain and fever. Calculate the molecular mass of 2-acetyloxybenzoic acid (aspirin) that has the following structural formula.

## 5:4  AVOGADRO'S NUMBER

As stated earlier, the mass of a single atom or molecule is so small it cannot be measured easily. Laboratory quantities require many millions of atoms. If we express the international atomic masses of elements in grams, the masses can be readily measured in the laboratory.

Since atomic masses are relative quantities, the atomic mass in grams of one element contains the same number of atoms as the atomic mass in grams of any other element. It has been found that the atomic mass in grams of any element contains $6.022\ 045 \times 10^{23}$ atoms. This number is called **Avogadro's number,** and is abbreviated, $N_A$. Another name for this quantity is the mole.

## 5:5 THE MOLE

The **mole** is the SI unit for amount of substance, and its symbol is mol. It represents both a formula mass and a number of formula units. Just as one million equals $1 \times 10^6$ things, one dozen equals 12 things, and one gross equals 144 things, one mole is $6.02 \times 10^{23}$ things. Depending on the substance, the mass of the mole will be different. The mole is an important quantitative unit used in most chemical calculations. It is always understood to refer to one formula mass in grams, one atomic mass in grams, or one molecular mass in grams.

An element that is diatomic (such as nitrogen) can be measured as one mole of molecules or as one mole of atoms. Note the difference in Table 5-1.

**Table 5-1**

| Mole Relationships | | | |
|---|---|---|---|
| **Substance** | **Mass** | **Number of particles** | **Moles** |
| C | 12.0 g | $6.02 \times 10^{23}$ atoms | 1 mol C |
| $K^+$ | 39.1 g | $6.02 \times 10^{23}$ ions | 1 mol $K^+$ |
| $CO_2$ | 44.0 g | $6.02 \times 10^{23}$ molecules | 1 mol $CO_2$ |
| NaCl | 58.5 g | $6.02 \times 10^{23}$ ion pairs | 1 mol NaCl |
| $N_2$ | 28.0 g | $6.02 \times 10^{23}$ molecules | 1 mol $N_2$ |
| N | 14.0 g | $6.02 \times 10^{23}$ atoms | 1 mol N |

These relationships are important in a number of different chemical calculations. They will be used in this chapter and in subsequent chapters.

Conversion ratios are used to convert from one unit (such as grams) to a different unit (such as moles). Since the atomic mass in grams of an element = 1 mole of the element = $6.02 \times 10^{23}$ atoms of an element, four conversion factors can be written.

$$\frac{1 \text{ mol } K^+}{39.1 \text{ g } K^+} \quad \text{or} \quad \frac{39.1 \text{ g } K^+}{1 \text{ mol } K^+}$$

$$\frac{1 \text{ mol } K^+}{6.02 \times 10^{23} \text{ K}^+} \quad \text{or} \quad \frac{6.02 \times 10^{23} \text{ K}^+}{1 \text{ mol } K^+}$$

The actual form used depends upon the units desired in the answer.

## Example 3

Calculate the mass in grams of 2.23 mol of nitrogen molecules.
**Solving Process:**
To convert from moles to grams, use the conversion ratio 28.0 g $N_2$/mol $N_2$. This ratio gives the answer in grams by dividing out the unit mol.

$$\text{mass } N_2 = \frac{2.23 \text{ mol } N_2}{} \left| \frac{28.0 \text{ g } N_2}{1 \text{ mol } N_2} \right.$$

$$= 62.4 \text{ g } N_2$$

## Example 4

Determine the number of atoms in 2.23 mol nitrogen molecules, $N_2$.
**Solving Process:**
The number of molecules in a mole is given by Avogadro's number. To obtain atoms, this number must be multiplied by two, since $N_2$ is diatomic.

$$\text{atoms } N = \frac{2.23 \text{ mol } N_2}{} \left| \frac{6.02 \times 10^{23} \text{ molecules } N_2}{1 \text{ mol } N_2} \right| \frac{2 \text{ atoms } N}{1 \text{ molecule } N_2}$$

$$= 2.68 \times 10^{24} \text{ atoms } N$$

## Example 5

Find the number of atoms in 16.0 g sulfur.
**Solving Process:**
Convert from grams to moles of sulfur, then from moles of sulfur to atoms of sulfur. This conversion will involve two ratios.

$$\text{atoms } S = \frac{16.0 \text{ g } S}{} \left| \frac{1 \text{ mol } S}{32.1 \text{ g } S} \right| \frac{6.02 \times 10^{23} \text{ atoms } S}{1 \text{ mol } S}$$

$$= 3.00 \times 10^{23} \text{ atoms}$$

## PROBLEMS

3. Calculate the mass in grams of 0.354 mol of each of the following.
   a. ammonia gas, $NH_3$         c. cholesterol, $C_{27}H_{46}O$
   b. platinum metal, Pt          d. iron(II) ferricyanide, $Fe_3(Fe(CN)_6)_2$
4. Calculate the number of moles in 50.0 g of each of the following.
   a. borazon, BN                 c. calcium propanoate, $Ca(C_3H_5O_2)_2$
   b. thallium(I) sulfate, $Tl_2SO_4$    d. penicillin G, $C_{16}H_{18}N_2O_4S$
5. Calculate the number of atoms, molecules, or ions for each of the following.
   a. 2.00 mol Na atoms           c. 3.00 mol $K^+$
   b. 46.0 g Na atoms             d. 68.0 g $H_2S$ molecules

6. Calculate the mass in grams of each of the following.

    **a.** $6.02 \times 10^{23}$ atoms of Na

    **b.** $3.01 \times 10^{23}$ formula units of $Sr(OH)_2$

    **c.** $1.20 \times 10^{24}$ molecules of $CO_2$

    **d.** $1.50 \times 10^{23}$ ions of $Na^+$

# 5:6 MOLARITY

The mole is also used to express the concentration of a solution. A 1 molar solution contains 1 mole of solute dissolved in enough solvent (usually water) to make 1 cubic decimeter of solution.

$$\text{molarity } (M) = \frac{\text{number of moles of solute}}{\text{cubic decimeter of solution}}$$

Chemists express concentration in terms of **molarity** because they measure most solutions by volume and because they are interested in obtaining a certain number of particles. One mole of sodium chloride, NaCl, is 58.5 grams. If 2 moles of NaCl (117.0 grams) are dissolved in enough water to make 1 cubic decimeter of solution, the solution is a 2M solution. Fifty cubic centimeters of a solution will have the same concentration, 2M. The total number of particles changes when the volume is changed but the concentration of particles (the number of particles per unit volume) does not change.

## Example 6

Calculate the molarity of $1.50$ $dm^3$ of solution that contains $200.0$ g of $MgCl_2$.

**Solving Process:**

The problem requires the calculation of molarity. Molarity is moles of solute per (divided by) $dm^3$ of solution. Therefore, the data concerning solute is placed in the numerator, and the data concerning the solution in the denominator. The solute data in the numerator is then converted to moles, and the solution data in the denominator to $dm^3$.

$$\text{molarity} = \frac{200.0 \text{ g } \cancel{MgCl_2}}{1.50 \text{ dm}^3} \left| \frac{1 \text{ mol } MgCl_2}{95.3 \text{ g } \cancel{MgCl_2}} \right.$$

$$= 1.40 \text{ mol/dm}^3 = 1.40M$$

## Example 7

Calculate the molarity of a solution that contains $10.0$ g of sodium hydroxide in $5.00 \times 10^2$ $cm^3$ of solution.

**Solving Process:**

Convert $10.0$ g of NaOH per $5.00 \times 10^2$ $cm^3$ to moles of NaOH per $dm^3$ of solution.

$$\text{molarity} = \frac{10.0 \text{ g } \cancel{NaOH}}{5.00 \times 10^2 \text{ } \cancel{cm^3}} \left| \frac{1 \text{ mol NaOH}}{40.0 \text{ g } \cancel{NaOH}} \right| \frac{1000 \text{ } \cancel{cm^3}}{1 \text{ dm}^3}$$

$$= 0.500 \text{ mol/dm}^3 = 0.500M$$

## PROBLEMS

7. Calculate the molarity of each of the following solutions.
   a. 0.500 dm$^3$ containing 30.0 g of acetic acid, $CH_3COOH$
   b. 2.000 dm$^3$ containing 49.0 g of phosphoric acid, $H_3PO_4$
   c. 1.50 dm$^3$ containing 102 g of potassium hydroxide, KOH
8. Calculate the mass of solute in the following solutions:
   a. 750.0 cm$^3$ of $CaCl_2$ solution that is 0.500$M$
   b. 3000.0 cm$^3$ of a KOH solution that is 2.50$M$
   c. 250.0 cm$^3$ of a $Na_2SO_4$ solution that is 2.00$M$
9. How many cubic decimeters of each solution can be made according to the following specifications?
   a. a 2.00$M$ solution using 80.0 g sodium hydroxide
   b. a 0.500$M$ solution using 80.0 g sodium hydroxide
   c. a 1.50$M$ solution using 188 g silver nitrate, $AgNO_3$

## 5:7   PERCENTAGE COMPOSITION

The **percentage composition** of a compound gives the relative amount of each element present. The percent of an element in a compound is

$$\% = \frac{\text{number of atoms of element} \mid \text{atomic mass of element}}{\text{formula mass of compound}} \mid 100$$

To calculate percentage composition:
(a) calculate the total mass for each element,
(b) calculate the formula mass for the entire compound,
(c) divide the total mass of each element by the formula mass of the compound, and
(d) multiply by 100.

## Example 8

Find the percentage of nitrogen in ammonium nitrate, $NH_4NO_3$, an important source of nitrogen in fertilizers.

**Solving Process:**

Calculate the formula mass; then find the percentage.

$$
\begin{array}{lll}
\text{nitrogen} & 2 \times 14.0 & = 28.0 \\
\text{hydrogen} & 4 \times 1.01 & = 4.04 \\
\text{oxygen} & 3 \times 16.0 & = \underline{48.0} \\
& \text{Formula mass} & = 80.0
\end{array}
$$

$$\% \text{ N} = \frac{\text{total mass N} \mid 100}{\text{formula mass } NH_4NO_3 \mid}$$

$$= \frac{28.0 \text{ g} \mid 100}{80.0 \text{ g} \mid} = 35.0\% \text{ N}$$

## PROBLEMS

10. Calculate the percentage composition of the following compounds.
    **a.** $Fe_2O_3$     **b.** $Ag_2O$     **c.** $HgO$     **d.** $Na_2S$
11. Determine the percentage of sodium in sodium sulfate, $Na_2SO_4$.
12. Urea, $CO(NH_2)_2$, and ammonia, $NH_3$, are two compounds used as a source of nitrogen in fertilizers. Calculate the percentage of nitrogen in each.

# 5:8  HYDRATES

Some crystals form **hydrates.** These compounds have water molecules adhering to their crystal structure. There is a fixed ratio of water molecules per formula unit. Examples are copper(II) sulfate pentahydrate, $CuSO_4 \cdot 5H_2O$, and calcium sulfate dihydrate, $CaSO_4 \cdot 2H_2O$. The raised dot indicates that the water molecules are not held tightly and can be driven off by heating the hydrate.

## Example 9

In an experiment, a student gently heated a hydrated copper compound to remove the water of hydration. The following data was recorded:

1. mass of crucible, cover, and contents before heating     21.54 g
2. mass of empty crucible and cover     19.82 g
3. mass of crucible, cover, and contents after heating
   to constant mass     20.94 g

Calculate (a) the experimental percent of water in the compound and (b) the percent error assuming that the compound is copper(II) sulfate pentahydrate.

**Solving Process:**

The mass of the original compound is found by subtracting item 2 from item 1. Calculate the mass of water lost by subtracting item 3 from item 1. Then calculate the percent of water.

$$\% \ H_2O = \frac{g \ H_2O \ removed}{g \ original \ compound} \ \bigg| \ 100$$

$$= \frac{0.60 \ g}{1.72 \ g} \ \bigg| \ 100 = 34.9\%$$

To calculate the percent error, we compare the experimentally determined value for the percent water with the value calculated from the formula for copper(II) sulfate pentahydrate, $CuSO_4 \cdot 5H_2O$. The calculated percent of water in the compound is 36.0%. Therefore the absolute error is

$$36.0\% - 34.9\% = 1.1\%$$

The percent error is

$$\% \text{ error} = \frac{\text{absolute error}}{\text{actual percentage}} \bigg| 100 = \frac{1.1\%}{36.0\%} \bigg| 100 = 3.1\%$$

## PROBLEMS

13. Calculate the percentage of each of the following in the compound sodium sulfate decahydrate, $Na_2SO_4 \cdot 10H_2O$.

   **a.** Na    **b.** S    **c.** O    **d.** $H_2O$

14. Calcium chloride can exist as the anhydrous compound $CaCl_2$ or in three different hydrated forms that are mono-, di-, and hexahydrates. Calculate the following.

   **a.** the percent calcium in each compound
   **b.** the percent water in each of the three hydrates

15. In a laboratory experiment, barium chloride dihydrate was heated to completely remove its water of hydration. Calculate (a) the experimental percent of water, (b) the percent of $BaCl_2$, and (c) the percent error. The data below was obtained in the experiment.

   **1.** empty crucible and cover                          20.286 g
   **2.** crucible, cover, and contents before heating      21.673 g
   **3.** crucible, cover, and contents after heating       21.461 g

## 5:9  EMPIRICAL FORMULAS

Recall from Section 4:6 that the empirical formula of a compound is the smallest whole number ratio of the number of atoms of each element in the substance. The molecular formula of a compound indicates the number of each atom in a molecule.

There is a definite relationship between the empirical and the molecular formula. Note that the molecular formula is always a whole number multiple of the empirical formula. For example, the empirical formula for ethyne is $CH_2$ and the molecular formula is $C_2H_4$ (2 × $CH_2$). As can be seen in Table 4-4 the empirical formula and the molecular formula are sometimes identical. In Section 5:7, we used the formula of a compound to determine its percentage composition. Now we reverse the procedure and determine the empirical formula from the percentage composition. The elements in compounds combine in simple whole number ratios of atoms. To determine an empirical formula, masses of elements are converted to moles and then a ratio of moles is determined.

## Example 10

Determine the empirical formula for sodium sulfite. Sodium sulfite contains 36.5% sodium, 25.4% sulfur, and 38.1% oxygen.

**Solving Process:**

The percentage composition data indicates that there are 36.5 g Na, 25.4 g S, and 38.1 g O in 100 g of compound.

**Step 1.** Find the number of moles.

$$\text{Na} \quad \frac{36.5 \text{ g Na}}{} \left| \frac{1 \text{ mol Na}}{23.0 \text{ g Na}} \right. = 1.59 \text{ mol Na}$$

$$\text{S} \quad \frac{25.4 \text{ g S}}{} \left| \frac{1 \text{ mol S}}{32.1 \text{ g S}} \right. = 0.791 \text{ mol S}$$

$$\text{O} \quad \frac{38.1 \text{ g O}}{} \left| \frac{1 \text{ mol O}}{16.0 \text{ g O}} \right. = 2.38 \text{ mol O}$$

**Step 2.** Determine the ratio of moles.

$$\begin{array}{ccc} \text{Na} & \text{S} & \text{O} \\ \frac{1.59}{0.791} = 2.01 & \frac{0.791}{0.791} = 1.00 & \frac{2.38}{0.791} = 3.01 \end{array}$$

The ratio is 2.01:1.00:3.01, Na:S:O.
The empirical formula is $Na_2SO_3$.

## Example 11

What is the empirical formula of a compound that contains 53.73% Fe and 46.27% S?

**Solving Process:**

There are 53.73 g Fe and 46.27 g S in 100 g of compound.

**Step 1.** Find the number of moles.

$$\text{mol Fe} = \frac{53.73 \text{ g Fe}}{} \left| \frac{1 \text{ mol Fe}}{55.85 \text{ g Fe}} \right. = 0.9620 \text{ mol Fe}$$

$$\text{mol S} = \frac{46.27 \text{ g S}}{} \left| \frac{1 \text{ mol S}}{32.07 \text{ g S}} \right. = 1.443 \text{ mol S}$$

**Step 2.** Determine the ratio of moles.

$$\begin{array}{cc} \text{Fe} & \text{S} \\ \frac{0.9620}{0.9620} = 1.0000 & \frac{1.443}{0.9620} = 1.500 \end{array}$$

The ratio is 1.000:1.500, giving $FeS_{1.500}$

In the previous example problem, the relative numbers of atoms were small whole numbers and we could write the formula directly from them. The ratio 1 to 1.5 must be expressed in terms of whole numbers, since a fractional part of an atom does not exist. By multiplying both numbers in the ratio by two, we obtain two atoms Fe and three atoms S. The empirical formula is $Fe_2S_3$.

## PROBLEMS

16. Calculate the empirical formula for compounds with the following compositions.
    a. Fe 63.5%, S 36.5%
    b. Mn 63.1%, S 36.9%
    c. K 26.6%, Cr 35.4%, O 38.0%
17. Calculate empirical formulas for the following two compounds containing sodium, sulfur, and oxygen.
    a. Na 32.4%, S 22.6% O 45.0%
    b. Na 29.1%, S 40.5%, O 30.4%
18. Calculate the empirical formulas for the following three iron ores.
    a. Fe 77.7%, O 22.3%
    b. Fe 72.4%, O 27.6%
    c. Fe 70.0%, O 30.0%

## 5:10  MOLECULAR FORMULAS

The molecular formula indicates not only the ratio of the atoms of the elements in a compound but also the actual number of atoms of each element in one molecule of the compound.

The molecular formula calculation is the same as the empirical formula calculation, except that the molecular mass is used in an additional step. The molecular formula is always a whole number multiple of the empirical formula.

### Example 12

An organic compound is found to contain 92.25% carbon and 7.75% hydrogen. If the molecular mass is 78, what is the molecular formula?

**Solving Process:**

Determine the empirical formula.

**Step 1.** Find the number of moles.

$$C \quad \frac{92.25 \text{ g C}}{} \; \Big| \; \frac{1 \text{ mol C}}{12.01 \text{ g C}} = 7.681 \text{ mol C}$$

$$H \quad \frac{7.75 \text{ g H}}{} \; \Big| \; \frac{1 \text{ mol H}}{1.01 \text{ g H}} = 7.67 \text{ mol H}$$

**Step 2.** Divide by the smaller number of moles to determine ratio of moles.

$$
\begin{array}{cc}
H & C \\
\dfrac{7.67}{7.67} = 1.00 & \dfrac{7.681}{7.67} = 1.00
\end{array}
$$

**Step 3.** Use the empirical formula to find the molecular formula.

The empirical formula is CH. Since the CH unit has a formula mass of 13 u and a molecular mass of 78 u there will be six units in each molecule.

$$13x = 78$$
$$x = 78/13 = 6.0$$

Six times the molecular formula is $C_6H_6$.

## PROBLEMS

19. There are two oxides of phosphorus. Both oxides can exist in different forms depending on the temperature and the pressure. Calculate the empirical and molecular formulas from the following data.
    a. P 56.4%, O 43.7%, molecular mass 220
    b. P 43.6%, O 56.4%, molecular mass 284
20. The formula mass of a compound is 92. Analysis of the compound shows that there are 0.608 g of nitrogen and 1.388 g of oxygen. What is the molecular formula of this compound?

# 5:11   EMPIRICAL FORMULAS OF HYDRATES

The method used to calculate the formulas of hydrates is basically the same as that used to calculate other empirical formulas except that it is necessary to determine the number of moles of water involved.

## Example 13

A hydrated compound has an analysis of 18.29% Ca, 32.37% Cl, and 49.34% $H_2O$. What is its formula?

**Solving Process:**

**Step 1.** Find the number of moles.

$$\text{mol Ca} = \frac{18.29 \text{ g Ca}}{} \left| \frac{1 \text{ mol Ca}}{40.08 \text{ g Ca}} \right. = 0.4563 \text{ mol Ca}$$

$$\text{mol Cl} = \frac{32.37 \text{ g Cl}}{} \left| \frac{1 \text{ mol Cl}}{35.45 \text{ g Cl}} \right. = 0.9131 \text{ mol Cl}$$

$$\text{mol } H_2O = \frac{49.34 \text{ g } H_2O}{} \left| \frac{1 \text{ mol } H_2O}{18.02 \text{ g } H_2O} \right. = 2.738 \text{ mol } H_2O$$

**Step 2.** Determine ratio of moles.

| Ca | Cl | $H_2O$ |
|---|---|---|
| $\dfrac{0.4563}{0.4563} = 1.000$ | $\dfrac{0.9131}{0.4563} = 2.001$ | $\dfrac{2.738}{0.4563} = 6.000$ |

The empirical formula is $CaCl_2 \cdot 6H_2O$. The raised dot between the $CaCl_2$ and the $6H_2O$ means that this substance is a hydrated compound.

## PROBLEMS

21. The masses of the hydrates listed below were measured, heated to drive off the water of hydration, and cooled. Then the masses of the residues were measured. Find the formulas of the following hydrates.
    a. 1.62 g of $CoCl_2 \cdot xH_2O$ gave a residue of 0.88 g
    b. 1.21 g of $Pb(CH_3COO)_2 \cdot xH_2O$ gave a residue of 1.03 g
    c. 1.04 g $NiSO_4 \cdot xH_2O$ gave a residue of 0.61 g
    d. 1.26 g of $CaSO_4 \cdot xH_2O$ gave a residue of 0.99 g

22. A hydrated magnesium compound has a formula mass of about 174 and contains 31.0% water of hydration. From the following analysis, calculate the molecular formula: Mg 13.90%, P 17.74%, H 4.01%, O 64.30%.

## CHAPTER REVIEW PROBLEMS

1. Calculate the formula (or molecular) mass of the following compounds:
   a. $K_3AsO_4$
   b. $Na_2B_4O_7 \cdot 10H_2O$
   c. $MnCl_2 \cdot 4H_2O$
   d. $Al_2(SO_4)_3 \cdot 18H_2O$
   e. $N_2O_5$
   f. $(NH_4)_3PO_4$
   g. $Na_2CO_3$
   h. $CHCl_2COOH$
   i. $NaCl$

2. Hydrocarbons and various oxides of nitrogen react photochemically (a chemical process that requires light) to form a variety of pollutants. The formula of one of the pollutants, peroxyacetylnitrate, is

$$CH_3C \overset{O}{\underset{OONO_2}{\big\backslash}}$$

   What is the molecular mass of this compound?

3. An amino acid that cannot be made (synthesized) by the body and must be obtained in the diet is lysine. Determine the molecular mass of lysine, which has the formula

$$H_2N-(CH_2)_3-CHCOOH$$
$$| $$
$$NH_2$$

4. Calculate the mass in grams of each of the following.
   a. 6.38 mol $O_2$
   b. 4.00 mol Al
   c. 2.25 mol $H_2SO_4$
   d. 5.49 mol KI
   e. 1.500 mol $Ba(IO_4)_2$
   f. 0.602 mol $Ca(NO_3)_2 \cdot 3H_2O$

5. Calculate the number of moles in each of the following.
   **a.** 188.0 g Zn                    **d.** 32.0 g $SO_2$
   **b.** 160.0 g $Br_2$                **e.** 10.0 g $Na_2S$
   **c.** 293.0 g Fe                    **f.** 84.2 g $K_2SO_4$

6. Calculate the number of atoms, molecules, or ions in each of the following quantities.
   **a.** 20.0 g Ca atoms              **c.** 68.0 g $H_2S$ molecules
   **b.** 3.34 mol $CO_2$ molecules    **d.** 0.125 mol $Mg^{2+}$ ions

7. Calculate the mass in grams of each of the following.
   **a.** $3.01 \times 10^{23}$ atoms of S
   **b.** $2.41 \times 10^{24}$ molecules of $H_2O$

8. Calculate the molarity of each of the following solutions.
   **a.** 500.0 $cm^3$ that contains 82.0 g $Ca(NO_3)_2$
   **b.** 250.0 $cm^3$ that contains 50.0 g $NiSO_4 \cdot 6H_2O$

9. Calculate the mass of solute in each of the following solutions.
   **a.** 250.0 $cm^3$ of a $Na_2SO_4 \cdot 7H_2O$ solution that is 2.00$M$
   **b.** 1.500 $dm^3$ of $KH_2PO_4$ solution that is 0.240$M$

10. How many cubic decimeters of solution can be made from each of the following?
    **a.** a 0.100$M$ solution using 117 g NaCl
    **b.** a 1.25$M$ solution using 55.0 g $Na_2S_2O_3 \cdot 5H_2O$

11. The sugar substitute sodium benzosulfimide (sodium saccharin) has a sweetness of about 500 times that of sucrose. Calculate the percentage of sodium and carbon in the sweetener. Its formula is

12. Copper phthalocyanine is a complex organic molecule possessing a brilliant greenish blue color. Millions of pounds are produced yearly to color products such as plastics, automobile finishes, rubber goods, and printing inks. Determine the percent carbon in copper phthalocyanine that has the formula $Cu(C_8H_4N_2)_4$.

13. Determine the percent of water in $MgSO_4 \cdot 7H_2O$.

14. Two compounds are analyzed and found to contain:
    **a.** 0.89 g K, 1.18 g Cr, 1.27 g O
    **b.** 1.03 g K, 0.69 g Cr, 0.84 g O
    Determine the empirical formulas for these two compounds.

15. To find the experimental empirical formula of a compound, a student heats a uniform coil of magnesium ribbon 35.00 cm long in a crucible. The resulting mixed product is treated with water, and subsequent heating gives an oxide of magnesium. The data is recorded as follows:

    **1.** mass of empty crucible and cover                                   20.74 g
    **2.** mass of two meters of magnesium ribbon                         1.44 g
    **3.** mass of crucible, cover, and final product                     21.17 g

    Determine the empirical formula for the oxide of magnesium.

16. A fat is composed, in part, of long chains of carbon and hydrogen atoms. In a reaction with a strong base, a fat forms a soap and glycerol. What is the empirical formula of a fat containing 76.5% C, 11.3% O and 12.2% H, if it has a molecular mass of 847?

17. Citric acid, an organic acid found in lemons and other citrus fruits, contains 37.5% carbon, 58.3% oxygen, and 4.20% hydrogen. What is the empirical formula of citric acid if it has a molecular mass of 192?

# CHEMICAL REACTIONS

# 6

## 6:1 REPRESENTING CHEMICAL CHANGES

Scientists rely on a variety of shorthand methods for expressing chemical information. You have already seen how chemical symbols are used for the names of elements and chemical formulas for the names of compounds. A **chemical equation** is a shorthand expression that represents a chemical reaction. A **chemical reaction** is the process by which one or more substances are changed into one or more new substances. A chemical equation shows the relative amount of each substance taking place in a chemical reaction.

The starting substances in a chemical reaction are called **reactants.** The substances that are formed are called **products.** The general format for a chemical equation is

$$CO_2(g) + H_2O(l) \quad \rightarrow \quad H_2CO_3(aq)$$
$$\text{reactants} \qquad \text{yield} \quad \text{products}$$

Reactants are generally written on the left side of chemical equations; products are written on the right side.

The letters in parentheses indicate the physical state of each substance involved in the reaction. The following symbols should be used in your work.

(g) gas      (cr) crystalline solid
(l) liquid    (aq) water solution

## 6:2 BALANCING EQUATIONS

The first step in writing a chemical equation is writing a word equation. It is composed of the names of the substances that are involved in a chemical reaction.

copper(I) chloride + hydrogen sulfide →
copper(I) sulfide + hydrochloric acid

The second step is writing a skeleton equation. This equation includes the chemical symbols and formulas for all the reactants and products identified in the word equation.

$$CuCl(aq) + H_2S(g) \rightarrow Cu_2S(cr) + HCl(aq)$$

The third step in writing a chemical equation is balancing the equation. The balanced equation includes the coefficients, numbers placed directly in front of the chemical formulas and symbols. The coefficients indicate the relative proportions of each substance involved in the chemical reaction.

$$2CuCl(aq) + H_2S(g) \rightarrow Cu_2S(cr) + 2HCl(aq)$$

This equation states that two moles of CuCl(aq) react with one mole of $H_2S$(g) producing one mole of $Cu_2S$(cr) and two moles HCl(aq).

## Example 1

Sodium reacts with water to produce a metallic hydroxide and hydrogen gas. Write a balanced equation for the reaction.

**Solving Process:**

**Step 1.** Write the word equation. Determine the products and reactants.

sodium + water $\rightarrow$ sodium hydroxide + hydrogen

**Step 2.** Write a skeleton equation. Since hydrogen is a diatomic gas, its formula is $H_2$. The formula for water may be written as HOH; this may make it easier to balance the equation.

$$Na + HOH \rightarrow NaOH + H_2$$

**Step 3.** Balance the equation. The metallic element sodium is balanced. One atom of sodium is on each side of the equation. There is one hydrogen atom on the reactant side (the H in OH has been accounted for) and 2 hydrogen atoms on the product side. Place a 2 in front of the HOH to balance the hydrogen atoms

$$Na + 2HOH \rightarrow NaOH + H_2$$

There are now 2OH on the left and 1 on the right. Place a 2 in front of the NaOH to give the same number of OH on each side.

$$Na + 2HOH \rightarrow 2NaOH + H_2$$

Put a 2 in front of the sodium metal. The balanced equation reads

$$2Na(cr) + 2HOH(l) \rightarrow 2NaOH(aq) + H_2(g)$$

Check to see if the equation is balanced.

|    | Reactants | Products |
|----|-----------|----------|
| Na | 2         | 2        |
| H  | 4         | 4        |
| O  | 2         | 2        |

## PROBLEMS

Balance each of the following chemical reactions.

1. $Mg(cr) + O_2(g) \rightarrow MgO(cr)$
2. $Fe(cr) + O_2(g) \rightarrow Fe_2O_3(cr)$
3. $H_2O(l) + N_2O_3(g) \rightarrow HNO_2(aq)$
4. $Na_2O(cr) + H_2O(l) \rightarrow NaOH(aq)$
5. $Fe(cr) + H_2O(l) \rightarrow Fe_3O_4(cr) + H_2(g)$

Write equations for the following chemical reactions.

6. magnesium bromide(aq) + chlorine(g) $\rightarrow$ magnesium chloride(aq) + bromine(g)
7. chlorine(g) + sodium iodide(cr) $\rightarrow$ sodium chloride(cr) + iodine(g)

8. potassium nitrate(cr) $\rightarrow$ potassium nitrite(cr) + oxygen(g)

9. zinc(cr) + hydrochloric acid(aq) $\rightarrow$ zinc chloride(aq) + hydrogen(g)

10. calcium oxide(cr) + hydrochloric acid(aq) $\rightarrow$ calcium chloride(aq) + water(l)

# 6:3   CLASSIFYING CHEMICAL CHANGES

The products of a chemical reaction may often be predicted by applying known facts about common reaction types. While there are hundreds of different "kinds" of chemical reactions, only four general types of reactions will be considered: single displacement, double displacement, decomposition, and synthesis.

**Single Displacement.** One element displaces another element in a compound. A single displacement has the general form

*element + compound* $\rightarrow$ *element + compound*

$$A + BX \rightarrow AX + B$$

The following are some general types of single displacement reactions.

1. An active metal will displace the metallic ion in a compound of a less active metal.

$$Fe(cr) + Cu(NO_3)_2(aq) \rightarrow Fe(NO_3)_2(aq) + Cu(cr)$$

2. Some active metals such as sodium and calcium will react with water to give a metallic hydroxide and hydrogen gas.

$$Ca(cr) + 2H_2O(l) \rightarrow Ca(OH)_2(aq) + H_2(g)$$

3. Active metals such as zinc, iron, and aluminum will displace the hydrogen in acids to give a salt and hydrogen gas.

$$Zn(cr) + 2HCl(aq) \rightarrow ZnCl_2(aq) + H_2(g)$$

4. An active nonmetal will displace a less active nonmetal.

$$Cl_2(g) + 2NaBr(aq) \rightarrow 2NaCl(aq) + Br_2(aq)$$

## PROBLEMS

*Balance the following reactions.*

11. $Al(cr) + Pb(NO_3)_2(aq) \rightarrow Al(NO_3)_3(aq) + Pb(cr)$

12. $Cu(cr) + AgNO_3(aq) \rightarrow Cu(NO_3)_2(aq) + Ag(cr)$

13. $K(cr) + H_2O(l) \rightarrow KOH(aq) + H_2(g)$

14. $Cl_2(g) + LiI(aq) \rightarrow LiCl(aq) + I_2(g)$

*Balance each of the following reactions after predicting the products.*

15. aluminum(cr) + hydrochloric acid(aq) $\rightarrow$

16. iron(cr) + copper(II) sulfate(aq) $\rightarrow$ (iron(II) compound is formed)

17. zinc(cr) + sulfuric acid(aq) $\rightarrow$

18. chlorine(g) + magnesium iodide(aq) $\rightarrow$

19. sodium(cr) + water(l) $\rightarrow$

20. magnesium(cr) + hydrochloric acid(aq) $\rightarrow$

**Double Displacement.** The positive and negative ions of two compounds are interchanged in a double displacement reaction. The form of these reactions is easy to recognize.

$$compound + compound \rightarrow compound + compound$$
$$AX + BY \rightarrow AY + BX$$

The following are some general types of double displacement reactions.

1. A reaction between an acid and a base yields a salt and water. Such a reaction is a neutralization reaction.

$$2KOH(aq) + H_2SO_4(aq) \rightarrow K_2SO_4(aq) + 2H_2O(l)$$

2. Reaction of a salt with an acid forms a salt of the acid and a second acid that is volatile.

$$2KNO_3(aq) + H_2SO_4(aq) \rightarrow K_2SO_4(aq) + 2HNO_3(g)$$

This same reaction of a salt with an acid or base may yield a compound that can be decomposed. $H_2CO_3$, $H_2SO_3$, and $NH_3(aq)$ decompose to give a gas and $H_2O$.

$$CaCO_3(aq) + 2HCl(aq) \rightarrow CaCl_2(aq) + H_2CO_3(aq)$$
$$H_2CO_3(aq) \rightarrow CO_2(g) + H_2O(l)$$

3. Reactions of some soluble salts produce an insoluble salt and a soluble salt.

$$AgNO_3(aq) + NaCl(aq) \rightarrow AgCl(cr) + NaNO_3(aq)$$

## PROBLEMS

*Balance the following equations.*

**21.** $Ca(OH)_2(aq) + HCl(aq) \rightarrow CaCl_2(aq) + H_2O(l)$

**22.** $KOH(aq) + H_3PO_4(aq) \rightarrow K_3PO_4(aq) + H_2O(l)$

**23.** $Al(NO_3)_3(aq) + H_2SO_4(aq) \rightarrow Al_2(SO_4)_3(aq) + HNO_3(aq)$

**24.** $Na_2SO_3(aq) + HCl(aq) \rightarrow NaCl(aq) + H_2O(l) + SO_2(g)$

*Balance each of the following reactions after predicting the products.*

**25.** sodium hydroxide(aq) + phosphoric acid(aq) $\rightarrow$

**26.** ammonium sulfate(aq) + calcium hydroxide(aq) $\rightarrow$

**27.** silver nitrate(aq) + potassium chloride(aq) $\rightarrow$

**28.** magnesium hydroxide(aq) + phosphoric acid(aq) $\rightarrow$

**29.** iron(II) sulfide(cr) + hydrochloric acid(aq) $\rightarrow$

**30.** ammonium sulfide(aq) + iron(II) nitrate(aq) $\rightarrow$

**Decomposition.** When energy in the form of heat, electricity, light, or mechanical shock is supplied, a compound may decompose to form simpler substances. The general form for this type of reaction is

$$compound \rightarrow two\ or\ more\ substances$$
$$AX \rightarrow A + X$$

The following are some general types of decomposition reactions.

1. When some acids are heated, they decompose to form water and an acidic oxide.

$$H_2CO_3(aq) \rightarrow CO_2(g) + H_2O(l)$$

2. When some metallic hydroxides are heated, they decompose to form a metallic oxide and water.

$$Ca(OH)_2(cr) \rightarrow CaO(cr) + H_2O(g)$$

3. When some metallic carbonates are heated, they decompose to form a metallic oxide and carbon dioxide.

$$Li_2CO_3(cr) \rightarrow Li_2O(cr) + CO_2(g)$$

4. When metallic chlorates are heated, they decompose to form metallic chlorides and oxygen.

$$2KClO_3(cr) \rightarrow 2KCl(cr) + 3O_2(g)$$

5. Most metallic oxides are stable, but a few decompose when heated.

$$2HgO(cr) \rightarrow 2Hg(l) + O_2(g)$$

6. Some compounds cannot be decomposed by heat, but can be decomposed into their elements by electricity.

$$2NaCl(l) \rightarrow 2Na(cr) + Cl_2(g)$$

## PROBLEMS

*Balance the following equations.*

**31.** $KNO_3(cr) \rightarrow KNO_2(cr) + O_2(g)$

**32.** $PbO_2(cr) \rightarrow PbO(cr) + O_2(g)$

**33.** $NaOH(cr) \rightarrow Na_2O(cr) + H_2O(l)$

**34.** $MgCO_3(cr) \rightarrow MgO(cr) + CO_2(g)$

*Balance each of the following reactions after predicting the products.*

**35.** When heated, sulfurous acid, $H_2SO_3 \rightarrow$

**36.** When heated, calcium carbonate $\rightarrow$

**37.** When heated, iron(III) hydroxide $\rightarrow$

**38.** When heated, sodium chlorate $\rightarrow$

**39.** When heated, silver oxide $\rightarrow$

**40.** By electricity, water $\rightarrow$

**Synthesis.** In a synthesis reaction two or more simple substances are combined to form one new and more complex substance. Here the general form is

*element or compound + element or compound $\rightarrow$ compound*

$$A + X \rightarrow AX$$

The following are some general types of synthesis reactions.

1. Two or more elements combine to form a compound.

$$Fe(cr) + S(l) \rightarrow FeS(cr)$$

2. An acid anhydride, nonmetallic oxide, combines with water to give an acid.

$$SO_2(g) + H_2O(l) \rightarrow H_2SO_3(aq)$$

3. A basic anhydride, metallic oxide, combines with water to form a base.

$$Na_2O(cr) + H_2O(l) \rightarrow 2NaOH(aq)$$

4. A basic oxide combines with a nonmetallic oxide to form a salt.

$$CO_2(g) + Na_2O(cr) \rightarrow Na_2CO_3(cr)$$

## PROBLEMS

*Balance the following equations.*

**41.** $Na(cr) + Cl_2(g) \rightarrow NaCl(cr)$
**42.** $Br_2(g) + H_2O(l) + SO_2(g) \rightarrow HBr(aq) + H_2SO_4(aq)$
**43.** $CaO(cr) + H_2O(l) \rightarrow Ca(OH)_2(aq)$
**44.** $P_2O_5(cr) + BaO(cr) \rightarrow Ba_3(PO_4)_2(cr)$

*Balance each of the following reactions after predicting the products.*

**45.** barium oxide(cr) + water(l) →
**46.** sulfur(IV) oxide(g) + magnesium oxide(cr) →
**47.** carbon dioxide(g) + water(l) →
**48.** magnesium(cr) + oxygen(g) →
**49.** nitrogen(III) oxide(g) + water(l) →
**50.** iron metal(cr) + oxygen(g) → (iron(III) compound is formed)

## 6:4   MASS-MASS RELATIONSHIPS

**Stoichiometry** is the study of quantitative relationships in chemical reactions. A basic idea used in solving stoichiometric problems is the mole concept (see Chapter 5). If you are given the mass of one substance and know the balanced equation, you can calculate the reactants needed or the products produced because the equation shows relative number of moles of reactants and products. A general procedure for mass-mass problems uses the following steps.

1. Write a balanced equation.
2. Convert from mass of given material to moles.
3. Determine the mole ratio from the coefficients of the balanced equation and convert from moles of given material to moles of required material.
4. Express the moles of required material in grams.

The setup for a mass-mass calculation follows the format given below.

$$\left(\begin{array}{c}start\ with\\grams\ given\end{array}\right) \rightarrow \left(\begin{array}{c}grams\\to\ moles\end{array}\right) \rightarrow \left(\begin{array}{c}use\\mole\ ratio\end{array}\right) \rightarrow \left(\begin{array}{c}moles\\to\ grams\end{array}\right) \rightarrow \left(\begin{array}{c}end\ with\\grams\ required\end{array}\right)$$

## Example 2

Calculate the mass of HCl needed to react with 10.0 g Zn.

**Solving Process:**

**Step 1.** Begin with the balanced equation.

$$Zn(cr) + 2HCl(aq) \rightarrow ZnCl_2(aq) + H_2(g)$$

**Step 2.** Convert grams of zinc to moles.

$$\frac{10.0 \text{ g Zn}}{} \quad \bigg| \quad \frac{1 \text{ mol Zn}}{65.4 \text{ g Zn}}$$

**Step 3.** Determine the mole ratio that exists between Zn and HCl and convert from moles Zn to moles HCl.

1 mole Zn reacts with 2 moles HCl

$$\frac{10.0 \text{ g Zn}}{} \quad \bigg| \quad \frac{1 \text{ mol Zn}}{65.4 \text{ g Zn}} \quad \bigg| \quad \frac{2 \text{ mol HCl}}{1 \text{ mol Zn}}$$

**Step 4.** Convert moles of HCl to grams of HCl.

$$\text{grams HCl} = \frac{10.0 \text{ g Zn}}{} \quad \bigg| \quad \frac{1 \text{ mol Zn}}{65.4 \text{ g Zn}} \quad \bigg| \quad \frac{2 \text{ mol HCl}}{1 \text{ mol Zn}} \quad \bigg| \quad \frac{36.5 \text{ g HCl}}{1 \text{ mol HCl}}$$

$$= 11.2 \text{ g HCl}$$

Note that the conversion ratios are chosen and arranged so all the units divide out except the desired unit, in this case, grams of HCl. Since all the ratios are equal to 1, multiplying by one of them, or by all of them, changes only the units of the answer.

## Example 3

Calculate the mass of $O_2$ produced if 2.50 g $KClO_3$ are completely decomposed by heating.

**Solving Process:**

**Step 1.** Write the balanced equation.

$$2KClO_3(cr) \rightarrow 2KCl(cr) + 3O_2(g)$$

**Step 2.** Convert mass of $KClO_3$ to moles.

$$\frac{2.50 \text{ g KClO}_3}{} \quad \bigg| \quad \frac{1 \text{ mol KClO}_3}{123 \text{ g KClO}_3}$$

**Step 3.** Determine the mole ratio that exists between $KClO_3$ and $O_2$.

2 moles $KClO_3$ yield 3 moles $O_2$

$$\frac{2.50 \text{ g KClO}_3}{} \quad \bigg| \quad \frac{1 \text{ mol KClO}_3}{123 \text{ g KClO}_3} \quad \bigg| \quad \frac{3 \text{ mol O}_2}{2 \text{ mol KClO}_3}$$

**Step 4.** Convert moles of $O_2$ to grams.

$$\text{grams O}_2 = \frac{2.50 \text{ g KClO}_3}{} \quad \bigg| \quad \frac{1 \text{ mol KClO}_3}{123 \text{ g KClO}_3} \quad \bigg| \quad \frac{3 \text{ mol O}_2}{2 \text{ mol KClO}_3} \quad \bigg| \quad \frac{32.0 \text{ g O}_2}{1 \text{ mol O}_2}$$

$$= 0.976 \text{ g O}_2$$

## PROBLEMS

*Solve the following problems. The reactions may not be balanced.*

51. If 20.0 g of magnesium react with excess hydrochloric acid, how many grams of magnesium chloride are produced?

$$Mg(cr) + HCl(aq) \rightarrow MgCl_2(aq) + H_2(g)$$

52. How many grams of chlorine gas must be reacted with excess sodium iodide if 10.0 g of sodium chloride are needed?

$$NaI(aq) + Cl_2(g) \rightarrow NaCl(aq) + I_2(cr)$$

53. How many grams of oxygen are produced in the decomposition of 5.00 g of potassium chlorate?

$$KClO_3(cr) \rightarrow KCl(cr) + O_2(g)$$

54. What mass of copper is required to replace silver from 4.00 g of silver nitrate dissolved in water?

$$Cu(cr) + AgNO_3(aq) \rightarrow Cu(NO_3)_2(aq) + Ag(cr)$$

55. If excess ammonium sulfate reacts with 20.0 g of calcium hydroxide, how many grams of ammonia are produced?

$$(NH_4)_2SO_4(aq) + Ca(OH)_2(cr) \rightarrow CaSO_4(cr) + NH_3(g) + H_2O(l)$$

56. If excess sulfuric acid reacts with 30.0 g of sodium chloride, how many grams of hydrogen chloride are produced?

$$NaCl(aq) + H_2SO_4(aq) \rightarrow HCl(g) + Na_2SO_4(aq)$$

57. How much silver phosphate is produced if 10.0 g of silver acetate react with excess sodium phosphate?

$$AgCH_3COO(aq) + Na_3PO_4(aq) \rightarrow Ag_3PO_4(cr) + NaCH_3COO(aq)$$

58. How many grams of sodium hydroxide are needed to completely neutralize 25.0 g of sulfuric acid?

$$NaOH(aq) + H_2SO_4(aq) \rightarrow Na_2SO_4(cr) + H_2O(g)$$

## CHAPTER REVIEW PROBLEMS

*Balance the following reactions.*

1. $HgO(cr) \rightarrow Hg(l) + O_2(g)$
2. $H_2O(l) \rightarrow H_2(g) + O_2(g)$
3. $Al(cr) + Pb(NO_3)_2(aq) \rightarrow Al(NO_3)_3(aq) + Pb(cr)$
4. $Cu(cr) + AgNO_3(aq) \rightarrow Cu(NO_3)_2(aq) + Ag(cr)$
5. $K(cr) + H_2O(l) \rightarrow KOH(aq) + H_2(g)$
6. $MnO_2(cr) + HCl(aq) \rightarrow MnCl_2(aq) + Cl_2(g) + H_2O(l)$
7. $Cl_2(g) + LiI(aq) \rightarrow LiCl(aq) + I_2(g)$
8. $F_2(g) + H_2O(l) \rightarrow HF(aq) + O_3(g)$
9. $AgNO_3(aq) + K_2SO_4(aq) \rightarrow Ag_2SO_4(aq) + KNO_3(aq)$

**10.** $NH_3(g) + O_2(g) \rightarrow N_2O_4(g) + H_2O(g)$

*Write a balanced equation and indicate the reaction type (single or double displacement, decomposition, or synthesis) for each of the following reactions.*

**11.** aluminum nitrate(aq) + sodium hydroxide(aq) →
    aluminum hydroxide(cr) + sodium nitrate(aq)

**12.** sulfur trioxide(g) → sulfur dioxide(g) + oxygen(g)

**13.** phosphoric acid(aq) + magnesium hydroxide(aq) →
    magnesium phosphate(cr) + water(l)

**14.** ammonium nitrite(cr) → nitrogen(g) + water(l)

**15.** ammonia(g) + oxygen(g) → nitrogen(II) oxide(g) + water(g)

**16.** barium chloride(aq) + sodium sulfate(aq) → sodium chloride(aq) +
    barium sulfate(cr)

**17.** iron(III) oxide(cr) + carbon monoxide(g) →
    iron(cr) + carbon dioxide(g)

**18.** magnesium hydroxide(aq) + ammonium phosphate(aq) →
    magnesium phosphate(cr) + ammonia(g) + water(l)

**19.** aluminum(cr) + copper(II) chloride(aq) →
    aluminum chloride(aq) + copper(cr)

**20.** iron(cr) + silver acetate(aq) → iron(II) acetate(aq) + silver(cr)

*Balance each of the following reactions after predicting the products.*

**21.** magnesium hydroxide(aq) + phosphoric acid(aq) →

**22.** iron(II) sulfide(cr) + hydrochloric acid(aq) →

**23.** ammonium sulfide(aq) + iron(II) nitrate(aq) →

**24.** sulfuric acid(aq) + potassium hydroxide(aq) →

**25.** aluminum sulfate(aq) + calcium phosphate(cr) →

**26.** barium carbonate(cr) + hydrochloric acid(aq) →

**27.** silver acetate(aq) + potassium chromate(aq) →

**28.** ammonium phosphate(aq) + barium hydroxide(aq) →

**29.** chromium(III) sulfite(aq) + sulfuric acid(aq) →

**30.** calcium hydroxide(aq) + nitric acid(aq) →

**31.** In a series of steps in an experiment, copper metal is converted into various compounds and then back to copper metal by treating the original copper stepwise with nitric acid, sodium hydroxide, heat, sulfuric acid, and zinc metal. Write the five equations representing these chemical changes if the overall experiment can be represented as:

$$Cu \rightarrow Cu(NO_3)_2 \rightarrow Cu(OH)_2 \rightarrow CuO \rightarrow CuSO_4 \rightarrow Cu$$

**32.** One type of fire extinguisher contains concentrated sulfuric acid that reacts with a solution to produce carbon dioxide. What solution, sodium hydrogen carbonate or sodium carbonate, would give the greater amount of carbon dioxide in a reaction with the same amount of acid?

33. If iron pyrite, $FeS_2$, is not removed from coal, oxygen from the air will combine with both the iron and the sulfur as the coal burns. Write a balanced chemical equation illustrating the formation of iron(III) oxide and sulfur dioxide.

34. Sodium sulfite, $Na_2SO_3$, can be used for the removal of $SO_2$ produced as a by-product in manufacturing operations. The $SO_2$ reacts with a sodium sulfite solution to form sodium hydrogen sulfite. The $NaHSO_3$ solution is heated to regenerate the original sodium sulfite for reuse. Write the equation for this reaction.

35. Molten iron and carbon monoxide are produced in a blast furnace by the reaction of iron(III) oxide and coke (carbon). If 25.0 kg of pure $Fe_2O_3$ are used, how many moles of iron can be produced?

36. Ammonia gas produced as a by-product in an industrial reaction can be reacted with sulfuric acid in order that the gas does not escape into the atmosphere. The product, ammonium sulfate, can be used as a fertilizer. Determine how many kilograms of acid are required to produce 1000.0 kg of $(NH_4)_2SO_4$.

37. Coal gasification is a process that is carried out industrially in a series of steps. The net reaction involves coal (carbon) reacting with water to form methane, $CH_4$, and carbon dioxide. How many kilograms of methane can be produced from $1.00 \times 10^3$ kg of coal?

38. A source of acid rain is automobile exhaust. Nitric oxide, formed in an internal combustion engine, reacts with oxygen in the air to produce nitrogen dioxide. The $NO_2$ reacts with water to form nitric acid. It is determined that the average car produces $10.0 \, m^3$ of exhaust gas per mile driven. Assume that the average concentration of $NO_2$ in auto exhaust is $100.0 \, \mu g/m^3$ and that traffic surveys have shown an average of $2.00 \times 10^6$ vehicle miles driven per day. From this data, determine the kilograms of nitric acid that could be produced annually.

$$2NO_2 + H_2O \rightarrow HNO_2 + HNO_3$$

39. Photosynthesis is a complex process composed of many steps. The initial reactants are carbon dioxide and water and the final products are glucose and oxygen gas. If a plant needs to make 30.0 g of glucose, $C_6H_{12}O_6$, through the process of photosynthesis, how many grams of water are required?

# ATOMIC STRUCTURE 7

## 7:1 EARLY ATOMIC THEORIES

Scientists use models to explain atomic structure, because atoms cannot be seen directly. Models help provide mental images for concepts such as atomic structure. The research and theories described in this section will help you develop a mental model for what scientists believe atoms would look like if individual atoms could be seen.

In the 1800's John Dalton proposed an atomic theory of matter. His theory had four main points: (1) all matter is composed of atoms which cannot be broken apart; (2) all atoms of the same element are identical in mass (and other properties); (3) atoms of different elements are different in mass (and other properties); (4) atoms unite in definite ratios to form compounds. Dalton's theory is that atoms have fixed masses. An atom of one element has the same mass no matter what other elements it combines with. In a given chemical compound, the elements are always combined in the same proportion by mass. This statement is the **law of definite proportions.** Dalton's theory was modified when subatomic particles and isotopes were discovered.

Since the late 1800's there has been a great deal of scientific research to determine the actual structure of atoms. In 1897, J. J. Thompson used cathode ray tubes in a magnetic field to determine the charge to mass ratio for an electron. A few years later, Robert Millikan designed his "oil drop" experiment to provide the data needed to calculate the mass of the electron. In 1913, Henry Moseley used X rays to find the relationship between wavelength and atomic number. Based on his work we know that the number of protons determines the identity of the element.

Niels Bohr and Ernest Rutherford used spectroscopy to expand their knowledge of atomic structure. They viewed the atom as a central nucleus of positive charge surrounded by electrons. Today we know that absorption and emission spectra are like fingerprints for the elements. Bohr pictured the hydrogen atom as an electron circling a nucleus. The electron moves from its ground state or normal state if it absorbs a photon, energy of a certain frequency. When an electron drops from a larger orbit to a smaller one, a definite amount of energy is radiated.

## 7:2 ISOTOPES AND ATOMIC NUMBER

The **atomic number** of an element is represented by the symbol $Z$. The atomic number is the number of protons in the nucleus. Since an atom is electrically neutral, the number of electrons must equal the number of protons. The atomic number can be found in the table of atomic masses inside the back cover of this book. The number of protons determines the identity of the element.

**Isotopes** are atoms of an element that are exactly alike chemically but slightly different in mass. Isotopes have the same number of protons but a different number of neutrons. The number of neutrons determines the particular isotope of the element.

The particles that make up an atomic nucleus are called **nucleons.** The total number of nucleons, protons plus neutrons, in an atom is called the **mass number,** $A$. Thus, the number of neutrons $= A - Z$. Isotopes are often symbolized by placing the atomic number and mass number to the left of the chemical symbol. The mass number is a superscript, the atomic number a subscript. The isotope of radon, an indoor air pollutant, is

$$\text{mass number (protons + neutrons)} \atop \text{atomic number (protons)} \quad {}^{222}_{86}\text{Rn}$$

The name of this isotope is radon-222.

## Example 1

Compute the number of electrons, protons, and neutrons in the atom of carbon with $A = 14$, and write its nuclear symbol.

**Solving Process:**

The atomic number, $Z$, is read from the table of atomic masses. The atomic number (number of protons) of carbon is 6. Because the atom is electrically neutral, the number of electrons equals the atomic number. The mass number, $A$, is the total number of nucleons. This particular isotope of carbon has a mass number of 14.

$$\text{number of neutrons} = A - Z = 14 - 6 = 8$$

In carbon-14, there are 6 protons, 8 neutrons, and 6 electrons. Its nuclear symbol is ${}^{14}_{6}\text{C}$.

## PROBLEMS

1. Use the table of atomic masses inside the back cover to compute the number of electrons, neutrons, and protons in the following nuclides. Write the symbol for each nuclide.

   **a.** Cr   $A = 50$      **d.** Ir   $A = 193$
   **b.** Cl   $A = 37$      **e.** Si   $A = 29$
   **c.** Mg  $A = 26$      **f.** Ne  $A = 22$

2. Moseley used X rays to determine the atomic numbers of the elements. Identify each of the following elements by name.

   **a.** 1 proton           **d.** 12 protons
   **b.** 4 protons          **e.** 20 protons
   **c.** 8 protons          **f.** 30 protons

# 7:3  AVERAGE ATOMIC MASS

The atomic mass unit, u, is used to measure atomic mass. The carbon-12 nuclide is the standard for the atomic mass scale. One carbon-12 atom has a mass of 12 atomic mass units. The subatomic particles that we have studied have the following atomic masses.

$$\text{electron} = 9.109\ 53 \times 10^{-28}\ \text{g} = 0.000\ 549\ \text{u}$$
$$\text{proton} = 1.672\ 65 \times 10^{-24}\ \text{g} = 1.0073\ \text{u}$$
$$\text{neutron} = 1.674\ 95 \times 10^{-24}\ \text{g} = 1.0087\ \text{u}$$

As you can see, the masses of the protons and neutrons in an atom make up nearly all of the atom's mass.

The **average atomic mass** of an element can be determined from relative amounts of each isotope. In a naturally occurring element, the fractional abundance is the fraction of a particular isotope in the total sample of atoms. The atomic masses in the atomic mass table and the periodic table are based on the weighted average of the masses of all isotopes of an element. The average atomic mass of the element is used in most chemical calculations.

## Example 2

Chlorine has two isotopes. Chlorine-35 has an actual mass of 34.9689 u and chlorine-37 has a mass of 36.9659 u. In any sample of chlorine atoms, 75.771% will be chlorine-35 and 24.229% will be chlorine-37. Calculate the average atomic mass of chlorine.

**Solving Process:**

Each of the isotopic masses is multiplied by its fractional abundance. Then the products are added.

$$(34.9689)(0.75771) + (36.9659)(0.24229) = 35.453\ \text{u}$$

## PROBLEMS

3. Calculate the average atomic mass of magnesium using the following data for three magnesium isotopes.

| isotope | mass (u) | fractional abundance |
|---------|----------|----------------------|
| Mg-24 | 23.985 | 0.7870 |
| Mg-25 | 24.986 | 0.1013 |
| Mg-26 | 25.983 | 0.1117 |

4. Calculate the average atomic mass of iridium using the following data for two iridium isotopes.

| isotope | mass (u) | fractional abundance |
|---------|----------|----------------------|
| Ir-191 | 191.0 | 0.3758 |
| Ir-193 | 193.0 | 0.6242 |

## CHAPTER REVIEW PROBLEMS

*Indicate whether each of the following statements is true or false. Correct the false statements.*

1. Dalton's atomic theory includes a statement that says atoms of the same element are identical.
2. Dalton's theory states that atoms have variable masses.
3. J. J. Thompson is credited with the "oil drop" experiment.
4. The mass of an electron is equal to the mass of a proton.
5. The mass of a proton is approximately equal to the mass of a neutron.
6. Millikan devised an experiment to determine the charge on an electron.
7. The atomic number represents the number of protons in a nucleus and is represented by the symbol Na.
8. The proton has a mass of approximately 1 u.
9. The difference in mass of isotopes of the same element is due to the different number of protons in the nucleus.
10. The isotope carbon-12 is used as the relative mass standard for the atomic mass scale.
11. Calculate the average atomic mass of chromium.

    | isotope | mass (u) | fractional abundance |
    |---------|----------|----------------------|
    | Cr-50   | 49.946   | 0.043 500            |
    | Cr-52   | 51.941   | 0.838 00             |
    | Cr-53   | 52.941   | 0.095 000            |
    | Cr-54   | 53.939   | 0.023 500            |

12. How many protons are in the nucleus of each of the following elements?

    **a.** uranium       **c.** helium
    **b.** selenium      **d.** unnilseptium

13. Give the number of neutrons in each of the following isotopes.

    **a.** titanium-46    **c.** $^{34}_{16}S$
    **b.** nitrogen-15    **d.** $^{65}_{29}Cu$

14. Fill in the blanks in the table below for neutral atoms. Use only the information given in the table.

    |                | Atomic Number | Mass Number | Number of protons | Number of neutrons | Number of electrons |
    |----------------|---------------|-------------|-------------------|--------------------|---------------------|
    | calcium-43     |               |             | 20                |                    |                     |
    | lead-211       |               |             |                   | 129                |                     |
    | plutonium-242  | 94            |             |                   |                    |                     |
    | chromium-50    |               |             |                   |                    | 24                  |

# ELECTRON CLOUDS AND PROBABILITY  8

## 8:1 QUANTUM NUMBERS

Einstein demonstrated that light not only has wave properties but also particle properties. DeBroglie reasoned that if light, which is considered a wave, has particle properties then particles of matter might show wave characteristics. Schrödinger expanded these concepts to describe electrons and to develop a theory called quantum mechanics or wave mechanics. **Quantum mechanics** allows us to determine the probability of finding an electron at a certain place in the atom. We do not know an electron's exact position. In fact, *it is impossible to know both the position and speed of an electron with absolute certainty.* This statement is the **Heisenberg Uncertainty Principle.**

Quantum mechanics uses four different **quantum numbers** to describe each electron in an atom. Three of the quantum numbers, $n$, $l$, and $m$, describe the atomic orbital. An **atomic orbital** is a region in space where there is a high probability of finding the electrons. The fourth quantum number, $s$, is used to designate a magnetic property of electrons called spin.

The **principal quantum number,** $n$, is used to describe the energy of the electron. The energy of an electron is determined by its average distance from the nucleus. The energy level in an atom is related to the radius of the electron cloud. The $n$ quantum number can have values of 1, 2, 3, ... $n$. Each energy level, or quantum number, has $n$ different sublevels. Each sublevel is described by the second quantum number $l$. The numerical values for $l$ are the integers from 0 to $(n - 1)$. The $l$ values are usually designated by letters, $s$ for $l = 0$, $p$ for $l = 1$, $d$ for $l = 2$, and $f$ for $l = 3$. All of the sublevels, except the $s$ sublevel, have more than one orbital. Each orbital in a sublevel will have the same energy and usually the same shape as all the others in that sublevel.

The orbitals differ in their orientation in space around the nucleus. The third quantum number, $m$ (magnetic quantum number), is used to describe each orbital within a sublevel. The values for $m$ are integers from $-l$ to $+l$. For example, when $l = 1$, the sublevel is $p$. Since $m$ can have any value from $+l$ to $-l$, its values are $-1$, 0, and $+1$. Thus there are three orbitals in the $p$ sublevel, one located along each of the three perpendicular axes.

When an electron moves, it generates a magnetic field. The fourth quantum number, s, describes the direction of electron spin around its axis. There are two values permitted by the theory, $+1/2$ and $-1/2$. These values can be thought of as describing clockwise and counterclockwise electron rotation around its axis. According to the **Pauli Exclusion Principle** *no two electrons in an atom can have the same set of quantum numbers.* Thus, only two electrons, having opposite spins, can occupy an orbital. As a result, each sublevel can hold a maximum of twice as many electrons as the number of orbitals in the sublevel.

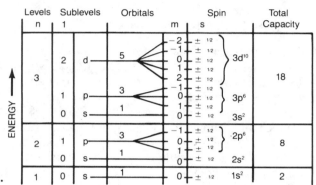

**FIGURE 8-1.**

PROBLEMS

1. Extend Figure 8-1 by showing the permitted values for each of the quantum numbers in the fourth energy level.

2. What is the maximum number of electrons that can occupy the fourth energy level?

3. Complete the following table.

| sublevel | s | p | d | f |
|----------|---|---|---|---|
| *l* value |   |   |   |   |

4. How many sublevels are there in the third energy level?

5. How many electrons can occupy any single orbital?

6. Complete the following table for the sublevels represented by the following quantum numbers.

| n | 2 |  | 4 | 4 | 5 |
|---|---|---|---|---|---|
| *l* | 0 | 2 |  | 3 |  |
| sublevel designation |  | 3d | 4p |  | 5s |

7. When $n = 5$, what are the possible values for $l$?

8. When $l = 2$, what are the possible values of $m$?

## 8:2   DIAGONAL RULE

The **electron configuration** of an atom is used to describe the electron distribution in the sublevels. Each sublevel symbol is written following a coefficient that represents the energy level containing the sublevel. Each sublevel symbol has a superscript on the right giving the number of electrons in the sublevel. For example, the electron configuration of the boron atom (atomic number 5) is written $1s^2 2s^2 2p^1$.

The order of filling corresponds to the increasing energy of the sublevels. By filling the sublevels of the lowest energy first, we have a model of an atom in the ground state. In many atoms with higher atomic numbers, the sublevels are not regularly filled. There is a rule of thumb that will give a correct configuration for most atoms in the ground state. We will explore the exceptions more fully in the next chapter. This rule of thumb is called the **diagonal rule** and is shown in Figure 8-2. If you follow the diagonal arrows from tail to head, listing the orbitals passed, you can find the electron configuration of most atoms.

**FIGURE 8-2.**

Example 1

Write the electron configuration of arsenic ($Z = 33$).

**Solving Process:**

The diagonal rule diagram gives us the order $1s$, $2s$, $2p$, $3s$, $3p$, $4s$, $3d$, $4p$. The sublevels are then filled to capacity with the 33 electrons present in arsenic beginning with $1s$, then $2s$, and so on. The final 3 electrons are placed in the $4p$. The electron configuration is $1s^2 2s^2 2p^6 3s^2 3p^6 4s^2 3d^{10} 4p^3$.

The sum of the superscripts equals the atomic number, 33.

## PROBLEMS

9. Which of the following show the correct order of filling?
   a. $1s2s2p$                     d. $1s2s2p3s3p4s$
   b. $1s2s2p3s3p$                 e. $1s2s2p3p3d4s$
   c. $1s2s3s$                     f. $1s2s2p3s3p4s4p$

10. Write the name of the element represented by each of the following configurations.
    a. $1s^22s^22p^5$                    c. $1s^22s^22p^63s^23p^64s^23d^{10}4p^1$
    b. $1s^22s^22p^63s^2$                d. $1s^22s^22p^63s^23p^4$

11. Write the electron configuration for each of the following elements using the diagonal rule.
    a. aluminum ($Z = 13$)          d. carbon ($Z = 6$)
    b. iron ($Z = 26$)              e. barium ($Z = 56$)
    c. cadmium ($Z = 48$)           f. hafnium ($Z = 72$)

## 8:3   ORBITAL FILLING DIAGRAMS

The electron configuration gives the number of electrons in each sublevel but does not show how the orbitals of a sublevel are occupied by the electrons. The result of Hund's Rule predicts that one electron enters each orbital of a sublevel before any orbital is doubly occupied. For example, the electron configuration for nitrogen is $1s^22s^22p^3$. Nitrogen has three electrons in the $2p$ sublevel, and each of these electrons occupies a separate orbital. In the orbital filling diagram each box stands for an orbital. Arrows are used to indicate the direction of electron spin.

## Example 2

Construct an orbital filling diagram for fluorine ($Z = 9$).
**Solving Process:**
**Step 1.** Write the electron configuration using the diagonal rule.

$$1s^22s^22p^5$$

**Step 2.** Construct an orbital filling diagram using a box for each orbital. Use arrows to represent the electrons in each orbital.

| 1s | 2s | 2p | | |
|----|----|----|----|----|
| ↑↓ | ↑↓ | ↑↓ | ↑↓ | ↑ |

Recall that each electron occupies an empty orbital within a sublevel, rather than pair with another.

# 8:4   ELECTRON DOT DIAGRAMS

The Lewis electron dot diagram is useful when showing how atoms bond together. In these diagrams the outer energy level electrons, those with the largest value of $n$, are represented by dots placed around the letter symbol of the element.

## Example 3

Write the Lewis electron dot diagram for selenium ($Z = 34$).

**Solving Process:**

**Step 1.** Write the orbital filling diagram for the outer energy level of selenium using the diagonal rule.

$$1s^2 2s^2 2p^6 3s^2 3p^6 4s^2 3d^{10} 4p^4 \qquad \begin{array}{c} 4s \\ \boxed{\uparrow\downarrow} \end{array} \qquad \begin{array}{c} 4p \\ \boxed{\uparrow\downarrow} \ \boxed{\uparrow} \ \boxed{\uparrow} \end{array}$$

**Step 2.** The symbol of the element represents the nucleus and all the electrons except those in the outer energy level. Each "side" (above, below, left, right) of the symbol represents an orbital. Draw dots on the sides to represent only the outer electrons ($4s$ and $4p$). Show them as paired or unpaired based on the orbital diagram.

## PROBLEMS

12. Predict electron configurations using the diagonal rule for atoms of the following elements.

| | | | |
|---|---|---|---|
| **a.** Li | **c.** Be | **e.** B | **g.** C |
| **b.** N | **d.** O | **f.** F | **h.** Ne |

13. Draw orbital filling diagrams for the elements listed in problem 12.

14. Draw Lewis electron dot diagrams for the elements in problem 12.

## CHAPTER REVIEW PROBLEMS

1. Heisenberg stated that, at the same time, it was impossible to know what two things about an electron?

2. How many quantum numbers are there?

3. What letter denotes the quantum number for the principal energy level?

4. What four letters are used to represent the sublevels within a principal energy level?

5. What is the maximum number of electrons that may occupy one orbital?

6. Who stated that no two electrons in the same atom could have the same set of four quantum numbers?

7. The Lewis electron dot diagram is used to represent only which electrons in an atom?

8. What is the diagonal rule used to predict?

9. How many sublevels are possible in the third energy level?

10. How many orbitals are there in an *f* sublevel?

11. What is the maximum number of electrons that can occupy a *d* sublevel?

12. Which sublevel may contain a maximum of three pairs of electrons?

13. What must be true about the spins of two electrons occupying the same orbital?

14. Write the electron configuration for each of the following elements.
    a. lithium ($Z = 3$)       d. mercury ($Z = 80$)
    b. radium ($Z = 88$)       e. tin ($Z = 50$)
    c. sodium ($Z = 11$)       f. krypton ($Z = 36$)

15. Draw the orbital filling diagrams for the following elements.
    a. titanium ($Z = 22$)     c. aluminum ($Z = 13$)
    b. sodium ($Z = 11$)       d. phosphorus ($Z = 15$)

16. Draw the Lewis electron dot diagram for the elements listed in problems 14 and 15.

# PERIODIC TABLE

# 9

## 9:1 MODERN PERIODIC TABLE

In 1869 Dmitri Mendeleev, a Russian chemist, prepared a periodic table of the elements. The elements were arranged in order of their atomic masses in horizontal rows so that the elements in any vertical column had similar properties. In 1914, Moseley determined the atomic numbers of the elements from their X-ray spectra. He then reordered the elements in the periodic table according to increasing atomic number. This arrangement gave rise to our modern **periodic law.** It states that *the properties of the elements are a periodic function of their atomic numbers.*

In the modern periodic table we place elements with similar electron configurations in the same column or group. We also list the elements in the column in order of their increasing principal quantum numbers. The numbers along the left side of the periodic table on the inside back cover are the values for *n*, the energy levels. The first two columns (1-2) consist of elements that have electrons filling the *s* sublevel. The elements in the last six columns on the right (13-18) are elements that have electrons filling the *p* sublevels. The 10 columns in the center of the chart (3-12) contain the transition elements whose electrons are filling an inner *d* sublevel having a quantum number of $(n - 1)$. The two horizontal rows at the bottom of the periodic table represent the elements with a quantum number of $(n - 2)$ whose electrons are filling the inner *f* sublevel.

## 9:2 ELECTRON CONFIGURATION

The periodic table can be used to read the electron configuration of an element. The written configuration of any element in Group IA (1) will end in $s^1$. The coefficient of $s^1$ is easily found from the table because the number of the period indicates the energy level. Group IIA (2) elements end their electron configuration with $s^2$. The same procedure can be used for Groups IIIA (13) through VIIIA (18). There the endings are $p^1$ through $p^6$ preceded by a coefficient that is the same number as the period. For example, arsenic $(Z = 33)$ is in period 4 and Group VA (15). Its electron configuration will end in $4p^3$.

For Groups IIIB (3) through IIB (12) the endings are $d^1$ through $d^{10}$ preceded by a coefficient that is one less than the period number. For the lanthanides, the endings are $f^1$ through $f^{14}$ preceded by a coefficient that is two less than the period number.

To understand some of the exceptions to the diagonal rule, it is necessary to know that there is a special stability associated with certain electron configurations in an atom. An atom with eight electrons in the outer level has a special stability. *An atom having a filled or half filled sublevel is also more stable.* For example, chromium is predicted to have two electrons in its $4s$ sublevel and four electrons in its $3d$ sublevel. Actually it has only one electron in its $4s$ sublevel and five electrons in its $3d$ sublevel. Thus, the atom has two half-full sublevels instead of one full sublevel and one with no special arrangement. Copper is similar. It has one electron in its $4s$ sublevel and ten electrons in its $3d$ sublevel. Most of the exceptions from predicted configurations can be explained in this way.

## PROBLEMS

1. Give the group number for the elements that have the following electron configurations.

   **a.** $1s^2 2s^2 2p^1$

   **b.** $1s^2 2s^2$

   **c.** $1s^2 2s^2 2p^6 3s^2 3p^5$

   **d.** $1s^2 2s^2 2p^6 3s^2 3p^4$

   **e.** $1s^2 2s^2 2p^6 3s^2 3p^6 4s^2 3d^3$

   **f.** $1s^2 2s^2 2p^6 3s^2 3p^6 4s^2 3d^{10}$

2. Give the names of each of the elements listed in problem 1.

3. Write the electron configurations for the following elements.

   **a.** potassium ($Z = 19$)

   **b.** mercury ($Z = 80$)

   **c.** lithium ($Z = 3$)

   **d.** phosphorus ($Z = 15$)

   **e.** calcium ($Z = 20$)

   **f.** indium ($Z = 49$)

4. In what period would the element with the configuration $1s^2 2s^2 2p^6 3s^2 3p^6 4s^2 3d^{10} 4p^6 5s^1$ be located?

5. Which two elements in the fourth period have configurations that are apparent contradictions to the diagonal rule?

## 9:3  METALS AND NONMETALS

Many of the columns in the table have family names. Group IA (1), except hydrogen, is called the **alkali metal family.** Group IIA (2) is called the **alkaline earth metal family.** Groups IA (1) and IIA (2) of the periodic table contain the most active metals.

On the other side of the table are the nonmetals. Group VIA (16) is called the **chalcogen** (KAL kuh juhn) **family.** Group VIIA (17) is known as the **halogen family.** The elements of Group VIIIA (18) are called the **noble gases.**

The majority of elements are **metals.** We are all familiar with typical metallic properties. Metals have a luster and are malleable. They conduct heat and electricity well. **Nonmetals** are generally gases or brittle solids at room temperature. They are usually poor conductors of heat and electricity. Exceptions are diamond, an excellent conductor of heat, and graphite, an electrical conductor. Elements with three or fewer electrons in the outer level are considered to be metals. Elements with five or more electrons in the outer level are considered to be nonmetals. There are some elements that have properties of both metals and nonmetals. These elements are called **metalloids.** These elements lie to the right and left of the stairstep line on the periodic table. Aluminum is usually considered to be a metal.

The elements in the B Groups are called **transition elements.** They all show metallic properties. The elements 57 through 70, the **lanthanides,** and 89 through 102, the **actinides,** have two electrons in the outer energy level and are metals.

## PROBLEMS

6. Classify the following elements as metal, metalloid, or nonmetal.
   **a.** cadmium        **c.** californium        **e.** calcium
   **b.** fluorine        **d.** carbon            **f.** germanium
7. Are the transition elements metals or nonmetals?

*Match each of the following terms with a letter from the periodic table.*

FIGURE 9-1.

 8. alkali metals              12. chalcogens
 9. alkaline earth metals      13. halogens
10. lanthanides                14. noble gases
11. actinides                  15. transition metals

## CHAPTER REVIEW PROBLEMS

1. How are substances that are gases or brittle solids at room temperature classified?

2. Would an element with two outer electrons be a metal or nonmetal?

3. What Russian scientist designed the first periodic table?

4. Which group of elements contains the most active metals?

5. Which group of elements has eight outer electrons?

6. To which quantum number is the period number of an element related?

7. For the transition elements, as the atomic number increases, to which sublevel are electrons being added?

8. According to the octet rule, how many pairs of outer electrons do the most stable atoms have?

9. In the lanthanide series, as the atomic number increases, to which sublevel are electrons being added?

10. Write the electron configurations of the following elements.
    a. silicon ($Z = 14$)          c. copper ($Z = 29$)
    b. krypton ($Z = 36$)          d. cesium ($Z = 55$)

11. Identify the elements whose electron configurations end with the following.
    a. $4s^2 3d^2$                 d. $7s^2 5f^6$
    b. $2s^2 2p^6$                 e. $4s^2 3d^{10} 4p^5$
    c. $4s^1 3d^5$                 f. $3s^1$

12. Write the electron configurations of the following elements.
    a. iodine ($Z = 53$)           c. nickel ($Z = 28$)
    b. oxygen ($Z = 8$)            d. strontium ($Z = 38$)

13. Classify the following elements as metals, metalloids, or nonmetals.
    a. chlorine ($Z = 17$)         d. arsenic ($Z = 33$)
    b. tungsten ($Z = 74$)         e. promethium ($Z = 61$)
    c. radium ($Z = 88$)           f. uranium ($Z = 92$)

# PERIODIC PROPERTIES 10

## 10:1 RADII OF ATOMS

The periodic table is a powerful tool of the chemist. Similar properties of the elements occur at predicted intervals. The properties are periodic because both the position and properties arise from the electron configurations of the atoms.

As you look at the periodic table from top to bottom, each period represents a new energy level. *As the principal quantum number increases, the size of the electron cloud increases.* Chemists discuss the size of atoms by referring to their radii. As you look across the periodic table, all the atoms in a period have the same principal quantum number. The positive charge on the nucleus increases by one proton for each element. This increase in charge results in the outer electron cloud being pulled closer to the nucleus. Thus, *atoms generally decrease slightly in size from left to right across a period.*

### PROBLEM

1. From each of the following pairs, use the periodic table to select the atom that is larger in radius.
   **a.** Sn, Sr     **c.** Na, Rb     **e.** S, P     **g.** B, Al
   **b.** Cl, I      **d.** Mg, Be    **f.** Ac, U    **h.** Au, Ba

## 10:2 RADII OF IONS

Generally, when atoms unite to form compounds, their structures become more stable. Ionic compounds are formed from atoms that have lost or gained electrons in order to obtain a noble gas configuration. A **noble gas configuration** is particularly stable because the eight outer electrons fill the outer sublevels. Metals, on the left and in the center of the table, tend to lose electrons, forming positive ions by losing electrons. This loss of electrons results in the formation of a smaller metallic ion. Nonmetals are located on the right side of the table. Nonmetallic ions are formed by atoms gaining electrons. The negatively charged nonmetallic ions are larger than the atoms from which they are formed.

### PROBLEM

2. From each of the following pairs of particles, select the particle that is larger in radius.
   **a.** Ca, $Ca^{2+}$    **c.** $As^{3-}$, $P^{3-}$    **e.** $Mg^{2+}$, $Be^{2+}$    **g.** C, $C^{4-}$
   **b.** $F^-$, $Cl^-$     **d.** $Pb^{4+}$, Pb    **f.** $Te^{2-}$, Te     **h.** Ag, $Ag^+$

## 10:3   PREDICTING OXIDATION NUMBERS

The outer, high energy electrons are involved in the reaction of atoms with each other. Recall that the noble gas configuration of eight outer electrons is stable. Filled $s$ and $p$ sublevels result in eight outer electrons. Oxidation numbers can be predicted from electron configurations.

Consider the metals in Group IA (1). Each atom has one electron in its outer level. The loss of this one electron will give these metals the same configuration as a noble gas. Group IA (1) metals have an oxidation number of 1+. In Group IIA (2) we would expect the loss of the two $s$ electrons for the atom to achieve the same configuration as the prior noble gas. That loss leads to a prediction of 2+ oxidation number for the alkaline earth metals.

In the B groups there are atoms in which the highest energy electrons are not in the outer level. Scandium has the configuration $1s^2 2s^2 2p^6 3s^2 3p^6 4s^2 3d^1$. Its outer level is the fourth level containing two electrons. Scandium's highest energy electron, however, is the one in the $3d$ sublevel. The transition elements may lose not only the outer level electrons, but also some lower electrons. Therefore, the transition elements have oxidation numbers varying from 2+ (representing loss of the two outer $s$ electrons) to 8+. We would expect scandium to show only 2+ and 3+ oxidation numbers. Titanium has one more $3d$ electron than scandium. Experiments show that it has the predicted 2+, 3+, and 4+ numbers. The trend continues across the fourth row. Vanadium has a maximum oxidation number of 5+, chromium 6+, and manganese 7+. Iron, with a configuration of $1s^2 2s^2 2p^6 3s^2 3p^6 4s^2 3d^6$, has oxidation numbers of 2+ and 3+. For iron to have oxidation numbers higher than 3+ would mean breaking up a half-full $3d$ sublevel. Recall that an atom with a half-full sublevel represents a particularly stable configuration.

Group IIIA (13) elements lose three electrons and have an oxidation number of 3+. Group IVA (14) may have a 2+ or 4+ oxidation number.

In Groups VA (15), VIA (16), and VIIIA (17), there is a general tendency to gain electrons to complete the octet. The outside level is already more than half-filled. These elements show oxidation numbers of 3−, 2−, and 1− respectively. It is also possible for these elements to lose electrons and have positive oxidation numbers. The tendency to lose electrons increases as we move down a column.

## PROBLEMS

3. Predict the oxidation numbers for the following elements.

| | | | |
|---|---|---|---|
| **a.** Al | **c.** Cl | **e.** Mg | **g.** Na |
| **b.** N | **d.** Zn | **f.** S | **h.** Mn |

4. Which electrons were gained or lost to complete the outer octet and produce the following ions?

| | | | |
|---|---|---|---|
| **a.** $K^+$ | **c.** $Ga^{3+}$ | **e.** $Sn^{4+}$ | **g.** $Ca^{2+}$ |
| **b.** $O^{2-}$ | **d.** $P^{3-}$ | **f.** $Br^-$ | **h.** $Sc^{3+}$ |

## 10:4   FIRST IONIZATION ENERGY

Some atoms tend to give up electrons and become positive ions. Other atoms tend to gain electrons and become negative ions. These atomic tendencies have a periodic nature.

The energy needed to remove an atom's most loosely held electron is called **first ionization energy.** It is measured in kilojoules per mole. A metal is characterized by a low first ionization energy. Nonmetals have high first ionization energies.

*In any column or group, there is a gradual decrease in ionization energy as atomic number increases.* The increased distance of the outer electrons from the nucleus and the **shielding effect** of the inner electrons tend to lower the ionization energy. Though it appears that the increased nuclear charge of an element with a greater atomic number would increase ionization energy, the lowering effects of increased distance and shielding are greater. Remember that the number of electrons in the outermost sublevel is the same for all elements in a column or group.

Ionization energy tends to increase as atomic number increases in any horizontal row or period. This increase is a result of the increasing nuclear charge. There are some deviations from this expected trend of increasing ionization energy. These deviations result from the factors listed in Table 10-1.

**Table 10-1**

| Factors Affecting Ionization Energy |
|---|
| 1. **Nuclear charge**—the larger the nuclear charge, the greater the ionization energy. |
| 2. **Shielding effect**—the greater the shielding effect, the less the ionization energy. |
| 3. **Radius**—the greater the distance between the nucleus and the outer electrons of an atom, the less the ionization energy. |
| 4. **Sublevel**—an electron from a full or half-full sublevel requires additional energy to be removed. |

It is possible to measure other (second, third, and so on) ionization energies of an atom. Ionization energy increases with the removal of each additional electron.

### PROBLEM

5. Which atom in each of the following pairs would have the lower first ionization energy?

| | | |
|---|---|---|
| **a.** N, O | **d.** C, Ge | **g.** I, Sb |
| **b.** Te, Sn | **e.** Br, I | **h.** Al, N |
| **c.** Ne, F | **f.** Mg, Ca | **i.** F, S |

## CHAPTER REVIEW PROBLEMS

1. Within a group, does the radii of atoms increase or decrease as the atomic number increases?

2. Does the radii of atoms within a period increase or decrease as the atomic number increases?

3. In each of the following pairs of atoms, pick the one that is larger.
   - **a.** Mg, Na
   - **b.** K, Ca
   - **c.** Al, B
   - **d.** Br, Cl
   - **e.** F, N
   - **f.** Ne, Ar

4. In each of the following pairs of particles, pick the one that is smaller.
   - **a.** Fe, $Fe^{3+}$
   - **b.** $S^{2-}$, S
   - **c.** $Ac^{3+}$, $U^{3+}$
   - **d.** $Br^-$, $Se^{2-}$
   - **e.** $Mo^{6+}$, Mo
   - **f.** $As^{3-}$, As

5. Predict the oxidation number of the following elements.
   - **a.** Li
   - **b.** Be
   - **c.** B
   - **d.** C
   - **e.** P
   - **f.** O
   - **g.** F
   - **h.** Ar
   - **i.** K

6. Predict the oxidation numbers of the following elements.
   - **a.** Rb
   - **b.** Co
   - **c.** Pu
   - **d.** Bi
   - **e.** V
   - **f.** Ba

7. In a group, will the ionization energy tend to increase or decrease with increasing atomic number?

8. In a period, will the ionization energy tend to increase or decrease with increasing atomic number?

9. Do metals or nonmetals generally have lower ionization energies?

10. Carbon has a first ionization energy of 1086.5 kJ/mol. Predict whether the first ionization energies of the following elements will be more or less than that of carbon.
    - **a.** helium
    - **b.** lithium
    - **c.** fluorine
    - **d.** silicon

11. As the distance between the nucleus and the outer electrons of an atom increases, will the ionization energy increase or decrease?

12. As the shielding effect increases, will the ionization energy increase or decrease?

13. As the positive charge on an ion increases, will the ionization energy increase or decrease?

# TYPICAL ELEMENTS

# 11

Elements in the same group on the periodic table have similar outer electron configurations. This arrangement gives them a similarity of properties and is the reason a group is sometimes called a family of elements. The similarity is particularly strong in Groups IA (1), IIA (2), VIIA (17), and VIIIA (18).

## 11:1  HYDROGEN

Hydrogen is a unique element and is thus a family by itself. The most abundant element in the universe, hydrogen is widely used in industry to make products as diverse as fertilizer, missile fuel, and margarine.

Hydrogen can react in four ways. It can lose its one electron to form the **hydrogen ion, H$^+$.** It can gain an electron as it forms the **hydride ion, H$^-$,** and combine with positive metal ions. Hydrogen can share electrons with most nonmetals. It can also act as a bridging atom between two atoms, such as boron.

## 11:2  REPRESENTATIVE METALS

Lithium, sodium, and potassium belong to Group IA (1), the alkali metals. These elements have low densities, are soft, and very reactive, forming 1+ ions. Reactivity increases as the atomic numbers of these metals increase. Their ionization energies become less because of the increased distance of the electrons from the nucleus and the shielding effect. Alkali metals form binary compounds with most nonmetals. Lithium is not typical of this group, since its reactions are more like magnesium, a Group IIA (2) element.

**FIGURE 11-1.**

Trends in Oxidation Numbers of the Elements

Group IIA (2) elements are known as alkaline earth metals. These elements are also reactive, and they form 2+ ions. Most compounds of these metals are soluble in water.

Aluminum, one of the Group IIIA (13) metals, is the most abundant metal in the earth's crust. It tends to share its three outer electrons, and is less reactive than the metals of Groups IA (1) and IIA (2).

## 11:3  REPRESENTATIVE NONMETALS

The elements of Group IVA (14) have atoms with four electrons in the outer level. These elements generally react by sharing electrons. Carbon is the first element in this group. The major part of carbon chemistry is classed as organic chemistry. **Catenation** occurs when carbon forms "chains" with other carbon atoms. Generally, compounds that do not contain carbon are called inorganic compounds. Different forms of the same element are called **allotropes.** Carbon has two allotropes: diamond and graphite.

Nitrogen and phosphorus differ greatly even though they are adjacent members of Group VA (15). Nitrogen occurs in oxidation states ranging from 3− through 5+. Phosphorus shows only 3−, 0, 3+, and 5+ oxidation states. Nitrogen gas, $N_2$, is very stable but many nitrogen compounds are relatively unstable. TNT, an explosive, is one example. Elemental phosphorus, solid at room temperature, occurs as $P_4$ molecules. White and red phosphorus are allotropes.

Oxygen, Group VIA (16), is the most plentiful element in the earth's crust. It gains two electrons to achieve a stable octet and forms $O^{2-}$ ions. Metallic oxides generally react with water to form basic solutions. Nonmetallic oxides generally form acidic solutions when dissolved in water. Some oxides, called amphoteric oxides, can produce either acidic or basic solutions, depending on the other substances present. Ozone, $O_3$ is a highly reactive allotrope of oxygen. The chemistry of sulfur is similar to that of oxygen.

Group VIIA (17) is the highly reactive halogen (salt forming) family. These elements exist as diatomic molecules. They react either by forming 1− ions or by sharing electrons. Fluorine is the most reactive of all elements, because of its small radius and limited shielding effect.

In 1962, the first "inert" gas compound was synthesized. Since that time the gases of Group VIIIA (18) have been called the noble gases. Xenon, krypton, and radon compounds have been made. However, the noble gases are generally considered the most stable elements.

## 11:4  TRANSITION METALS, LANTHANIDES AND ACTINIDES

The transition metals ("B" groups) are those elements whose highest energy electrons are in *d* sublevels. The *d* electrons may be lost, one at a time, after the outer $s$ electrons have been lost. The fourth period elements, titanium through zinc, are used primarily as structural metals. They can be used alone or as alloys. Chromium is a transition metal. It has multiple oxidation numbers. Because of its $4s^13s^5$ outer electron configuration, it is stable and resists corrosion. Zinc's behavior differs slightly from other transition elements due to a full $d$ sublevel, $4s^23d^{10}$.

All of the lanthanides show $3+$ as the most stable state. Neodymium, a soft reactive metal, is a typical example of the elements whose highest energy level electrons are in the $4f$ sublevel. The actinides are those elements whose highest energy level electrons are in the $5f$ sublevel. Curium, a silvery, hard metal of medium density is an example. It is reactive and highly toxic.

## CHAPTER REVIEW PROBLEMS

*Identify the false statements and correct them.*

1. Group IIA (2) elements that form $2+$ ions are known as alkali metals.

2. Graphite and diamond are isotopes of carbon.

3. The transition metals are those elements whose highest energy electrons are in the $4f$ sublevel.

4. The shielding effect blocks the attraction of the nucleus for outer electrons.

5. The tendency of carbon atoms to form long chains is called catenation.

6. When hydrogen gains one electron, it forms the hydrogen ion, $H^+$.

7. Organic chemistry is the chemistry of carbon compounds.

8. The family of elements having eight outer electrons, Group VIIIA (18), is called the halogens.

9. Amphoteric oxides react with water to form either acidic or basic solutions.

10. The most reactive elements on the periodic table are in Groups IIA (2) and VIIA (17).

# CHEMICAL BONDING 12

## 12:1  BOND CHARACTER

*The chemical bonds formed between atoms depend on two periodic properties: the electron configurations of the atoms and the attraction the atoms have for electrons.* The relative tendency of an atom to attract electrons to itself when bonded with another atom is called **electronegativity.** Examine Table A-9 in the Appendix. It shows that the variation in electronegativity follows the same trend as ionization energies.

When two atoms transfer electrons, ions are produced. The electrostatic force that holds two ions together due to their differing charges is the **ionic bond.** Ionic compounds have high melting points, conduct electricity in the molten state, tend to be soluble in water, and usually crystallize as well-defined crystals.

If two elements combine by sharing electrons, they are said to form a **covalent bond.** The shared pair or pairs of electrons constitute a covalent bond. The resulting particle is called a **molecule.** Covalent compounds typically have low melting points, do not conduct electricity, and are brittle.

Electronegativity differences can be used to determine whether a bond is ionic or covalent. Use Table 12-1 to find the percent ionic or covalent character of a bond. As you can see, most bonds show some ionic and covalent character. The character of bonds is on a continuum. The value of 1.67 is generally used for convenience as a dividing point. Electronegativity differences less than 1.67 are considered mainly covalent; differences above 1.67 are considered mainly ionic.

Table 12-1

| Character of Bonds | | | | | | | | | |
|---|---|---|---|---|---|---|---|---|---|
| Electronegativity Difference | 0.00 | 0.65 | 0.94 | 1.19 | 1.43 | 1.67 | 1.91 | 2.19 | 2.54 |
| Percent Ionic Character | | 0% | 10% | 20% | 30% | 40% | 50% | 60% | 70% |
| Percent Covalent Character | | 100% | 90% | 80% | 70% | 60% | 50% | 40% | |

## Example 1

Classify as ionic or covalent the bond that forms between calcium and oxygen.

**Solving Process:**

From Table A-9 the electronegativity of calcium is found to be 1.02 and oxygen is 3.37.

$$\text{Electronegativity difference} = 3.37 - 1.02 = 2.35$$

Use Table 12-1 to determine the percent ionic character. The difference of 2.35 is between 70% and 80%. The bond is considered to be an ionic bond.

## PROBLEMS

1. Classify the bonds between the following pairs of atoms as principally ionic or covalent.

   **a.** magnesium—chlorine      **d.** titanium—oxygen
   **b.** potassium—sulfur      **e.** copper—bromine
   **c.** cobalt—carbon      **f.** selenium—iodine

2. For each compound listed below, determine the character of the bond between the elements.

   **a.** NiO      **c.** $CaCl_2$      **e.** NaF
   **b.** BN      **d.** FeSi      **f.** $Zn_3P_2$

## 12:2  BOND LENGTH

The chemist makes use of four different types of radii—atomic, ionic, covalent, and van der Waals. Values for these radii can be found in your textbook and most chemical handbooks. We studied in Section 10:2 how ionic radii differ from atomic radii because of the loss or gain of electrons. Ionic radii are determined from ionic crystals. By adding the radii of two ions in a compound we may find their **internuclear distance** in a crystal.

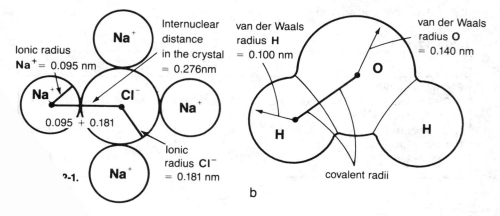

b

The distance between nuclei along the bond axis is called the **bond length.** This length is not really fixed because the atoms vibrate as though the bond were a spring. Bond lengths are average values. The bond length is the sum of the covalent radii of the atoms in the bond.

A certain minimum distance must be maintained between atoms that are not bonded to each other. This limitation exists because the electron cloud of one atom repels the electron cloud of other atoms. The radius of the imaginary rigid shell of an atom is called the van der Waals radius. It is named for the Dutch physicist Johannes van der Waals.

## PROBLEMS

*Use Figures 12-2a and b to answer the following questions.*

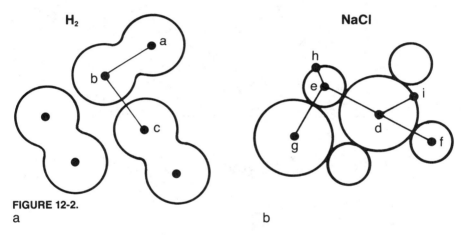

**FIGURE 12-2.**
a                                                        b

3. What are the names for the following lines?
   **a.** ab          **c.** di          **e.** df          **g.** eh
   **b.** bc          **d.** de          **f.** eg
4. What type of bonds does hydrogen have?
5. What type of bond exists between sodium and chlorine?

## 12:3   METALS

The properties of metals are not explained by ionic and covalent bonding theories. Metals conduct electricity, which indicates a ready source of electrons. Most metals have only one or two outer energy level electrons. These electrons are loosely held and readily move into the **conduction band** when an energy source is applied. Electrons are free to travel in the conduction band and are called **delocalized electrons.**

Metals differ from metalloids and nonmetals in that the energy gaps, the **forbidden zones,** in metals are very small, Figure 12-3. If sufficient energy is used the outer electrons in a semiconductor can be forced into the conduction band. The forbidden zone in nonmetals is too large an energy gap for electrons to pass over. For this reason, nonmetals are often referred to as insulators.

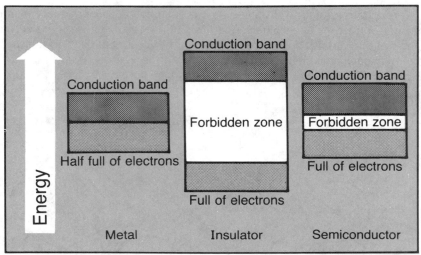

**FIGURE 12-3.**

## CHAPTER REVIEW PROBLEMS

1. Use Table A-9 to predict which of the following bonds will be ionic or covalent.

   **a.** Ca—F               **c.** H—O
   **b.** S—O                **d.** K—Cl

2. Answer the following questions about trends on the periodic table with "increases" or "decreases."

   **a.** Within a family of elements, what happens to the atomic radii as the atomic number increases?
   **b.** Within a family of elements, what happens to the electronegativity as the atomic number increases?
   **c.** Within a period, what happens to the electronegativity as the atomic number increases?

3. Match the following characteristics with the correct bond type—ionic, covalent, or metallic.

   **a.** electrons transferred shared
   **b.** electrons delocalized
   **c.** electrons shared

# MOLECULAR STRUCTURE  13

The structure of a substance determines its properties. It is, therefore, important to be able to predict the structure of molecules. Several theories have been proposed to explain the structure of molecules.

## 13:1 LEWIS ELECTRON DOT STRUCTURES

Being able to draw Lewis structures for polyatomic ions and molecules is very helpful in determining their structures. Guidelines for drawing these structures follow. Methane, $CH_4$, and the carbonate ion, $CO_3^{2-}$, are used as examples.

1. The first step is to decide what atoms are bonded together. The formula may suggest how the atoms are to be arranged. For those atoms given, the arrangements are

$$\begin{matrix} & H & & & O & & O \\ H & C & H & \text{and} & & C & \\ & H & & & & O & \end{matrix}$$

This choice is not always easy. For most binary covalent compounds and polyatomic ions, the central atom will be the atom that occurs once in the formula. For oxygen-containing acids, the hydrogens that are released from these compounds are bonded to oxygen. When in doubt, choose the most symmetrical atom arrangement.

2. Count the total number of outer level electrons in the ion or molecule. For $CH_4$, there are eight, four from carbon plus one from each of the four hydrogens. For $CO_3^{2-}$ there are twenty-four, four from carbon, six from each of the three oxygens, plus the two added to give the ion a charge of $2-$.

3. Place a pair of electrons (dots) between the central atom and each of the other atoms.

$$\begin{matrix} & H & & & O & O \\ H & \overset{..}{\underset{..}{C}} & H & & & \overset{..}{C} \\ & H & & & & O \end{matrix}$$

4. Distribute the remaining outer electrons so that each atom has a filled outer energy level, usually an octet of electrons. Some exceptions are H, which has two, and B, which will have six.

**83**

Our structure for $CH_4$ above is complete. We have used all eight electrons in such a way that carbon has eight and each hydrogen has two. However, we must add electrons to the carbonate unit.

$$\left[ \begin{array}{c} :\ddot{O}: \\ C \\ :\ddot{O}: \quad :\ddot{O}: \end{array} \right]^{2-} \quad \text{or} \quad \left[ \begin{array}{c} :\ddot{O}:C:\ddot{O} \\ :\ddot{O}: \end{array} \right]^{2-}$$

Neither structure meets the requirement of eight electrons around each atom. This leads to step 5.

5. When there are not enough electrons, make double or triple bonds. When there are extra electrons, place these on the central atom.

To have eight electrons on each atom, we move an additional pair of electrons between C and an O to create a double bond.

$$\left[ \begin{array}{c} :\ddot{O}:C::\ddot{O} \\ :\ddot{O}: \end{array} \right]^{2-} \quad \text{or} \quad \left[ \begin{array}{c} :\ddot{O}-C=\ddot{O} \\ | \\ :\ddot{O}: \end{array} \right]^{2-}$$

Thus, the unit contains 24 electrons arranged so that each atom has 8 electrons.

# 13:2   RESONANCE

The structure we have written for carbonate indicates one double and two single bonds. Double bonds are shorter than single bonds, but bond length measurements show that all three bonds are the same length. The values are intermediate between single and double. The Lewis structure doesn't match reality. We get around this problem by using a concept called **resonance** in which we represent a molecular structure as an average of two or more equivalent structures. For the carbonate ion, we write

$$\left[ \begin{array}{c} :\ddot{O} \\ \| \\ C \\ :\ddot{O}. \quad .\ddot{O}: \end{array} \right]^{2-} \leftrightarrow \left[ \begin{array}{c} :\ddot{O}: \\ | \\ C \\ :\ddot{O}. \quad \ddot{O}: \end{array} \right]^{2-} \leftrightarrow \left[ \begin{array}{c} :\ddot{O}: \\ \\ C \\ :\ddot{O} \quad .\ddot{O}: \end{array} \right]^{2-}$$

One carbonate ion exists. It has three bonds of equal length.

## PROBLEMS

1. Predict a reasonable arrangement of atoms in the following.
   a. $CO_2$         b. $BCl_3$         c. $NO_3^-$         d. $H_3PO_4$

2. Draw Lewis structures for each of the following.

a. $H_2S$      c. $NO_3^-$      e. $CCl_4$

b. $NH_4^+$      d. CO      f. HCOOH (one H bonds to C, one to O)

3. Which of the structures in question 2 involve resonance?

# 13:3 OUTER LEVEL ELECTRON PAIR REPULSION

One theory of molecular geometry holds that the outer level electron pair charge clouds repel each other. Thus, *the electron pairs, shared or unshared, stay as far apart as possible to minimize repulsion.*

This theory explains why $CO_2$ is linear, $H_2O$ is bent, or angular, and $CH_4$ is tetrahedral. See Table 13-1.

**Table 13-1**

| Molecular Geometry | | | |
|---|---|---|---|
| Number of Electron Clouds | Electron Geometry | Hybridization at Central Atom (A) and Examples | Shape |
| 2 | :—A—: <br> linear | $sp$ <br> (180°) <br> $BeCl_2$ <br> $CO_2$ | |
| 3 | trigonal planar | $sp^2$ <br> (120°) <br> $BF_3$ <br> $BCl_3$ | |
| 4 | tetrahedral | $sp^3$ <br> (109°28') <br> $CH_4$ <br> $CCl_4$ | |
| 5 | trigonal bipyramidal | $sp^3d$ or $dsp^3$ <br> (90°, 120°, 180°) <br> $PF_5$ <br> $AsCl_5$ | |
| 6 | octahedral | $sp^3d^2$ or $d^2sp^3$ <br> (90°, 180°) <br> $SF_6$ <br> $SeF_6$ | |

## Example 1

Predict the molecular structure of water, $H_2O$.

**Solving Process:**

The electron dot structure for water is H$:\overset{\displaystyle..}{\underset{\displaystyle H}{O}}:$ .

There are four electron pairs on oxygen. When these electron pairs are as far apart as possible, their clouds will point to the corners of a tetrahedron. Thus, the two hydrogen atoms form an angular molecule with oxygen, as their electron clouds are bent away from the two unshared electron pairs.

In a regular tetrahedron the bond angles are 109.5° as they are in $CH_4$ and $CCl_4$, each of which contains four shared electron pairs. The H-O-H bond angle in water is 104.5°. This angle is caused by the two unshared pairs of electrons that spread their charge clouds over a larger volume. The repulsion between unshared pairs is greater than that between shared pairs.

## 13:4  HYBRID ORBITALS

Another theory explains molecular shape in terms of the formation of orbitals that are hybrids of $s$, $p$, and $d$ orbitals. In this theory, bonding is viewed as an overlap of orbitals. The bonds between H and O in water are formed by the overlap of the half-filled $s$ orbital in H and a half-filled $p$ orbital in O.

To explain the bonding in compounds of beryllium, boron, carbon, and similar atoms, the idea of **hybrid orbitals** is used. For example, beryllium forms $BeH_2$. However, its electron configuration shows only paired outer electrons. The two Be—H bonds are accounted for by proposing the formation of two $sp$ orbitals.

Be   | ↑↓ |  |   |   |   |        Be   | ↓ | ↓ |   |   |   |
   2s          2p                  sp        2p

"hybrid"

One of the $2s$ electrons is "promoted" to a $2p$ orbital, and two equivalent hybrid orbitals result. The two $sp$ orbitals are directed in space to minimize repulsion. A linear structure results.

We predict $sp^2$ hybridization in boron that results in three orbitals in a triagonal planar arrangement, 120° bond angle. Carbon forms four $sp^3$ hybrid orbitals. These orbitals are directed in a tetrahedral arrangement, 109° bond angle.

Two different types of orbital overlap are observed. A bond formed by the direct overlap of two orbitals is called a **sigma bond** ($\sigma$). This type of overlap includes $s$-$s$, $s$-$p$, and $p$-$p$ overlap in an end-to-end manner. When two $p$ orbitals overlap sideways with their axes parallel, they form a **pi** ($\pi$)

**bond.** Single bonds can be considered as sigma bonds. A double bond is made up of one sigma bond and one pi bond. Molecules containing multiple bonds are usually more reactive than molecules containing only single bonds. A triple bond contains one sigma and two pi bonds.

# 13:5  MOLECULAR ORBITAL DIAGRAMS

Molecular orbital theory permits the study of the electron configuration of molecules in a manner similar to that of an atom's electron configuration. A molecular orbital is an area of high electron probability and has a definite energy.

As two hydrogen atoms collide, their $s$ orbitals overlap to form a low energy molecular orbital called a bonding orbital. The law of conservation of energy requires that a high energy, antibonding orbital also be formed. The bonding orbital is designated $\sigma_{1s}$ (sigma one ess), while the antibonding orbital is called $\sigma^*_{1s}$. The asterisk indicates an antibonding orbital.

The three $p$ atomic orbitals are perpendicular to each other, one lying along each of the three axes. They are labeled $p_x$, $p_y$, and $p_z$. As noted before, $p$ orbitals of different atoms can overlap side-to-side or end-to-end. If we label the ones that overlap end-to-end as $p_x$, the set of bonding and antibonding orbitals that form are $\sigma_{p_x}$ and $\sigma^*_{p_x}$. The $p_y$ and $p_z$ orbitals are perpendicular to the $p_x$ orbitals and overlap side to side, forming $\pi$-type molecular orbitals. These orbitals are $\pi_{p_y}$ and $\pi^*_{p_y}$, and $\pi_{p_z}$ and $\pi^*_{p_z}$.

Figure 13-1 shows the relative energies of these orbitals. The number of molecular orbitals formed equals the total number of atomic orbitals in the atoms combined. The electrons fill the lowest available orbitals first. The order of filling is

$$\sigma_{1s} < \sigma^*_{1s} < \sigma_{2s} < \sigma^*_{2s} < \pi_{2p_y} = \pi_{2p_z} < \sigma_{2p_x} < \pi^*_{2p_y}$$
$$= \pi^*_{2p_z} < \sigma^*_{2p_x}$$

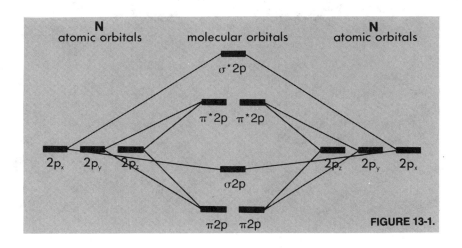

FIGURE 13-1.

A superscript is added to each orbital to indicate the number of electrons in the orbital. This notation is then referred to as the molecular orbital configuration. As with atomic electron configurations, electrons use unoccupied orbitals of the same energy before pairing up.

The number and strength of bonds that form between two atoms is measured by the **bond order.**

> bond order = 1 = single bond
> bond order = 2 = double bond
> bond order = 3 = triple bond

The bond order can be calculated from the molecular orbital configuration. Subtract the number of electrons in antibonding orbitals from the number of electrons in bonding orbitals and divide the difference by two. A bond order of zero means no stable molecule exists.

## Example 2

Use a molecular orbital diagram to write the molecular orbital configuration and compute the bond order for the nitrogen molecule, $N_2$.

**Solving Process:**

When the two nitrogen atoms combine, their atomic orbitals form the molecular orbitals shown in Figure 13-2. Each nitrogen atom has five outer

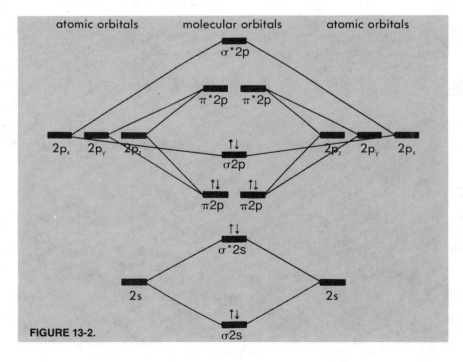

**FIGURE 13-2.**

electrons, $2s^2 2p^3$. Therefore, there would be ten electrons to place in molecular orbitals in the second energy level.

The molecular orbital configuration of $N_2$ is

$$(\sigma_{1s})^2 \, (\sigma^*_{1s})^2 \, (\sigma_{2s})^2 \, (\sigma^*_{2s})^2 \, (\pi_{2p_y})^2 \, (\pi_{2p_z})^2 \, (\sigma_{2p_x})^2$$

Since electrons in energy levels other than the outer level cancel, they can be omitted when calculating bond order.

$$\text{bond order} = \frac{\text{bonding} - \text{antibonding}}{2} = \frac{8 - 2}{2} = 3$$

Therefore, the $N_2$ molecule is stable and there is a triple bond between nitrogen atoms.

## PROBLEM

4. For each of the following, complete a molecular orbital diagram, write the molecular orbital configuration, and determine the bond order.
   - **a.** $Li_2$
   - **b.** $Be_2$
   - **c.** $C_2$

## CHAPTER REVIEW PROBLEMS

1. How many electrons should be shown in Lewis structures of each of the following?
   - **a.** $HNO_3$
   - **b.** $CN^-$
   - **c.** $O_2F_2$
   - **d.** $CS_2$
   - **e.** $POBr_3$
   - **f.** $C_2O_4{}^{2-}$

2. Draw Lewis structures for each of the following. Include all resonance structures.
   - **a.** $PH_3$
   - **b.** $CS_2$
   - **c.** $OH^-$
   - **d.** $NO^+$
   - **e.** $CO_3{}^{2-}$
   - **f.** $HCN$
   - **g.** $NH_3$
   - **h.** $SOCl_2$ (S is central atom)
   - **i.** $PCl_5$

3. Compare the C to O bond lengths in $CO_2$ and $CO_3{}^{2-}$.

4. Why is the N—H bond angle in $NH_3$ less than a tetrahedral angle of 109.5°?

5. Carbon uses four hybrid ($sp^3$) orbitals in the molecule, $CH_4$. Explain how these hybrid orbitals form.

6. Distinguish a sigma-bond from a pi-bond.

7. Predict the shape of the following using the electron pair repulsion model.
   - **a.** $BCl_3$
   - **b.** $MgI_2$
   - **c** $H_2S$
   - **d.** $CI_4$
   - **e.** $SiF_4$
   - **f.** $SCl_6$

**8. a.** Write a molecular orbital diagram for $He_2$.
   **b.** Compute the bond order for $He_2$.
   **c.** Write the molecular orbital configuration for $He_2$.
   **d.** Would you expect an $He_2$ molecule to exist?

**9. a.** Write the molecular orbital diagram for the BN molecule.
   **b.** Compute the bond order for BN.
   **c.** Write the molecular orbital configuration for BN.
   **d.** Would you expect a BN molecule to exist?

# POLAR MOLECULES 14

## 14:1 POLARITY

Most chemical bonds are neither 100% ionic nor 100% covalent. Atoms have different electron-attracting abilities, as measured by ionization energies and electronegativites. This difference results in unequal sharing of the bonding electrons, producing polar bonds and often polar molecules. A **polar bond** is one in which there is an uneven charge distribution. In the molecule HCl, for example, chlorine has a partial negative charge ($\delta^-$) and hydrogen a partial positive charge ($\delta^+$).

$$\overset{\delta^+}{H} -\overset{\delta^-}{Cl} \quad \text{or} \quad H \Rightarrow Cl$$

The electronegativity difference is $3.00 - 2.20 = 0.80$. The result is a polar bond, or dipole, and also a polar molecule. An arrow is used to represent a polar bond. The arrow points to the element with higher electronegativity.

Not all molecules having polar bonds are polar. Molecular geometry must be considered. If the polar bonds are arranged symmetrically, the polar effects cancel, as in $CO_2$, $BCl_3$, and $CCl_4$.

$$O \Lleftarrow C \Rrightarrow O \qquad \overset{Cl}{\underset{Cl \quad Cl}{\overset{\uparrow}{B}}} \qquad \overset{Cl}{\underset{Cl}{Cl \leftarrow C \rightarrow Cl}}$$

Unsymmetrical arrangements occur in $H_2O$ and $NH_3$, producing polar molecules.

Many physical properties of molecules, such as melting and boiling points and solubility are affected by the degree of polarity of molecules.

---

### Example 1

Determine the polarity of HCN and $SOCl_2$.

**Solving Process:**
Determine the molecular geometry by drawing Lewis structures and using the electron pair repulsion theory.

$$:\!\ddot{O}\!:\!\ddot{S}\!:\!\ddot{Cl}\!:$$
$$:\!\ddot{Cl}\!:$$

$$H:C:::N:$$
linear                    trigonal pyramid

Use electronegativities to determine bond polarity H = 2.20, C = 2.56, N = 2.81, S = 2.46, Cl = 3.00, O = 3.37. Electronegativity differences give these bond polarities:

$$H \rightarrow C \rightarrow N \qquad O \leftarrow S \rightarrow Cl$$
$$\downarrow$$
$$Cl$$

Since both arrangements are unsymmetrical, polar molecules result.

## PROBLEMS

1. Which of the following bonds is most polar? In each bond, indicate the atom that carries the partial negative charge.

   **a.** H-I          **b.** P-I          **c.** As-Br          **d.** N-S

2. Which of the following molecules are polar?

   **a.** $SO_2$          **b.** $AsCl_3$          **c.** $H_2Se$          **d.** $SO_3$

# 14:2  VAN DER WAALS FORCES

The attractive forces between molecules strongly influence their physical properties. Strong intermolecular attractions between molecules in solids and liquids affect the melting and boiling points of these substances. The stronger the forces, the higher these temperatures are. The chief forces of intermolecular attraction are dipole-dipole forces and London, or dispersion, forces. These forces are known as **van der Waals forces.**

Dipole-dipole forces exist between polar molecules. Dispersion forces are temporary dipoles in nonpolar molecules. These instantaneous dipoles are created as the movement of electrons shifts the electron density. The more electrons a molecule has the stronger the dispersion forces. In general, for molecules of approximately the same molecular mass, dipole-dipole forces are stronger than dispersion forces.

## PROBLEMS

3. Compare the strength of intermolecular forces in methane, $CH_4$ (molecular mass = 16) and ammonia, $NH_3$ (molecular mass = 17).

4. List these molecules in order of increasing van der Waals forces: $Br_2$, $F_2$, $Cl_2$, $I_2$.

# 14:3  COMPLEX IONS

Some polar molecules, such as $H_2O$ and $NH_3$, and some negative ions react with transition metal ions to form **complex ions** and coordination compounds. An example is $Fe(H_2O)_6{}^{2+}$, hexaaquoiron(II) ion. The polar molecules and negative ions, called **ligands,** bond by donating a pair of electrons to the central atom. In the resulting bond, called a **coordinate covalent bond,** both electrons come from one atom. Thus, when a complex ion combines with an oppositely charged ion to form a neutral species, it is called a coordination compound. The cancer drug, dichlorodiammineplatinum(II), $Pt(NH_3)_2Cl_2$, is a coordination compound.

# 14:4  NAMING COMPLEX IONS

In naming a complex ion, the ligands are named first, followed by the name of the central ion. Each type of ligand is preceded by a prefix designating the number of molecules or ions of that particular ligand present in the complex. The prefixes used are *di-, tri-, tetra-, penta-,* and *hexa-.*

**Table 14-1**

| Some Common Ligands | | | |
|---|---|---|---|
| Ligand | Name | Ligand | Name |
| $OH^-$ | hydroxo | $S_2O_3{}^{2-}$ | thiosulfato |
| $Br^-$ | bromo | $C_2O_4{}^{2-}$ | oxalato |
| $Cl^-$ | chloro | $H_2O$ | aquo |
| $F^-$ | fluoro | $NH_3$ | ammine |
| $I^-$ | iodo | $CO$ | carbonyl |
| $S^{2-}$ | thio | $NO$ | nitrosyl |
| $CN^-$ | cyano | | |

The order given in Table 14-1 represents the order in which the ligands appear in a name. Note that negative ions are named before molecules. If the complex as a whole possesses a negative charge, the name of the complex ion ends in *-ate.* If the central ion has more than one possible oxidation number, a Roman numeral in parentheses must follow the name of the central ion.

**Table 14-2**

| Latin Stems Used in Some Metal Complexes | | | |
|---|---|---|---|
| Metal | Latin Stem | Metal | Latin Stem |
| copper | cuprate | lead | plumbate |
| gold | aurate | silver | argentate |
| iron | ferrate | tin | stannate |

## Example 2

Name the complex ion $FeCO(CN)_5{}^{3-}$.

**Solving Process:**

In the complex ion there are two ligands, CO, carbonyl, and $CN^-$, cyano. The negative cyano ligand is named first, preceded by the prefix penta. Molecular ligands such as carbonyl are named second, followed by the name of the central ion. The ending on the word iron remains unchanged if the ion is positive, but in this example it is negative. The elements listed in Table 14-2 use the Latin stem when the ion is negative. Thus, iron becomes ferrate. Iron has more than one possible oxidation number, so its oxidation number is given in parentheses after its name. The name of the complex ion is written as one word. The name is

pentacyanocarbonylferrate(II) ion

## PROBLEMS

5. Name the following complex ions.
   a. $AuCl_4{}^-$
   b. $Cr(NH_3)_3Cl^{2+}$
   c. $Cu(NH_3)_4{}^{2+}$
   d. $HgI_4{}^{2-}$
6. Write formulas for the following complex ions.
   a. hexaaquochromium(III)
   b. hexaamminecobalt(III)

## CHAPTER REVIEW PROBLEMS

1. Use Table A-9 to arrange the following bonds in order of increasing polarity: H—O, H—H, H—Cl, H—S, H—Br, H—Ga. Indicate the atom in each bond that carries the partial negative charge.
2. Which of the following molecules are polar?
   a. CO
   b. $SiCl_4$
   c. $COCl_2$ (C is central atom)
   d. $HCBr_3$ (C is central atom)
3. Choose the substance in each of the following pairs that has the stronger intermolecular forces.
   a $CH_4$, $CH_3Cl$
   b. $H_2$, $N_2$
   c. $AsCl_3$, $AsBr_3$
   d. $SO_2$, $SO_3$
   e. $H_2S$, $H_2Se$
   f. $CH_4$, $CCl_4$
4. What two types of particles act as ligands?
5. How does a polar covalent bond differ from a nonpolar covalent bond?
6. What term is used to describe a particle that has ligands grouped around a central positive ion?
7. What type of molecules have polar bonds arranged in an asymmetrical pattern?

8. If two covalently bonded atoms have a large difference in electro-negativities, will the bond be polar or nonpolar?

9. Name the following complexes.

    **a.** $Zn(OH)_4{}^{2-}$    **b.** $Ag(S_2O_3)_2{}^{3-}$    **c.** $PbCl_4{}^{2-}$    **d.** $Ni(NH_3)_6{}^{2+}$

10. Write formulas for the following complex ions and predict their shapes.

    **a.** tetraammineiron(II) ion        **c.** diamminesilver ion
    **b.** hexaaquocopper(II) ion        **d.** hexahydroxostannate(IV) ion

11. The first complex ion synthesized in the laboratory was made in 1691 by the artist Dreisbach. This ion, $[Fe(CN)_6]^{4-}$, was used by the artist to make blue paints. What is the name of the ion?

12. If anhydrous $CuSO_4$ is dissolved in concentrated HCl(aq), $[CuCl_4]^{2-}$ ions form, causing the solution to turn yellow. A blue solution results when $CuSO_4$ is dissolved in water and $[Cu(H_2O)_4]^{2+}$ ions form. Name these two complex ions.

# KINETIC THEORY

# 15

## 15:1 GAS PRESSURE

The effect on matter of temperature and pressure is described by the kinetic theory. The **kinetic theory** assumes that all matter is made up of very small particles that are in constant motion and undergo perfectly elastic collisions.

Gas molecules collide with each other billions of times per second. Gas molecules also strike the walls of their container. It is the number of collisions and the force of the collisions that cause gas pressure. **Pressure** is force per unit area. The scientific standard for pressure is defined in pascals. One pascal (Pa) is the pressure of 1 newton per square meter ($N/m^2$). Normal air pressure at sea level is 101 325 Pa or 101.325 kilopascals (kPa).

An instrument called a **manometer** (mah NAHM uh tuhr) is used to measure pressure. There are two types of manometers. In the "open" type, air exerts pressure on the column of liquid on one arm of a U-tube. The gas being studied exerts pressure on the other arm. The difference in liquid level between the two arms is a measure of the gas pressure relative to the air pressure. The "closed" type has a vacuum above the liquid in one arm.

A **barometer** is a closed-arm manometer used to measure atmospheric pressure. Most barometers are calibrated to read millimeters of mercury (mm Hg). For converting units,

$$101.325 \text{ kPa} = 760 \text{ mm or } 1 \text{ kPa} = 7.50 \text{ mm Hg}$$

**FIGURE 15-1.**

Valve

Gas sample

58.5 mm

a

Valve

Gas sample

185 mm

b

## Example 1

In Figure 15-1a, the closed arm of the manometer is filled with oxygen. Compute the pressure of the oxygen in kilopascals. The difference in mercury levels is 58.5 mm and the atmospheric pressure is 98.95 kPa.

**Solving Process:**

The mercury is higher in the arm connected to the $O_2$. Thus, the pressure exerted by the $O_2$ must be less than that of the air. As a result, we must subtract the pressure of the mercury from the air pressure to get the $O_2$ pressure. Before subtracting, however, we must convert the 58.5 mm difference in height to kilopascals.

$$\text{number of kPa} = \frac{58.5 \text{ mm}}{} \left| \frac{1 \text{ kPa}}{7.50 \text{ mm}} \right. = 7.80 \text{ kPa}$$

Now we can subtract the two pressures.

$$\text{pressure of } O_2 = 98.95 - 7.80 = 91.15 \text{ kPa}$$

## Example 2

Suppose the difference in height of the two mercury levels in the closed manometer in Figure 15-1b is 185 mm. What is the pressure in kilopascals of the gas in the container?

**Solving Process:**

Since the column of mercury is 185 mm high and 7.50 mm of mercury equals 1 kPa, the pressure is

$$\text{pressure of gas} = \frac{185 \text{ mm}}{} \left| \frac{1 \text{ kPa}}{7.50 \text{ mm}} \right. = 24.7 \text{ kPa}$$

## PROBLEMS

1. A closed manometer is filled with mercury and connected to a container of sulfur dioxide gas. The difference in the height of mercury in the two arms is 560 mm. What is the pressure of the $SO_2$ in kilopascals?

2. An open manometer is filled with mercury and connected to a container of hydrogen. The mercury level is 78.0 mm higher in the arm of the tube connected to the air. Air pressure is 100.7 kPa. What is the pressure of the hydrogen in kilopascals?

3. An open manometer is filled with mercury and connected to a container of nitrogen. The level of mercury is 26.0 mm higher in the arm of the tube connected to the container of nitrogen. Air pressure is 99.6 kPa. What is the pressure, in kilopascals, of the nitrogen?

4. A closed manometer is filled with mercury and connected to a container of argon gas. The difference in height of mercury in the two arms is 116.0 mm. What is the pressure, in kilopascals, of the argon?

# 15:2 TEMPERATURE

Kinetic energy is the energy of motion. A measure of that kinetic energy is **temperature.** The average kinetic energy of molecules or atoms in a gas is the same for all samples at a particular temperature. The temperature and mass of gas particles determines their average speed. At a given temperature, a particle with large mass will move more slowly than a particle with small mass.

Particle speed is directly related to changes in temperature. Since molecular motion of a gas decreases as the temperature decreases, it should be possible theoretically to lower the temperature to a point where all molecular motion ceases. This temperature, known as **absolute zero,** is −273.15°C.

Scientists have made a temperature scale based on absolute zero. It is known as the absolute, or **kelvin scale.** The kelvin (K) is the SI unit of temperature. The zero point of the kelvin scale is absolute zero. The divisions, or degrees, are the same size as those of the Celsius scale. Thus,

$$K = °C + 273$$

## PROBLEMS

5. Convert the following temperatures from Celsius to kelvin.
   **a.** 29°    **b.** −56°    **c.** 344°    **d.** −38°    **e.** 100°    **f.** 25°
6. Convert the following temperatures from kelvin to Celsius.
   **a.** 168    **b.** 255    **c.** 546    **d.** 300    **e.** 53    **f.** 273

## CHAPTER REVIEW PROBLEMS

1. What is an instrument called that is used to measure gas pressure?
2. Which theory explains the effect of temperature and pressure on matter?
3. What name is used to describe a closed manometer that directly measures the absolute pressure of the atmosphere?
4. Theoretically, all molecular motion ceases at what temperature?
5. What is the standard pressure in kPa of air at sea level under normal conditions?
6. What is caused by the force and number of collisions that gas molecules have with the container's walls?
7. At the same temperature, which molecule will move faster, the lighter or heavier one?
8. An open manometer is filled with mercury and connected to a container of neon gas. The mercury level is 42.8 mm higher in the open arm. The barometric pressure is exactly 101.325 kPa. What is the pressure, in kilopascals, of the neon?

9. How does the amount of energy required to change the temperature 1 C° compare to that of one kelvin degree?

10. An open manometer is filled with mercury. The difference in the mercury level in the arms is 81.2 mm. The mercury level is higher in the gas sample arm. What is the pressure, in kilopascals, of the gas in the container if the air pressure is 95.6 kilopascals?

11. In a closed manometer assume that the height of the levels differs by 362 mm Hg. What is the pressure in kPa of the gas in the container?

12. Convert the following temperatures from one temperature scale to another as indicated.

   **a.** 516 K to °C        **c.** 26°C to K         **e.** 421°C to K
   **b.** 155°C to K         **d.** 14 K to °C         **f.** 373 K to °C

13. Suppose you have two vials at the same temperature, one containing sulfur dioxide, $SO_2$, and the other containing chlorine, $Cl_2$. When they are opened across the room from you, which would you expect to smell first?

# SOLIDS 16

## 16:1 UNIT CELLS

The chemist classifies solids as either crystalline or amorphous. **Crystals** are rigid bodies that have flat faces meeting at definite angles and having sharp melting points. When a crystal is cut, it is said to cleave. The two resulting pieces will have the same flat faces and definite angles. **Amorphous solids** such as glass or paraffin do not have definite shapes. They soften and then melt over a wide temperature range. When a glass breaks, it is said to fracture, which results in curved or irregular surfaces.

The **unit cell** is the simplest repeating unit in a crystal. The space lattice is formed by stacking identical unit cells together to form one of seven crystal systems. These crystal systems are described in Table 16-1.

Different unit cells can form the same crystal shape. In Figure 16-1 we observe that the cubic crystal can be formed from simple cubic, face-centered cubic, or body-centered cubic units cells.

**FIGURE 16-1.**

Face-centered cubic

Cubic

Body-centered cubic

## Table 16-1

| | Lengths of the Unit Cell Axes | Angles Between the Unit Cell Axes | Crystal System |
|---|---|---|---|
| **Seven Crystal Systems** | | | |
| | all equal | all = 90° | cubic |
| | 2 equal 1 unequal | all = 90° | tetragonal |
| | 3 equal 1 unequal | 1 = 90° 3 = 60° | hexagonal |
| | all equal | all ≠ 90° | rhombo-hedral |
| | all unequal | all = 90° | ortho-rhombic |
| | all unequal | 2 = 90° 1 ≠ 90° | monoclinic |
| | all unequal | all ≠ 90° | triclinic |

Most metals exhibit one of three types of crystal structure. Two of these arrangements are called closest packing structures. In hexagonal closest packing (HCP) and cubic closest packing (CCP or face-centered cubic), each metal atom has twelve neighboring atoms. The number of neighboring atoms or ions is called the coordination number. The atoms in HCP and CCP structures occupy 74% of the volume of the crystal. By comparison, simple cubic structures have coordination numbers of six with the atoms occupying 52% of the crystal volume.

The Group IA (1) as well as some other metals crystallize in the body-centered cubic (BCC) structure. For BCC structures the coordination number is eight and 68% of the volume is occupied by the atoms.

Some metals can be heat treated, or tempered, because the atoms change their packing as the temperature rises. In general, the trend is toward the HCP arrangement. A **polymorphous** substance has two or more crystal structures.

We must not assume that crystals have perfect order. There are defects in real crystals. Particles can be missing from their proper position; planes of particles can be misaligned. These defects are called dislocations. Sometimes a crystal is manufactured with a deliberate defect. For example, perfect crystals are "doped" to make semiconductors (transistors).

# 16:2  HYDRATES

A number of compounds called **hydrates** attract and hold water molecules in their crystal structure. The water is called **water of hydration** and may be removed by heating. The solid residue remaining after the water is removed is called the anhydrous material. **Anhydrous** means "without water."

In the formula of a hydrated compound, the number of water molecules involved is indicated by placing a raised dot after the anhydrous formula and writing the water formula with a coefficient if necessary. For example, $CuSO_4 \cdot 5H_2O$ is copper(II) sulfate pentahydrate. *Hydrate* means "water" and the Greek prefix *penta-* indicates the number of water molecules per formula unit of compound. For example:

| | |
|---|---|
| $Na_2CO_3$ | sodium carbonate |
| $Na_2CO_3 \cdot H_2O$ | sodium carbonate monohydrate |
| $Na_2CO_3 \cdot 7H_2O$ | sodium carbonate heptahydrate |
| $Na_2CO_3 \cdot 10H_2O$ | sodium carbonate decahydrate |

The ions of some anhydrous substances have such a strong attraction for water molecules that the dehydrated crystal will recapture and hold water molecules from the air. Such a substance is called a hygroscopic (hi gruh SKAHP ihk) substance. Some substances are so **hygroscopic** that they take up enough water from the air to dissolve and form a liquid solution. These substances are said to be **deliquescent** (del ih KWES uhnt). The opposite process can also occur. Water of hydration may be spontaneously released to the air. A substance that releases water molecules to the air from the crystal is said to be **efflorescent** (ef luh RES uhnt).

## PROBLEMS

1. Name each of the following compounds.
   a. $MgCO_3$
   b. $MgCO_3 \cdot 3H_2O$
   c. $MgCO_3 \cdot 5H_2O$
   d. $Nd(CH_3COO)_3 \cdot H_2O$
   e. $Ni(CN)_2 \cdot 4H_2O$
   f. $Pr_2(CO_3)_3 \cdot 8H_2O$

2. Write formulas for each of the following compounds.
   a. calcium oxalate monohydrate
   b. cerium(III) bromate nonahydrate
   c. hydrogen bromide hexahydrate
   d. iron(II) oxalate dihydrate
   e. iron(III) oxalate pentahydrate
   f. lithium iodide trihydrate

## CHAPTER REVIEW PROBLEMS

1. How is a crystal defined?

2. What is the simplest repeating unit in a crystal's geometric arrangement called?

3. What is the three-dimensional arrangement of unit cells repeated over and over in a definite arrangement called?

4. Each atom in a hexagonal closest packing arrangement is surrounded and touched by how many other atoms?

5. Almost all metals are packed into one of three kinds of unit cells. List the three most common unit cells for metals.

6. Do all natural crystals have perfect structures?

7. What term is used to describe the process of adding some impurities to crystals deliberately?

8. What term is used to describe a single substance that has two or more crystalline shapes?

9. Water molecules may be incorporated into the crystal structure. What do we call these crystals?

10. What is a substance called after the water of hydration has been removed?

11. Some crystals will recapture and hold water molecules from the air. What is such a substance called?

12. Some substances will absorb enough water from the air to dissolve and form a solution. What term is applied to these substances?

13. What term is used to describe a substance that releases water molecules to the air from the crystal?

14. How are the particles arranged in an amorphous solid?

15. What common substance is an excellent example of an amorphous material?

16. Name the following compounds.
    a. $NiCl_2 \cdot 6H_2O$
    b. $Mg(ClO_4)_2 \cdot 6H_2O$
    c. $Mg_3(PO_4)_2 \cdot 4H_2O$
    d. $Ca(NO_3)_2 \cdot 3H_2O$

17. Write the formula for the following hydrates.
    a. cobalt(II) chloride hexahydrate
    b. barium hydroxide octahydrate
    c. gallium(III) oxide monohydrate
    d. magnesium hydrogen arsenate heptahydrate

# LIQUIDS

# 17

## 17:1  PHASE DIAGRAMS

The solid, liquid, and gas phases of a substance exist at different temperatures and pressures. The **phase diagram** is a convenient way to represent graphically the conditions at which a particular phase is stable.

Figure 17-1 is a phase diagram for $CO_2$, carbon dioxide. There are three lines that divide the diagram into solid, liquid, and gas regions. Each point on a line represents a temperature and pressure at which the two phases are in equilibrium. The normal boiling point and normal melting point occur where the equilibrium line is cut by the standard atmospheric pressure line 101.325 kPa. The **triple point** indicates the temperature and pressure at which all three phases are in equilibrium.

**Phase Diagram of CO₂**    FIGURE 17-1.

In a closed system, liquid and gaseous carbon dioxide can be in equilibrium. Above the critical temperature there is only one phase, gaseous carbon dioxide. The **critical temperature,** $T_c$, is the temperature above which no amount of pressure will liquefy the gas. At the critical temperature the minimum pressure necessary to liquefy the gas is called the **critical pressure,** $P_c$. A high critical temperature indicates that the attractive force between the particles is strong. Methyl chloride, $CH_3Cl$, has a $T_c = 144°C$

**105**

and $P_c = 6685$ kPa. It can be liquified by increasing the pressure. By compressing the gas the molecules come close enough that van der Waals forces can hold them together.

**FIGURE 17-2**

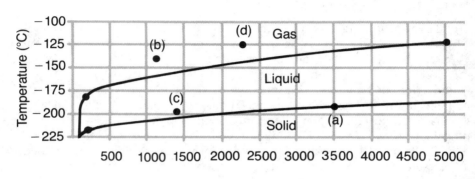

**Phase Diagram for $O_2$**

Temperature (°C) / Pressure (kPa)

1. Using Figure 17-2, determine the following for oxygen.
   a. critical temperature          c. normal melting point
   b. critical pressure             d. normal boiling point
2. Using Figure 17-1, determine the state of matter that exists for $CO_2$ under the following conditions.
   a. 4000 kPa and $-100°C$          c. 3000 kPa and $-25°C$
   b. 1000 kPa and $10°C$            d. 101.3 kPa and $0°C$
3. What transition would occur at the labeled points on Figure 17-2 when the following changes occur?
   a. at point A if temperature increased
   b. at point B if temperature decreased
   c. at point C if pressure increased
   d. at point D if pressure decreased

# 17:2   ENERGY AND CHANGE OF STATE

When a substance is heated, the energy of its particles is increased. If the kinetic energy is increased, the result is an increase in the temperature of the substance. If the increase is in potential energy, the physical state of the substance will change. The change, or combination of changes, that will take place depends upon the starting temperature of the substance. Similar considerations can be applied to removing energy from (cooling) a substance.

The changes of state from solid to liquid and liquid to solid take place at the same temperature, which is labeled the **melting point** or **freezing point.** The changes from liquid to gas and gas to liquid take place at the same temperature, which is labeled the **boiling point** or **condensing point.** The amount of energy required for a state change depends on the nature and amount of a substance. If we use $q$ to represent the quantity of energy needed to melt a substance, then

$$q = m(H_{fus})$$

where $m$ is the mass of the substance and $H_{fus}$ is a property of a substance called **enthalpy of fusion.** Similarly, to boil a substance, the relationship is

$$q = m(H_{vap})$$

where $H_{vap}$ is a property of a substance called its **enthalpy of vaporization.** Table 17-1 lists the enthalpies of fusion and vaporization for several substances.

**Table 17-1**

| Molar Enthalpies of Fusion and Vaporization for Some Substances (in kJ/mol) | | | |
|---|---|---|---|
| **Fusion($H_{fus}$)** | | **Vaporization ($H_{vap}$)** | |
| aluminum | 10.5 | aluminum | 291 |
| arsenic | 93.7 | benzene | 30.8 |
| gold | 12.8 | gold | 343 |
| indium | 3.26 | helium | 0.08 |
| iron | 13.8 | iron | 340 |
| steel | 13.8 | selenium | 59.7 |
| titanium | 18.8 | sodium | 99 |
| water | 6.02 | water | 40.7 |

## Example 1

How much energy is required to melt 86.3 g of iron at its melting point?

**Solving Process:**

The energy required for this phase change depends upon the mass, 86.3 g, and enthalpy of fusion, 13.8 kJ/mol. To make use of the $H_{fus}$ value, the quantity of iron must be in units of moles. Thus, the solution is

$$q = mass \times enthalpy\ of\ fusion \times mole\ conversion$$

$$= \frac{86.3\ g\,Fe}{} \left| \frac{13.8\ kJ}{1\ mol\,Fe} \right| \frac{1\ mol\,Fe}{55.8\ g\,Fe} = 21.3\ kJ$$

The amount of energy required to change the temperature of a substance depends upon the amount and nature of the substance as well as the extent of the temperature change. The energy required is calculated by

$$q = m(\Delta T)C_p$$

where $q$ is the energy added (or removed), $m$ is the mass of the substance, $\Delta T$ is the change in temperature, and $C_p$ is a property of the substance called its **specific heat.** Review Section 3:5 for an example problem.

You may be asked to do calculations that involve both temperature and state changes. For such problems, each step involving a temperature or state change is solved separately. The sum of the energy changes for all the steps is the solution to the problem. For example, suppose you are asked to start with a solid substance below its melting point and determine the energy required to change that substance to a gas above its boiling point. The following steps must be taken.

    **a.** heat the solid to its melting point
    **b.** melt the solid
    **c.** heat the liquid to its boiling point
    **d.** boil the liquid
    **e.** heat the gas to the required temperature

## Example 2

How much energy is released when 42.5 g of aluminum vapor are cooled from 4750°C to 25.0°C?

| | |
|---|---|
| freezing point = 660.0°C | boiling point = 2467°C |
| $H_{vap}$ = 291 kJ/mol | $H_{fus}$ = 10.5 kJ/mol |
| $C_p(g)$ = 1.05 J/g·C° | $C_p(l)$ = 0.869 J/g·C° |
| $C_p(cr)$ = 0.900 J/g·C° | |

**Solving Process:**

It is often helpful in problems of this type to draw a graph to indicate the steps in changing the vapor to solid.

FIGURE 17-3.

Temperature (°C)

Energy (J)

**Step 1:** Calculate the energy released as the Al gas is cooled to the condensing point, 2467°C. Convert joules to kilojoules so the units in each step will be the same.

$q = m(\Delta T)C_p$

$$= \frac{42.5\,\cancel{g} \quad\bigg|\quad 2283\,\cancel{°C} \quad\bigg|\quad 1.05\,\cancel{J} \quad\bigg|\quad 1\,kJ}{\cancel{g\cdot °C} \quad\bigg|\quad 1000\,\cancel{J}} = 102\,kJ$$

**Step 2:** Calculate the energy released as the Al gas is condensed. You must convert grams of Al to moles because $H_{vap}$ is given in kJ/mol.

$q = mass \times mole\ conversion \times enthalpy\ of\ vaporization$

$$= \frac{42.5\,\cancel{g} \quad\bigg|\quad 1\,\cancel{mol} \quad\bigg|\quad 291\,kJ}{27.0\,\cancel{g} \quad\bigg|\quad 1\,\cancel{mol}} = 458\,kJ$$

**Step 3:** Calculate the energy released as the liquid Al is cooled to the freezing point, 660.0°C.

$$q = \frac{42.5\,\cancel{g} \quad\bigg|\quad 1807\,\cancel{°C} \quad\bigg|\quad 0.869\,\cancel{J} \quad\bigg|\quad 1\,kJ}{\cancel{g\cdot °C} \quad\bigg|\quad 1000\,\cancel{J}} = 66.7\,kJ$$

**Step 4:** Calculate the energy released as the liquid Al is frozen.

$q = mass \times mole\ conversion \times enthalpy\ of\ vaporization$

$$= \frac{42.5\,\cancel{g} \quad\bigg|\quad 1\,\cancel{mol} \quad\bigg|\quad 10.5\,kJ}{27.0\,\cancel{g} \quad\bigg|\quad 1\,\cancel{mol}} = 16.5\,kJ$$

**Step 5:** Calculate the energy released as the solid Al is cooled to 25.0°C.

$$q = \frac{42.5\,\cancel{g} \quad\bigg|\quad 635\,\cancel{°C} \quad\bigg|\quad 0.900\,\cancel{J} \quad\bigg|\quad 1\,kJ}{\cancel{g\cdot °C} \quad\bigg|\quad 1000\,\cancel{J}} = 24.3\,kJ$$

The total energy released is the sum of all five steps.

$$102\,kJ + 458\,kJ + 66.7\,kJ + 16.5\,kJ + 24.3\,kJ = 668\,kJ$$

## PROBLEMS

4. Compute the energy changes associated with the following transitions.
   a. melting 55.8 g Ti at 1667°C
   b. condensing 14.2 g $H_2O$ at 100.0°C
   c. boiling 53.5 g $C_6H_6$, benzene, at 80.1°C
   d. freezing 27.3 g Al at 660°C
   e. melting 76.4 g Au at 1064°C
5. Compute the energy changes associated with the following transitions.
   a. heating 49.2 g acetic acid, $CH_3COOH$, from 24.1°C to 67.3°C
   b. heating 9.61 g toluene, $C_6H_5CH_3$, from 19.6°C to 75.0°C
   c. heating 2.47 g kerosene from 17.1°C to 46.7°C
   d. cooling 31.9 g chalk from 83.2°C to 55.5°C
   e. cooling 63.6 g glass from 95.5°C to 42.3°C

## CHAPTER REVIEW PROBLEMS

1. In a closed, insulated system, ice is floating in water. The temperature is 0°C. Will all of the water freeze?

2. Water is boiling at 100°C. The hot plate's surface temperature is increased. Will the water now boil at a higher temperature?

3. Will a gas liquefy above the critical temperature when the pressure increases a large amount?

4. Are the vapor pressure of the liquid phase and the vapor pressure of the gas phase equal at the boiling point?

5. Are the attractive forces between the particles strong or weak when the vapor pressure of a substance is high?

6. Gas can be liquified when what temperature and pressure changes occur?

7. Using the phase diagram for compound x, Figure 17-4, answer the following questions.
   a. At what temperature does the vapor pressure of the solid equal atmospheric pressure?
   b. What is the temperature of the triple point?
   c. What is the critical temperature?
   d. What is the critical pressure?
   e. At what labeled point does boiling occur?
   f. At what point do solid and liquid phases exist in equilibrium?

FIGURE 17-4.

*Use Tables 17-1 and A-8 to answer the following questions.*

8. How much energy is required to raise the temperature of 91.4 g solid steel from 25.0°C to 76.1°C?

9. How much energy is required to raise the temperature of 4.66 g kerosene from 10.9°C to 26.8°C?

10. How much energy is required to raise the temperature of 175 g $H_2O$ from −11.0°C to 140.0°C?

11. If 100.0 g of pure water at 27°C are placed into an insulated flask, how many grams of ice at 0.0°C must be added to lower the temperature of the water to 5.0°C? (recall: energy lost = energy gained)

# GASES 18

Air in a tire exerts pressure. A partially filled balloon will expand if it is placed over a hot radiator. In marked contrast to solids and liquids, gas volumes change noticeably with small changes in pressure and temperature. These changes were studied by experimenting with real gases and the relations obtained were reduced to equations that defined the behavior of gases. These equations, known as the gas laws, are valid only for an ideal gas. An **ideal gas** is one composed of particles with no attractive forces and no volume. Although ideal gases do not actually exist, they give good approximations in most situations for real gases.

## 18:1  BOYLE'S LAW

What is pressure? As gas molecules hit the walls of a container, the particles exert a force on the container. The number of collisions and the force of the collisions cause gas pressure. The standard unit for pressure is the pascal, which represents force per unit area. One pascal (Pa) is the pressure of one newton per square meter ($N/m^2$). Air pressure at sea level has been used as a scientific standard of pressure. However, this pressure changes with changing weather conditions. Normal air pressure at sea level is 101 325 Pa or 101.325 kilopascals (kPa).

A **barometer** is used to measure atmospheric pressure. Most barometers are calibrated in millimeters of mercury (mm Hg). For converting units, 101.325 kPa = 760 mm or 1 kPa = 7.50 mm Hg.

If the pressure on an ideal gas in a confined container is increased, the volume decreases. When the pressure is doubled, the new gas volume is half the original gas volume. If the pressure is decreased to half the original pressure, the new volume is double the old volume. Robert Boyle found that gas volume and pressure vary inversely. **Boyle's law** is *the volume of an enclosed gas varies inversely as the pressure, if the temperature remains constant.*

Our primary interest in solving Boyle's law problems is to find a new volume when the original volume and the change in pressure are known. The change in pressure can be represented by a pressure ratio. The new volume of a gas after a change in pressure at a constant temperature is calculated by

$$V_2 = V_1 \frac{P_1}{P_2}$$

where $V_1$ is the initial volume and $P_1$ is the initial pressure. The given values can be substituted into the equation or the changes in the gas volume can be visualized using Boyle's law.

The preferred volume unit is cubic meters ($m^3$). However, cubic decimeters ($dm^3$) and cubic centimeters ($cm^3$) are also used.

Mentally determine whether the new volume will be larger or smaller than the old volume and arrange the pressure ratio accordingly. If the new volume will be larger, multiply by a ratio that is greater than 1; if smaller, multiply by a ratio less than 1. The following points should be considered when solving Boyle's law problems.

1. A pressure increase decreases the volume, which means the pressure ratio should be less than 1.
2. A pressure decrease increases the volume, which means the pressure ratio should be greater than 1.
3. To calculate a new pressure when the old pressure and the volume change are known, use the relationship:

*new pressure = old pressure × volume ratio*

4. The volume and pressure vary inversely.

## Example 1

If 425 $cm^3$ of oxygen are collected at a pressure of 9.80 kPa what volume will the gas occupy if the pressure is changed to 9.40 kPa?

**Solving Process:**

The pressure decreases from 9.80 to 9.40 kPa. The volume should increase according to Boyle's law. To have a volume increase, the pressure ratio must be greater than 1. The pressure ratio is

$$\frac{9.80 \text{ kPa}}{9.40 \text{ kPa}}$$

In calculations, use the relationship:

*new volume = old volume × pressure ratio*

$$= \frac{425 \text{ cm}^3}{} \left| \frac{9.80 \text{ kPa}}{9.40 \text{ kPa}} \right. = 443 \text{ cm}^3$$

## Example 2

Calculate the pressure of a gas that occupies a volume of 125 $cm^3$, if at a pressure of 95.0 kPa, it occupies a volume of 219 $cm^3$.

**Solving Process:**

The volume decreases from 219 $cm^3$ to 125 $cm^3$. The pressure must increase, so the volume ratio must be greater than 1, or

$$\frac{219 \text{ cm}^3}{125 \text{ cm}^3}$$

*new pressure = old pressure × volume ratio*

$$= \frac{95.0 \text{ kPa}}{} \left| \frac{219 \text{ cm}^3}{125 \text{ cm}^3} \right. = 166 \text{ kPa}$$

## PROBLEMS

1. Correct the following gas volumes from the initial conditions to the new conditions (assume the temperature remains constant).
   a. 100.0 cm³ oxygen at 10.50 kPa to 9.91 kPa
   b. 50.0 cm³ hydrogen at 97.3 kPa to 101 000 Pa
   c. 500.0 cm³ sulfur dioxide at 95.6 kPa to 101.3 kPa
   d. 150.0 cm³ nitrogen at 101.30 kPa to 120.0 kPa
   e. 2.00 m³ nitrogen at 158.0 kPa to 109.0 kPa
   f. 1.50 dm³ neon at 98.2 kPa to 150 kPa

2. A flask containing 90.0 cm³ of hydrogen was collected under a pressure of 97.5 kilopascals. At what pressure would the volume be 70.0 cm³, assuming the temperature is kept constant?

3. A gas has a volume of 275 cm³ when measured at a pressure of 9.80 × 10⁴ Pa. If the temperature is not changed, what would the gas volume be at standard pressure?

4. A gas has a volume of 50.0 m³ at standard pressure. Assuming no temperature change, what volume will the gas occupy
   a. if the pressure is doubled?
   b. if the pressure is tripled?
   c. if the original pressure is cut in half?

5. What is the volume occupied by 10.0 dm³ of gas at standard pressure after it has been compressed at constant temperature to 500.0 kPa?

6. A gas is confined in a cylinder with a movable piston at one end. When the volume of the cylinder is 760.0 cm³ the pressure of the gas is 125.0 kPa. When the cylinder volume is reduced to 450.0 cm³, what is the pressure?

# 18:2  DALTON'S LAW OF PARTIAL PRESSURE

If a mixture consists of two or more gases, each gas exerts a partial pressure independently of the other gases present. The partial pressure of a gas in a mixture is the pressure that the gas would exert if it were the only gas in the container. The total pressure is equal to the sum of the individual gas pressures. **Dalton's law of partial pressure** can be stated as *the sum of the partial pressures of a mixture of gases is the total pressure exerted by the enclosed gases.*

In the chemistry laboratory, gases (such as oxygen, nitrogen, and hydrogen) bubble through water as they are collected. As a result, water vapor molecules exert a pressure along with the collected gas. The pressure of the dry gas can be found only by deducting the pressure due to water molecules. Vapor pressure depends upon the temperature. The warmer the gas, the greater the pressure of the water vapor. Table A-14 lists the vapor pressure of water at varying temperatures.

## Example 3

A quantity of gas is collected over water at 10.0°C in a 125 cm³ vessel. The manometer indicates a pressure of 98.0 kPa. What volume would the dry gas occupy at standard pressure and 10.0°C?

**Solving Process:**

We must determine what part of the total pressure is due to water vapor. Table A-14 indicates that at 10.0°C, water has a vapor pressure of 1.2 kPa. To find the pressure of the collected gas:

$$P_{gas} = P_{total} - P_{water}$$

$$= 98.0 \text{ kPa} - 1.2 \text{ kPa}$$

$$= 96.8 \text{ kPa}$$

Since this pressure is less than standard, the gas would have to be compressed to change it to standard. The pressure ratio by which the volume is to be multiplied must be less than 1.

$$\text{new volume} = \frac{125 \text{ cm}^3}{} \left| \frac{96.8 \text{ kPa}}{101.3 \text{ kPa}} \right. = 119 \text{ cm}^3$$

## PROBLEMS

7. Determine the partial pressure of oxygen collected over water if the temperature is 28°C and the total gas pressure is 98.74 kPa.

8. The partial pressure of helium is 13.5 kPa in a mixture of helium, oxygen, and methane gases. If the total pressure is 96.4 kPa and the partial pressure of oxygen is 29.3 kPa, what is the partial pressure of the methane gas?

9. A 79.9 cm³ sample of oxygen is collected by water displacement at 24°C. What volume would the gas occupy at standard pressure if the gas is collected originally at a pressure of 98.5 kPa?

10. In a series of laboratory experiments, different gases were collected over water at the indicated water temperature and pressure. Correct each volume to the volume the dry gas would occupy at standard pressure. The temperature is constant.

   a. 52.0 cm³ gas at 18°C and 94.5 kPa
   b. 75.0 cm³ gas at 23°C and 97.2 kPa
   c. 135 cm³ gas at 21°C and 98.4 kPa
   d. 225 cm³ gas at 27°C and 102.5 kPa

# 18:3   KELVIN TEMPERATURE

All gases (in contrast to solids and liquids) expand and contract at approximately the same rate. When a gas is heated, it expands by 1/273 of its volume at 0° Celsius for each temperature increase of one Celsius degree. When a gas is cooled, it contracts 1/273 of its volume at 0° Celsius for each Celsius degree the temperature is lowered.

No gas has ever been cooled to −273°C. All gases liquefy or solidify at temperatures higher than −273°C. The temperature −273°C is called absolute zero. It is written zero kelvin or 0 K. To convert from °C to K, add 273 to the Celsius temperature.

$$K = 273 + C°$$

Scientists have chosen 273 K (0°C) as a standard temperature for working with gases.

## 18:4  CHARLES' LAW

If the temperature of an ideal gas increases, the volume increases, when the pressure remains constant. If the temperature of a gas decreases, the volume decreases. **Charles' law** can be stated as *the volume of a quantity of gas varies directly as the kelvin temperature, if the pressure remains constant.* Note that temperature must be expressed in kelvin.

It is possible to predict the new volume of a gas when the old volume and the temperature change are known. The temperature change is expressed as an absolute temperature ratio. The equation used to calculate the new volume is

*new volume = old volume × kelvin temperature ratio*

$$V_2 = V_1 \frac{T_2}{T_1}$$

The subscripts represent the initial and final conditions, as in the Boyle's law relationship. The following points should be considered when solving Charles' law problems.

1. An absolute temperature increase gives a volume increase, which means an absolute temperature ratio greater than 1.

2. An absolute temperature decrease gives a volume decrease, which means an absolute temperature ratio less than 1.

3. The new temperature in kelvins can be calculated when the initial kelvin temperature and new and old volumes are known:

   *new temperature* (K) = *old temperature* (K) × *volume ratio*

4. The kelvin temperature varies directly as the volume.

## Example 4

What volume will a sample of nitrogen occupy at 28.0°C if the gas occupies a volume of 457 cm$^3$ at a temperature of 0.0°C? Assume the pressure remains constant.

**Solving Process:**
Convert the temperatures from Celsius to kelvin.

$$K = 273 + °C$$

$$K = 273 + 28.0°C = 301 \text{ K} \quad \text{and} \quad K = 273 + 0.0°C = 273 \text{ K}$$

A kelvin temperature increase (from 273 K to 301 K) will cause a volume increase. The kelvin temperature ratio must be greater than 1.

$$\frac{301 \text{ K}}{273 \text{ K}}$$

new volume = old volume × kelvin temperature ratio

$$= \frac{457 \text{ cm}^3}{} \left| \frac{301 \cancel{K}}{273 \cancel{K}} \right. = 504 \text{ cm}^3$$

## Example 5

If a gas occupies a volume of 733 cm$^3$ at 10.0°C, at what temperature, in °C, will it occupy a volume of 1225 cm$^3$ if the pressure remains constant?

**Solving Process:**
An increase in volume (from 733 cm$^3$ to 1225 cm$^3$) indicates a temperature increase. The volume ratio must be greater than 1.

$$\frac{1225 \text{ cm}^3}{733 \text{ cm}^3}$$

$$T_2 = \frac{T_1}{} \left| \frac{V_2}{V_1} \right.$$

$$= \frac{283 \text{ K}}{} \left| \frac{1225 \cancel{\text{cm}^3}}{733 \cancel{\text{cm}^3}} \right. = 473 \text{ K}$$

Convert 473 K to °C.

$$°C = 473 \text{ K} - 273 = 200°C$$

## PROBLEMS

11. A gas has a volume of 10.0 m$^3$ at standard temperature. Assuming no pressure change, what volume will the gas occupy
    **a.** if the kelvin temperature is doubled?
    **b.** if the original kelvin temperature is halved?

12. Correct the following gas volumes from the initial conditions to the new conditions (assume that the pressure remains constant).
    **a.** 250.0 cm$^3$ chlorine at 10.0°C to 60.0°C
    **b.** 75.0 cm$^3$ hydrogen at 20.0°C to −10.0°C
    **c.** 100.0 cm$^3$ oxygen at 27.0°C to standard temperature
    **d.** 300.0 cm$^3$ nitrogen at 15.0°C to 38.0°C
    **e.** 2.30 dm$^3$ nitrogen dioxide at standard temperature to 40.0°C
    **f.** 35.0 cm$^3$ helium at 285 K to 92 K

**13.** A gas occupies a volume of 560 cm³ at a temperature of 120°C. To what temperature must the gas be lowered, if it is to occupy 400.0 cm³? Assume a constant pressure.

# 18:5  COMBINED GAS LAW

Boyle's and Charles' laws can be used together to form a combined gas law. This law can be used in a situation where both a pressure and a temperature change occur. A pressure ratio and a kelvin temperature ratio are needed to calculate the new volume.

*new volume = old volume × pressure ratio × kelvin temperature ratio*

Each ratio is considered independently in setting up the expression. You will want to construct a pressure-volume-temperature data table.

| Value | Old conditions | New conditions | What happens to the gas volume? |
|---|---|---|---|
| *Pressure* | | | |
| *Volume* | | | |
| *Temperature* | | | |

"What happens to the gas volume?" is answered with the word "decrease" or "increase," depending upon whether the pressure or temperature ratio is larger or smaller than 1.

The initials STP are often used in gas law problems. **STP** means standard temperature and pressure. The **standard pressure** for measuring gases is 101 325 Pa (101.325 kPa). For convenience in solving problems 101.3 kPa is used. **Standard temperature** is 0°C or 273 K. All temperature ratios must be expressed in kelvin.

## Example 6

Calculate the volume of a gas at STP if 502 cm³ of the gas are collected at 29.7°C and 96.0 kPa.

**Solving Process:**

Organize the data given as shown and convert the Celsius temperatures to kelvins.

| Value | Old conditions | New conditions | What happens to the gas volume? |
|---|---|---|---|
| *P* | 96.0 kPa | 101.3 kPa | decreases |
| *V* | 502 cm³ | ? | ? |
| *T* | 302.7 K | 273.2 K | decreases |

*new volume = old volume × pressure ratio × kelvin temperature ratio*

$$= \frac{502 \text{ cm}^3}{} \left| \frac{96.0 \text{ kPa}}{101.3 \text{ kPa}} \right| \frac{273.2 \text{ K}}{302.7 \text{ K}} = 429 \text{ cm}^3$$

## Example 7

If 400.0 cm$^3$ of oxygen are collected over water at 20.0°C, and the atmospheric pressure is 97.0 kPa, what is the volume of the dry oxygen at STP?

**Solving Process:**

Organize the data. Convert C° to K and correct the total pressure for water vapor pressure.

Note that the gas is not actually wet when it is collected over water. When a gas is collected over water, some of the water molecules inevitably escape from the liquid surface and form water vapor. The collected gas, therefore, contains both gas and water molecules. To find the pressure due to gas molecules, you must account for and deduct the pressure due to water vapor molecules.

| Value | Old conditions | New conditions | What happens to the gas volume? |
|-------|----------------|----------------|---------------------------------|
| P | 97.0 − 2.3 = 94.7 kPa | 101.3 kPa | decreases |
| V | 400.0 cm³ | ? | ? |
| T | 293 K | 273 K | decreases |

*new volume = old volume × pressure ratio × kelvin temperature ratio*

$$= \frac{400.0 \text{ cm}^3}{} \left| \frac{94.7 \text{ kPa}}{101.3 \text{ kPa}} \right| \frac{273 \text{ K}}{293 \text{ K}} = 348 \text{ cm}^3$$

## PROBLEMS

14. Convert the following gas volumes to the new conditions using the combined gas law.
    a. 5.00 × 10$^2$ cm$^3$ hydrogen at 20.0°C and 120 kPa to STP
    b. 2.50 × 10$^2$ cm$^3$ oxygen at 27°C and 95.0 kPa to STP
    c. 1.00 × 10$^2$ cm$^3$ chlorine at STP to 20.0°C and 98.0 kPa
    d. 140 cm$^3$ hydrogen at 15°C and 110.0 kPa to 40.0°C and 94.5 kPa

15. The following gases are collected over water at the given conditions. Calculate the volume occupied by the dry gas at standard conditions.
    a. 2.00 × 10$^2$ cm$^3$ oxygen at 15°C and 94 000 Pa
    b. 125 cm$^3$ hydrogen at 20.0°C and 97 500 Pa
    c. 50.0 cm$^3$ nitrogen at 28°C and 99 500 Pa
    d. 325 cm$^3$ oxygen at 25°C and 98.6 kPa

16. A gas occupied 550.0 cm$^3$ at a pressure of 9.95 × 10$^4$ Pa and a temperature of 21°C. Several days later it was measured at a pressure of 9.78 × 10$^4$ Pa and temperature of 15°C. What volume did the gas occupy under these new conditions?

17. A 47.0 cm$^3$ volume of nitrogen gas is collected over water at a water temperature of 18°C and a pressure of 98.5 kPa. What volume will the gas occupy at standard conditions?

18. An automobile tire has a pressure of 210.0 kPa at 20.0°C. What will be the tire pressure after driving, if the tire temperature rises to 35.0°C?

19. The respiratory rate for a person is about 15 breaths per minute. Assume that each average breath is about 510 cm$^3$ of air at 20.0°C and 99.5 kPa. What volume of air in cubic meters, corrected to standard conditions, does the individual breathe in one day?

# 18:6   GAS DENSITY

The volume of a gas changes with change in temperature or pressure. Specifically, if we increase the pressure on a gas we decrease the volume; thus, we would have a greater density. If we increase the temperature of a gas, the volume increases, and the density is lower. The density of a gas varies directly with the pressure and inversely with the temperature.

For convenience, gas density is usually expressed in grams per cubic decimeter. Using g/cm$^3$ would give very small numbers for gas densities. Remember that 1000 cm$^3$ equal 1 dm$^3$.

## Example 8

If the density of oxygen is 1.43 g/dm$^3$ at standard pressure and temperature, what is the density of oxygen at 99.0 kPa and 27.0°C?

**Solving Process:**

The original density must be adjusted by a pressure ratio and a kelvin temperature ratio to the new conditions.

| Value | Old conditions | New conditions | What happens to the density? |
|-------|----------------|----------------|------------------------------|
| P | 101.3 kPa | 99.0 kPa | decreases |
| T | 273 K | 300.0 K | decreases |
| D | 1.43 g/dm$^3$ | ? | ? |

The pressure decreases and the temperature increases. A temperature increase gives a density decrease. The pressure and temperature ratios are

$$\frac{99.0 \text{ kPa}}{101.3 \text{ kPa}} \qquad \frac{273 \text{ K}}{300.0 \text{ K}}$$

$$new\ density = old\ density \times pressure\ ratio \times temperature\ ratio$$

$$= \frac{1.43\ g}{dm^3} \left| \frac{99.0\ kPa}{101.3\ kPa} \right| \frac{273\ K}{300.0\ K} = 1.27\ g/dm^3$$

## PROBLEMS

20. Sulfur dioxide has a density of 2.927 g/dm$^3$ at STP. What is its density at a pressure of 120.0 kPa and a temperature of 50.0°C?
21. A gas has a density of 3.472 g/dm$^3$ at STP. Determine its density at a pressure of 95.0 kPa and a temperature of 27.0°C.
22. A gas has a density of 2.851 g/dm$^3$ at STP. The pressure is dropped by 20.0 kPa in order to attempt to change the density to 2.000 g/dm$^3$. What must be the new temperature to achieve this lower density?

## 18:7   GAS DIFFUSION AND GRAHAM'S LAW

If a gas molecule having an odor is moving at 200 meters per second, why does it take several minutes before it is detected across the room? Although the molecules of a gas move in a straight line, they travel only a relatively short distance before colliding with another molecule. These collisions result in a time-consuming zig-zag path across the room. The dispersion of gases from an area of high concentration to an area of low concentration is called **diffusion.**

**Effusion** occurs when a gas passes through a small hole into a vacuum. In 1846 Thomas Graham discovered a relationship between molecular mass and effusion rate. **Graham's law** states that *the relative rate at which two gases at the same temperature and pressure will effuse varies inversely as the square root of the ratio of the molecular masses of the gases.*

## Example 9

Calculate the ratio of rates of effusion of N$_2$ molecules to that of CO$_2$ molecules from the same container at the same temperature and pressure.

**Solving Process:**

The two rates of effusion vary inversely as the square root of the ratio of their molecular masses.

$$\frac{rate\ N_2}{rate\ CO_2} = \sqrt{\frac{mass\ CO_2}{mass\ N_2}}$$

The molecular mass of N$_2$ is 28.0 u. The molecular mass of CO$_2$ is 44.0 u. Substitute these masses into the equation.

$$\frac{rate\ N_2}{rate\ CO_2} = \sqrt{\frac{44.0}{28.0}} = \frac{1.25}{1}$$

The N$_2$ gas molecules effuse 1.25 times faster than the CO$_2$ molecules.

## PROBLEMS

23. What is the ratio of the speed of hydrogen molecules to the speed of neon atoms when both gases are at the same temperature and pressure?

24. At a certain temperature, the velocity of chlorine molecules, $Cl_2$, is 0.0410 m/s. What is the velocity of sulfur dioxide molecules, $SO_2$, at the same temperature and pressure?

## CHAPTER REVIEW PROBLEMS

1. Correct the following gas volumes from the initial conditions to the new conditions. Assume that the pressure or temperature is constant, if not given.
   a. 45.0 $cm^3$ at 49°C to −29°C
   b. 270.0 $cm^3$ at standard temperature to 25°C
   c. 75.0 $cm^3$ at standard pressure to 90.8 kPa
   d. 165 $cm^3$ at 75 000 Pa to 84 000 Pa
   e. 95.0 $cm^3$ at STP to 24°C and 91.5 kPa
   f. 1.50 $dm^3$ at STP to −15°C and 110.0 kPa
   g. 325 $cm^3$ at 30.0°C and 95.0 kPa to STP
   h. 240 $cm^3$ at 5°C and 92.0 kPa to 40.0°C and 105.0 kPa

2. Oxygen has a density of 1.429 $g/dm^3$ at STP. Which change will result in a greater change in density? What is the new density?
   a. decreasing the temperature from 0.0°C to −40.0°C
   b. increasing the pressure from 100.0 kPa to 114.5 kPa

3. What is the density of a gas at STP if its density is 1.75 $g/dm^3$ at 110.0 kPa and 45°C?

4. At STP, the density of a gas is 3.24 $mg/cm^3$. What is its density in $g/dm^3$ at 30.0°C and 95.0 kPa?

5. If the pressure on 100 $cm^3$ of a gas is doubled, what volume will the gas occupy, assuming no other changes?

6. The volume of a gas at a pressure of 90.0 kPa is doubled and the temperature remains constant. What is the final pressure exerted by the gas?

7. An unbreakable meteorological balloon is released from the ground. Ground level pressure is 98.5 kPa and the temperature is 18°C. The balloon contains 74.0 $dm^3$ of hydrogen gas. As the balloon ascends, the pressure drops to 7.0 kPa.
   a. What is the new volume of the balloon, assuming no temperature change?
   b. If a temperature drop of 79° occurs, what is the new volume of the balloon after the temperature change?
   c. Of the two factors, pressure and temperature, which had the greatest effect in changing the volume of the balloon?

8. If the temperature of a gas is 0°C and the temperature is changed so that the gas volume doubles, what is the new temperature of the gas?

9. A balloon will burst at a volume of 2.0 dm³. If the gas in a partially filled balloon occupies 0.75 dm³ at a temperature of 21°C and a pressure of $9.90 \times 10^4$ Pa, what is the temperature at which it will burst if the pressure is $1.01 \times 10^5$ Pa at the time it breaks?

10. What is the ratio of the speed of carbon monoxide, CO, molecules to that of nitrogen(II) oxide, NO, molecules when both gases are at the same temperature?

# GASES AND THE MOLE

# 19

## 19:1 AVOGADRO'S PRINCIPLE AND MOLAR VOLUME

What is the relationship between the mass of a gas and its volume? **Avogadro's principle** states that *equal volumes of all gases, measured under the same conditions of pressure and temperature, contain the same number of particles.* It has been found experimentally that 1 mole of any gas at STP contains $6.02 \times 10^{23}$ particles. This number is called **Avogadro's number** of particles. One mole of any gas has a mass equal to its molecular mass. For example:

$$1 \text{ mole } N_2 = 28.0 \text{ g } N_2 = 6.02 \times 10^{23} \text{ molecules of } N_2$$
$$1 \text{ mole } CO_2 = 44.0 \text{ g } CO_2 = 6.02 \times 10^{23} \text{ molecules of } CO_2$$

The volume of one mole of a gas at STP is the molar volume of the gas. One mole of a gas at STP occupies 22.4 cubic decimeters ($dm^3$). This volume is the same for all gases at STP. The mass and volume of any gas are related as follows:

$$1 \text{ mole of any gas} = \text{molecular mass} = 22.4 \text{ dm}^3$$

### Example 1

How many grams of carbon dioxide, $CO_2$, will occupy a volume of 500.0 $cm^3$ at STP?

**Solving Process:**

The conversion equalities are

$$1 \text{ mol } CO_2 = 22.4 \text{ dm}^3 CO_2 \text{ (STP)}$$
$$1 \text{ mol } CO_2 = 44.0 \text{ g } CO_2$$

$$\text{grams } CO_2 = \frac{500.0 \text{ cm}^3 \text{ CO}_2}{} \left| \frac{1 \text{ dm}^3}{1000 \text{ cm}^3} \right| \frac{1 \text{ mol}}{22.4 \text{ dm}^3} \left| \frac{44.0 \text{ g } CO_2}{1 \text{ mol } CO_2} \right.$$

$$= 0.982 \text{ g}$$

## PROBLEMS

*Assume the volumes given are at STP unless other conditions are specified.*

1. Calculate the number of moles contained in each of the following gas volumes.

   **a.** $5.00 \times 10^4$ cm$^3$ H$_2$          **d.** 15 000 cm$^3$ NH$_3$
   **b.** $1.000 \times 10^3$ cm$^3$ N$_2$          **e.** 2500 cm$^3$ O$_2$
   **c.** 6500 cm$^3$ SO$_2$                         **f.** $2.000 \times 10^3$ cm$^3$ CO$_2$

2. Calculate the mass of each of the following volumes of gas.

   **a.** 20.0 m$^3$ CH$_4$          **d.** 0.300 m$^3$ N$_2$O
   **b.** 1500.0 cm$^3$ Cl$_2$       **e.** 3.0 m$^3$ N$_2$
   **c.** 70.0 cm$^3$ SO$_3$          **f.** 3500.0 cm$^3$ H$_2$S

3. Calculate the volume in dm$^3$ of each of the following.

   **a.** 4.0 mol Br$_2$             **e.** 2.50 mol NH$_3$
   **b.** 200.0 g H$_2$S             **f.** 50.0 g NO$_2$
   **c.** 25.5 g SO$_2$              **g.** 7.00 mol O$_2$
   **d.** 600.0 g Cl$_2$             **h.** 10.0 g HCl

## 19:2  IDEAL GAS EQUATION

The **ideal gas equation** combines the four physical variables (pressure, volume, temperature, and number of particles) for gases into one equation. Remember that an ideal gas is composed of point masses with no mutual attraction. All real gases deviate somewhat from the gas laws since the molecules of real gases occupy volume and attract one another.

The ideal gas equation is $PV = nRT$, where $P$ is the pressure in kilopascals. $V$ is the volume in cubic decimeters and $T$ is the temperature in kelvin. The $n$ represents the number of moles of a gas. With these units, the value of the constant $R$ is 8.31 dm$^3$·kPa/mol·K. There are other values of $R$ depending upon the units used to derive $R$.

We can use the ideal gas equation to determine the molecular mass ($M$) of a gas. The number of moles ($n$) of any species is equal to its mass ($m$) divided by the molecular mass ($M$). Thus, the ideal gas equation can also be written as

$$PV = nRT \quad \text{or} \quad PV = \frac{m}{M} RT \quad \text{or} \quad M = \frac{mRT}{PV}$$

## Example 2

How many moles of gas will a 1250 cm$^3$ flask hold at 35.0°C and a pressure of 95.4 kPa?

**Solving Process:**

The ideal gas equation can be solved for the number of moles, $n$, of a substance.

$$PV = nRT \quad \text{or} \quad n = \frac{PV}{RT}$$

Before we can substitute the known values into the ideal gas equation, 35.0°C must be converted to 308.2 K. We get the following expression.

$$n = \frac{\overset{P}{95.4\;\cancel{kPa}}}{\underset{R}{8.31\dfrac{\cancel{dm^3}\cdot\cancel{kPa}}{mol\cdot\cancel{K}}}} \left| \begin{array}{c} \overset{V}{1250\;\cancel{cm^3}} \\ \hline \end{array} \right. \left| \begin{array}{c} \overset{}{1\;\cancel{dm^3}} \\ \hline 1000\;\cancel{cm^3} \end{array} \right. = 0.0466 \text{ mol}$$

The solution is 0.0466 mol. Note that all other units in the problem divide out.

## Example 3

A flask has a volume of 258 cm³. A gas with mass 1.475 g is introduced into the flask at a temperature of 302.0 K and a pressure of $9.86 \times 10^4$ Pa. Calculate the molecular mass of the gas using the ideal gas equation.

**Solving Process:**

The number of moles, $n$, of a substance is equal to mass, $m$, divided by the molecular mass, $M$. Therefore, the ideal gas equation may be written

$$PV = \frac{mRT}{M}, \quad \text{or} \quad M = \frac{mRT}{PV}$$

$$M = \frac{1.475 \text{ g}}{9.86 \times 10^4\;\cancel{Pa}} \left| \begin{array}{c} 8.31\dfrac{\cancel{dm^3}\cdot\cancel{kPa}}{mol\cdot\cancel{K}} \end{array} \right. \left| \begin{array}{c} 302.0\;\cancel{K} \\ 258\;\cancel{cm^3} \end{array} \right. \left| \begin{array}{c} 1000\;\cancel{Pa} \\ 1\;\cancel{kPa} \end{array} \right.$$

$$\left| \begin{array}{c} 1000\;\cancel{cm^3} \\ 1\;\cancel{dm^3} \end{array} \right. = 146 \text{ g/mol}$$

Remember that the units of volume, pressure, temperature, and quantity of gas must be consistent with the value of $R$.

## PROBLEMS

4. What is the molecular mass of sulfur dioxide, $SO_2$, if 300.0 cm³ of the gas has a mass of 0.855 g at STP?

5. A sample of hydrogen iodide, HI, has a mass of 2.28 g and occupies 400.0 cm³ at STP. What is the molecular mass of this compound?

6. If 0.179 g of methane, $CH_4$, occupy 0.250 dm³, what is the molecular mass of methane if the volume is given at standard conditions?

7. From the volume, temperature, and pressure, calculate the number of moles for each gas listed using the ideal gas equation.
   a. 750.0 cm³ $O_2$ at 27°C and 99.0 kPa
   b. 3.00 dm³ $CO_2$ at −15°C and 103.0 kPa

8. Calculate the volume each gas will occupy under the conditions listed using the ideal gas equation.
   **a.** 3.00 mol $H_2$ at 24°C and 100.5 kPa
   **b.** 150.0 g $Cl_2$ at −12.5°C and 98.5 kPa
9. The density of a sample of phosphorus trifluoride, $PF_3$, is 3.90 g/dm³. What is the molecular mass of this gas at STP?

$$\left( \text{Hint: } D = \frac{m}{V} = \frac{MP}{RT} \right)$$

# 19:3   MASS-GAS VOLUME PROBLEMS

Many chemical reactions involve gases. It is often necessary to know the volume of gas involved with a known mass of material in a reaction. Problems of this type are similar to mass-mass problems, however one additional piece of information is needed. In mass-volume problems, mass is changed to moles of the desired substance and then converted to volume using the relationship:

1 mole of any gas = 22.4 dm³ of that gas at STP

The reverse calculation may also be done. Volume is changed to moles and moles are changed to mass.

## Example 4

Calculate the volume of oxygen produced at STP by the decomposition of 10.0 g of potassium chlorate, $KClO_3$.

**Solving Process:**

Write the balanced equation.

$$2KClO_3(cr) \rightarrow 2KCl(cr) + 3O_2(g)$$

Start with the known mass of $KClO_3$ given in the problem and convert to volume of oxygen at STP.

|  | grams of given | convert to moles | mole ratio |  |
|---|---|---|---|---|
| volume $O_2$ = | $\dfrac{10.0 \text{ g } KClO_3}{}$ | $\dfrac{1 \text{ mol } KClO_3}{123 \text{ g } KClO_3}$ | $\dfrac{3 \text{ mol } O_2}{2 \text{ mol } KClO_3}$ |  |

$$\frac{\text{convert to}}{dm^3 \text{ of unknown}}$$

$$\frac{22.4 \text{ dm}^3}{1 \text{ mol } O_2} = 2.73 \text{ dm}^3$$

## Example 5

A student performs an experiment involving the reaction of magnesium metal with hydrochloric acid to form hydrogen gas. From the given data, calculate the mass of magnesium.

    **1.** volume of hydrogen gas formed       42.0 cm³

2. temperature of hydrogen                          20.0°C
3. pressure                                         99.3 kPa
4. vapor pressure of water                           2.3 kPa
5. pressure of dry hydrogen (99.3 − 2.3)   97.0 kPa

**Solving Process:**

Determine the volume of dry hydrogen at STP. Use the combined gas law.

$$\text{volume dry } H_2 = \frac{42.0 \text{ cm}^3 \ H_2}{} \left| \frac{97.0 \text{ kPa}}{101.3 \text{ kPa}} \right| \frac{273.2 \text{ K}}{293.2 \text{ K}}$$

$$= 37.5 \text{ cm}^3$$

Use the volume of dry $H_2$ (37.5 cm³) and the molar volume to find the moles of hydrogen gas formed at STP.

$$\text{mol } H_2 = \frac{37.5 \text{ cm}^3 \ H_2}{} \left| \frac{1 \text{ mol } H_2}{22.4 \text{ dm}^3 \ H_2} \right| \frac{1 \text{ dm}^3}{1000 \text{ cm}^3}$$

$$= 1.67 \times 10^{-3} \text{ mol}$$

Write a balanced equation and use it to find the mass of magnesium.

$$Mg(cr) + 2HCl(aq) \rightarrow MgCl_2(aq) + H_2(g)$$

$$\text{mass Mg} = \frac{1.67 \times 10^{-3} \text{ mol } H_2}{} \left| \frac{1 \text{ mol Mg}}{1 \text{ mol } H_2} \right| \frac{24.3 \text{ g Mg}}{1 \text{ mol Mg}} = 0.0406 \text{ g}$$

## PROBLEMS

*Assume that all volumes are at STP.*

10. How many cm³ of hydrogen are produced if 4.00 g zinc react with excess hydrochloric acid?

$$Zn(cr) + 2HCl(aq) \rightarrow ZnCl_2(aq) + H_2(g)$$

11. If excess chlorine gas reacts with a solution containing 20.0 g of potassium bromide, how many cubic centimeters of bromine gas can be produced?

$$2KBr(aq) + Cl_2(g) \rightarrow 2KCl(aq) + Br_2(g)$$

12. How many grams of copper(II) oxide can be reduced to copper metal with 10.0 dm³ of $H_2$?

$$CuO(cr) + H_2(g) \rightarrow Cu(cr) + H_2O(g)$$

13. Calculate the cm³ of oxygen that can be produced by the electrolysis of 5.00 g of water.

$$2H_2O(l) \rightarrow 2H_2(g) + O_2(g)$$

14. In the reaction between aluminum and oxygen, how many grams of aluminum are required to react with 5.00 dm³ of oxygen?

$$4Al(cr) + 3O_2(g) \rightarrow 2Al_2O_3(cr)$$

# 19:4   VOLUME-VOLUME PROBLEMS

It is possible to calculate the volume of a gas in a reaction when the volume of another gas in the reaction is known. Two methods can be used in solving these volume-volume problems. The first method is the same as the mass-mass or mass-volume method.

The steps are

**Step 1.** Convert the given volume to moles.

**Step 2.** From the balanced equation, convert the moles of given substance to moles of required substance.

**Step 3.** Convert the moles of required substance back to its volume.

In each case, the temperature and pressure must be taken into consideration. Two methods of solving for gas volume are given. The second method usually involves only an inspection and simple mental calculation. It can be used easily when the temperature and pressure remain constant.

## Example 6

If 6.00 $dm^3$ of oxygen are available to burn carbon disulfide, $CS_2$, how many $dm^3$ of carbon dioxide are produced? The products of the combustion of carbon disulfide are carbon dioxide and sulfur dioxide.

**Solving Process:**

Balance the equation for this reaction.

$$CS_2(l) + 3O_2(g) \rightarrow CO_2(g) + 2SO_2(g)$$

Convert 6.00 $dm^3$ $O_2$ to $dm^3$ of $CO_2$.

$$\text{volume } CO_2 = \frac{6.00 \text{ dm}^3 \text{ O}_2}{} \left| \frac{1 \text{ mol O}_2}{22.4 \text{ dm}^3 \text{ O}_2} \right| \frac{1 \text{ mol CO}_2}{3 \text{ mol O}_2} \right|$$

$$\frac{22.4 \text{ dm}^3 \text{ CO}_2}{1 \text{ mol CO}_2} = 2.00 \text{ dm}^3$$

Therefore, 6.00 $dm^3$ $O_2$ will produce 2.00 $dm^3$ $CO_2$. Note that the changes to and from moles divide out.

**Alternate Method:** *Temperature and Pressure Constant*

The balanced equation indicates the relative number of moles of reactant and product. The coefficients also indicate the relative volumes of the gases at constant temperature and pressure. The relationship is a result of the principle stated in Avogadro's hypothesis: *equal volumes of gases at the same temperature and pressure contain the same number of particles.* If the gases are measured under the same conditions of temperature and pressure then 3 volumes $O_2$ : 1 volume $CO_2$ or 3 $dm^3$ $O_2$ : 1 $dm^3$ $CO_2$. The volume of $CO_2$ will be one-third the volume of $O_2$. Since the $O_2$ volume is 6.00 $dm^3$, the $CO_2$ volume is 2.00 $dm^3$. Conversion ratios could be used as follows.

$$\text{volume CO}_2 = \frac{6.00 \text{ dm}^3 \text{ O}_2}{} \left| \frac{1 \text{ dm}^3 \text{ CO}_2}{3 \text{ dm}^3 \text{ O}_2} \right.$$

$$= 2.00 \text{ dm}^3$$

## PROBLEMS

15. In the electrolysis of water, 75.0 cm$^3$ of oxygen gas are produced. How many cm$^3$ of hydrogen are produced?

$$2H_2O(l) \rightarrow 2H_2(g) + O_2(g)$$

16. If an electric discharge produces 20.0 cm$^3$ of ozone, $O_3$, how many cubic centimeters of oxygen are required?

$$3O_2(g) \rightarrow 2O_3(g)$$

17. Ammonia can be produced by the Haber process. If 60.0 dm$^3$ of $NH_3$ are produced, how many dm$^3$ of hydrogen and nitrogen are necessary?

$$3H_2(g) + N_2(g) \rightarrow 2NH_3(g)$$

18. How many cm$^3$ of chlorine gas are required to produce 50.0 cm$^3$ of hydrogen chloride gas?

$$H_2(g) + Cl_2(g) \rightarrow 2HCl(g)$$

19. The residue from the complete decomposition of potassium chlorate is found to contain 1.80 g of potassium chloride. Determine the following:

   a. grams of $KClO_3$ originally present
   b. grams of oxygen produced
   c. cubic centimeters of oxygen at STP

## 19:5  LIMITING REACTANTS

Many reactions continue until one of the reactants is consumed. The reactant that is used up first is called the **limiting reactant.** The other reactant is said to be in *excess.* When discussing limiting reactants, we will deal only with nonreversible reactions. It is possible to determine whether a material is in excess or is deficient in a reaction by experiment or by calculation.

Limiting reactant problems are most easily solved by comparing the moles of the reactants present using the following steps.

**Step 1.** Write a balanced equation.

**Step 2.** Change both given quantities to moles.

**Step 3.** From the balanced equation, determine the moles of required substance that each given quantity will produce.

**Step 4.** Complete the problem using the quantity that yields the lesser amount of product. This reactant is the limiting reactant.

## Example 7

If 40.0 g of $H_3PO_4$ react with 60.0 g of $MgCO_3$, calculate the volume of $CO_2$ produced at STP.

**Solving Process:**

**Step 1.** Write the balanced equation.

$$2H_3PO_4(aq) + 3MgCO_3(cr) \rightarrow Mg_3(PO_4)_2(cr) + 3CO_2(g) + 3H_2O(l)$$

**Step 2.** Change grams of reactant to moles of reactant.

$$\text{mol } H_3PO_4 = \frac{40.0 \text{ g } H_3PO_4}{} \left| \frac{1 \text{ mol } H_3PO_4}{98.0 \text{ g } H_3PO_4} \right. = 0.408 \text{ mol}$$

$$\text{mol } MgCO_3 = \frac{60.0 \text{ g } MgCO_3}{} \left| \frac{1 \text{ mol } MgCO_3}{84.3 \text{ g } MgCO_3} \right. = 0.712 \text{ mol}$$

**Step 3.** From the balanced equation determine the moles of $CO_2$ that will be produced by each reactant.

$$\text{mol } CO_2 = \frac{0.408 \text{ mol } H_3PO_4}{} \left| \frac{3 \text{ mol } CO_2}{2 \text{ mol } H_3PO_4} \right. = 0.612 \text{ mol}$$

$$\text{mol } CO_2 = \frac{0.712 \text{ mol } MgCO_3}{} \left| \frac{3 \text{ mol } CO_2}{3 \text{ mol } MgCO_3} \right. = 0.712 \text{ mol}$$

**Step 4.** Use the limiting reactant to complete the problem.

$$\text{volume } CO_2 = \frac{0.612 \text{ mol } CO_2}{} \left| \frac{22.4 \text{ dm}^3}{1 \text{ mol } CO_2} \right. = 13.7 \text{ dm}^3 \text{ at STP.}$$

Therefore, 40.0 g of $H_3PO_4$ will produce 13.7 $dm^3$ of $CO_2$ measured at standard temperature and pressure.

The same approach for finding limiting reactants can also be used in mass-mass or volume-volume problems.

## PROBLEMS

20. If 20.0 g of NaOH react with 30.0 g of $H_2SO_4$ to produce $Na_2SO_4$, which reactant is limiting?

$$2NaOH(aq) + H_2SO_4(aq) \rightarrow Na_2SO_4(aq) + 2 H_2O(l)$$

21. If 5.00 g of copper metal react with a solution containing 20.0 g of $AgNO_3$ to produce silver metal, which reactant is limiting?

$$Cu(cr) + 2AgNO_3(aq) \rightarrow Cu(NO_3)_2(aq) + 2Ag(cr)$$

22. What reactant is limiting if 3.00 $dm^3$ of $Cl_2$ at STP react with a solution containing 25.0 g of NaBr to produce $Br_2$?

23. If 20.0 g of KOH react with 15.0 g of $(NH_4)_2SO_4$, calculate the $dm^3$ of $NH_3$ produced at STP.

24. Magnesium acetate can be prepared by a reaction involving 15.0 g of iron(III) acetate with either 10.0 g of $MgCrO_4$ or 15.0 g of $MgSO_4$. Which reaction will give the greatest yield of $Mg(CH_3COO)_2$? How many grams of $Mg(CH_3COO)_2$ will be produced?

$$2Fe(CH_3COO)_3(aq) + 3MgCrO_4(cr) \rightarrow$$
$$3Mg(CH_3COO)_2(aq) + Fe_2(CrO_4)_3(cr)$$

$$2Fe(CH_3COO)_3(aq) + 3MgSO_4(cr) \rightarrow$$
$$3Mg(CH_3COO)_2(aq) + Fe_2(SO_4)_3(cr)$$

# 19:6    NONSTANDARD CONDITIONS

Gas volume changes dramatically when pressure or temperature change. The molar volume is 22.4 $dm^3$ only at STP. If the experimental conditions are different from STP in a problem, it is still necessary to calculate the gas volume at STP.

The secret to success in these problems is to remember that the central step (moles of given to moles of unknown) must take place at STP. Thus, if you are given a volume of gas at other than STP, you must convert to STP before performing the moles to moles step in the solving process. On the other hand, if you are requested to find the volume of a gas at conditions other than STP, you must convert the volume after the moles to moles step.

## Example 8

How many grams of ammonium sulfate must react with excess sodium hydroxide to produce 408 $cm^3$ of ammonia measured at 27°C and 98.0 kPa?

**Solving Process:**

Write the balanced equation.

$$(NH_4)_2SO_4(cr) + 2NaOH(aq) \rightarrow Na_2SO_4(aq) + 2NH_3(g) + 2H_2O(l)$$

Convert 408 $cm^3$ $NH_3$ at 27°C and 98.0 kPa to STP and then convert to g of $(NH_4)_2SO_4$. Since the temperature decreases, the volume decreases and the absolute temperature ratio is

$$\frac{273\ K}{300\ K}$$

Since pressure increases, volume decreases and the pressure ratio is

$$\frac{98.0\ kPa}{101.3\ kPa}$$

$$\frac{mass}{(NH_4)_2SO_4} = \frac{408\ cm^3\ NH_3}{} \left| \frac{273\ K}{300\ K} \right| \frac{98.0\ kPa}{101.3\ kPa} \left| \frac{1\ mol\ NH_3}{22.4\ dm^3} \right|$$

$$\left| \frac{1\ mol\ (NH_4)_2SO_4}{2\ mol\ NH_3} \right| \frac{132\ g\ (NH_4)_2SO_4}{1\ mol\ (NH_4)_2SO_4} \left| \frac{1\ dm^3}{1000\ cm^3} \right| = 1.06\ g$$

To produce 408 cm$^3$ NH$_3$ at 27°C and 98.0 kPa, it is necessary to react 1.06 g (NH$_4$)$_2$SO$_4$ with excess sodium hydroxide.

## Example 9

What volume of hydrogen collected over water at 27°C and 97.5 kPa is produced by the reaction of 3.00 g of Zn with an excess of sulfuric acid? The vapor pressure of water at 27°C is 3.6 kPa.

**Solving Process:**
Write the balanced equation.

$$Zn(cr) + H_2SO_4(aq) \rightarrow ZnSO_4(aq) + H_2(g)$$

The cubic decimeters of H$_2$ at STP must be converted to the conditions given in the problem. As the temperature is increased, the volume will increase, so the absolute temperature ratio is

$$\frac{300 \text{ K}}{273 \text{ K}}$$

As pressure is decreased volume will increase, so the pressure ratio is

$$\frac{101.3 \text{ kPa}}{97.5 \text{ kPa}}$$

This ratio must be corrected for the vapor pressure of water, which is 3.6 kPa at this temperature. The corrected ratio is

$$\frac{101.3 \text{ kPa}}{97.5 - 3.6 \text{ kPa}} \quad \text{or} \quad \frac{101.3 \text{ kPa}}{93.9 \text{ kPa}}$$

Convert from grams of Zn to cubic decimeters of dry H$_2$ at 27°C and 97.5 kPa. Then convert to cubic decimeters of H$_2$ at STP by using the absolute temperature and pressure ratios.

$$\text{volume H}_2 = \frac{3.00 \text{ g Zn}}{} \left| \frac{1 \text{ mol Zn}}{65.4 \text{ g Zn}} \right| \frac{1 \text{ mol H}_2}{1 \text{ mol Zn}} \left| \frac{22.4 \text{ dm}^3 \text{ H}_2}{1 \text{ mol H}_2} \right|$$

$$\left| \frac{300 \text{ K}}{273 \text{ K}} \right| \frac{101.3 \text{ kPa}}{93.9 \text{ kPa}} = 1.22 \text{ dm}^3 \text{ H}_2$$

Hence, 3.00 g Zn will react with excess H$_2$SO$_4$ to give 1.22 dm$^3$ of H$_2$ measured at 27°C and 97.5 kPa over water.

## PROBLEMS

**25.** If 14.7 g of sodium peroxide (Na$_2$O$_2$) react with water to produce sodium hydroxide and oxygen gas, how many dm$^3$ of oxygen are produced at 22°C and 1.12 × 10$^5$ Pa?

**26.** How many dm$^3$ of chlorine gas measured at 18.5°C and 98.0 kPa can be produced by the electrolysis of 62.3 g NaCl to give sodium metal and chlorine gas?

27. How many $dm^3$ of nitrogen measured at 21.5°C and $9.55 \times 10^4$ Pa are required to react with excess calcium carbide, $CaC_2$, to produce 100.0 g of calcium cyanamid, $CaCN_2$, and carbon?

28. How many grams of iron metal must react with excess steam to produce 10.0 $dm^3$ of hydrogen collected over water at 20.0°C and $9.90 \times 10^4$ Pa? The other product is iron(II,III) oxide, $Fe_3O_4(Fe_3O_4$ is actually $FeO·Fe_2O_3$).

## CHAPTER REVIEW PROBLEMS

1. One mole of He has a mass of 4.0026 g and 1.000 $dm^3$ of He (at STP) has a mass of 0.1787 g. Calculate the molar volume of helium.

2. A sample of gas has a mass of 1.248 g and occupies 300.0 $cm^3$ at STP. What is the molecular mass of this gas?

3. From the volume, temperature, and pressure data given, calculate the number of moles and the mass in grams for each gas listed using the ideal gas equation.
   a. 2000.0 $cm^3$ $NH_3$ at 10.0°C and 105.0 kPa
   b. 5.00 $dm^3$ $SO_2$ at 21.0°C and 100.0 kPa

4. Calculate the volume each gas will occupy under the conditions listed using the ideal gas equation.
   a. 5.00 mol $CH_4$ at 27.0°C and 97.2 kPa
   b. 200.0 g $NH_3$ at 12.0°C and 104.5 kPa

5. What is the molecular mass of a gas if 5.75 g of the gas occupy a volume of 3.50 $dm^3$? The pressure was recorded as $9.525 \times 10^4$ Pa and the temperature is 52°C.

6. How many cubic centimeters of hydrogen at STP are produced by the reaction of 0.750 g of sodium metal with excess water?

$$2Na(cr) + 2H_2O(l) \rightarrow 2NaOH(aq) + H_2(g)$$

7. What mass of magnesium will react with excess hydrochloric acid to produce $5.00 \times 10^2$ $cm^3$ of $H_2$ at STP?

$$Mg(cr) + 2HCl(aq) \rightarrow MgCl_2(aq) + H_2(g)$$

8. When lead(II) sulfide is burned in air, lead(II) oxide and sulfur dioxide are produced. If 20.0 $dm^3$ of sulfur dioxide were produced, how many cubic decimeters of oxygen gas were required to react with the lead(II) sulfide?

$$2PbS(cr) + 3O_2(g) \rightarrow 2PbO(cr) + 2SO_2(g)$$

9. In a reaction involving carbon monoxide and iron(III) oxide, the products are iron metal and carbon dioxide. If 84.75 $dm^3$ of carbon dioxide are produced, how many $dm^3$ of carbon monoxide are required?

10. Calcium carbide ($CaC_2$) reacts with water to produce calcium hydroxide and acetylene ($C_2H_2$). What volume of the gas at STP could be produced from the reaction of 50.0 g of $CaC_2$ and 50.0 g of water?

11. Hydrogen burns to give water. If 200.0 cm$^3$ of H$_2$ reacts with 150.0 cm$^3$ of O$_2$, what volume of water vapor is produced? How many cubic centimeters of gas remain unreacted and what gas remains? Assume that all volumes are measured at any given temperature above the normal boiling point of water.

12. How many grams of sodium hydrogen carbonate, NaHCO$_3$, must be heated to produce 2.50 dm$^3$ of carbon dioxide measured at 22.5°C and 97.5 kPa? The other products are sodium carbonate and water.

13. If 3.20 g of aluminum react with excess hydrochloric acid, how many cm$^3$ of hydrogen collected over water at 20.0°C and 99.5 kPa are produced?

# ENERGY AND DISORDER 20

## 20:1 ENTHALPY, ENTROPY, AND FREE ENERGY

All chemical changes are accompanied by changes in energy and the degree of disorder for the particles involved. The study of matter and energy interactions is called **thermodynamics.** Thermodynamic calculations can be kept simple if we reduce all variables to a set of standard conditions. These standards are 25°C, 101.3 kPa, and 1 molar solutions.

The variables of interest to the chemist studying the thermodynamics of chemical reactions include

$H$, the **enthalpy,** or heat content, of a substance

$S$, the **entropy,** or disorder, of a substance

$G$, the **free energy,** or chemical potential, of a substance

The changes in these variables during a reaction is the difference between the values for the products and the reactants.

Chemists are interested in $\Delta H$ since if $\Delta H < 0$ the reaction is **exothermic,** that is, energy is given off. On the other hand if $\Delta H > 0$, the reaction is **endothermic,** that is, energy is taken in. The chief use of $\Delta S$ is as a step in determining $\Delta G$. Of course, if $\Delta S > 0$ there is an increase in disorder and if $\Delta S < 0$ there is a decrease in disorder. $\Delta G$ is important because if $\Delta G < 0$ the reaction is spontaneous and if $\Delta G > 0$ the reaction is not spontaneous.

Enthalpy and free energy quantities are relative values compared to free elements defined as having zero enthalpy and zero free energy. The enthalpy and free energy of each substance are therefore represented by $\Delta H_f^\circ$ and $\Delta G_f^\circ$, respectively. The superscript "°" designates standard conditions. The subscript "f" designates "of formation" since the formation of the substance from the free elements is the enthalpy or free energy. The reactants (in this case the free elements) would be equal to zero. At standard conditions, the equations become

$$\Delta H^\circ_{(reaction)} = \Sigma \Delta H_f^\circ{}_{(products)} - \Sigma \Delta H_f^\circ{}_{(reactants)}$$
$$\Delta G^\circ_{(reaction)} = \Sigma \Delta G_f^\circ{}_{(products)} - \Sigma \Delta G_f^\circ{}_{(reactants)}$$
$$\Delta S^\circ_{(reaction)} = \Sigma S^\circ_{(products)} - \Sigma S^\circ_{(reactants)}$$

## Example 1

What is the enthalpy change for the following reaction?

$$Cl_2(g) + 2HBr(g) \rightarrow 2HCl(g) + Br_2(g)$$

135

**Solving Process:**

From Table A-10 of thermodynamic values in the Appendix, we find the following $\Delta H_f^\circ$ values:

$$HBr = -36.2 \text{ kJ/mol}$$
$$HCl = -92.3 \text{ kJ/mol}$$

By definition, the enthalpy of formation for $Cl_2$ and $Br_2$ is 0.

$$\Delta H^\circ = \Sigma \Delta H_{f\,(\text{products})}^\circ - \Sigma \Delta H_{f\,(\text{reactants})}^\circ$$

$$\Delta H^\circ = \left[ \frac{1\text{ mol Br}_2}{\text{mol Br}_2} \cdot \frac{0 \text{ kJ}}{} + \frac{2\text{ mol HCl}}{\text{mol HCl}} \cdot \frac{(-92.3) \text{ kJ}}{} \right] -$$

$$\left[ \frac{1\text{ mol Cl}_2}{\text{mol Cl}_2} \cdot \frac{0 \text{ kJ}}{} + \frac{2\text{ mol HBr}}{\text{mol HBr}} \cdot \frac{(-36.2) \text{ kJ}}{} \right]$$

$$= -112.2 \text{ kJ}$$

The negative sign indicates that the products have less enthalpy, than the reactants. Thus, energy must have been released, and the reaction is exothermic.

## Example 2

For the reaction

$$Ca(cr) + 2H_2O(l) \rightarrow Ca(OH)_2(cr) + H_2(g)$$
$$\Delta S^\circ = 25.7 \text{ J/K}$$

What is $S^\circ$ for $Ca(OH)_2(cr)$?

**Solving Process:**

From Table A-10 we find the following $S^\circ$ values:

$$Ca(cr) = 41.6 \text{ J/mol·K}$$
$$H_2O(l) = 70.0 \text{ J/mol·K}$$
$$H_2(g) = 131 \text{ J/mol·K}$$

$$\Delta S^\circ = \Sigma S_{(\text{products})}^\circ - \Sigma S_{(\text{reactants})}^\circ$$

$$25.7 \text{ J/K} = \left[ \frac{1 \text{ mol Ca(OH)}_2}{} \cdot x + \frac{1 \text{ mol H}_2}{} \cdot \frac{131 \text{ J}}{\text{mol H}_2 \cdot \text{K}} \right] -$$

$$\left[ \frac{1 \text{ mol Ca}}{} \cdot \frac{41.6 \text{ J}}{\text{mol Ca·K}} + \frac{2 \text{ mol H}_2\text{O}}{} \cdot \frac{70.0 \text{ J}}{\text{mol H}_2\text{O·K}} \right]$$

$$x = 76.3 \text{ J/mol·K}$$

## PROBLEMS

1. Find $\Delta H^\circ$ for the following reactions.
   a. $2KBr(cr) + H_2SO_4(l) \rightarrow K_2SO_4(cr) + 2HBr(g)$
   b. $Mg_3N_2(cr) + 6H_2O(l) \rightarrow 3Mg(OH)_2(cr) + 2NH_3(g)$
   c. $NH_4NO_3(cr) \rightarrow N_2O(g) + 2H_2O(l)$

2. Find $\Delta S°$ for the following reactions.
   a. $Zn(NO_3)_2(aq) + 2NaOH(aq) \rightarrow Zn(OH)_2(cr) + 2NaNO_3(aq)$
   b. $2NO_2(g) + H_2O(l) \rightarrow HNO_2(aq) + HNO_3(aq)$
   c. $Mg(cr) + 2HNO_3(aq) \rightarrow Mg(NO_3)_2(aq) + H_2(g)$

# 20:2   SPONTANEOUS REACTIONS

An American chemist, J. Willard Gibbs, discovered the relationship among entropy, enthalpy, and free energy to be

$$\Delta G° = \Delta H° - T\Delta S°$$

where $T$ is the absolute temperature. A **spontaneous reaction** is one in which $\Delta G$ is negative. Using tables of thermodynamic values we can predict whether a reaction is spontaneous at standard conditions. If a table includes values of $\Delta G_f°$, the $\Delta G°$ for the reaction can be calculated directly as in the previous section. $\Delta G°$ can also be calculated using $\Delta H°$, $T$, and $\Delta S°$.

## Example 3

Is the following reaction spontaneous?
$$2H_2O_2(l) \rightarrow 2H_2O(l) + O_2(g)$$

**Solving Process:**
From the table of thermodynamic values in the Appendix, we obtain the following $\Delta G_f°$ values:

$$H_2O_2 = -118 \text{ kJ/mol}$$
$$H_2O = -237 \text{ kJ/mol}$$
$$O_2 = 0 \text{ kJ}$$

$$\Delta G° = \Sigma\Delta G°_{f(products)} - \Sigma\Delta G°_{f(reactants)}$$

$$\Delta G° = \left[ \frac{2 \text{ mol } H_2O}{} \middle| \frac{(-237) \text{ kJ}}{\text{mol } H_2O} + \frac{1 \text{ mol } O_2}{} \middle| \frac{0 \text{ kJ}}{\text{mol } O_2} \right] -$$
$$\left[ \frac{2 \text{ mol } H_2O_2}{} \middle| \frac{(-118) \text{ kJ}}{\text{mol } H_2O_2} \right]$$

$$= -238 \text{ kJ}$$

$\Delta G°$ is negative, so the reaction is spontaneous at standard conditions. Note, however, the term spontaneous tells us nothing about how long a reaction will take.

## Example 4

Calculate the standard enthalpy of formation, $\Delta H_f°$, of iron(III) oxide at 298 K by the thermite welding process.
$$2Al(cr) + Fe_2O_3(cr) \rightarrow 2\ Fe(cr) + Al_2O_3(cr)$$

Use thermodynamic values from Table A-10 and the following data for Fe(cr): $\Delta H_f^\circ = 0$ kJ/mol, $\Delta G_f^\circ = 0$ kJ/mol, and $S^\circ = 32.7$ J/mol·K.

**Solving Process:**

**a.** Since the enthalpy change for the thermite reaction is not given, we must calculate it from the relationship, $\Delta G^\circ = \Delta H - T\Delta S$. We must first calculate $\Delta G^\circ$ and $\Delta S^\circ$. It is best to organize the data you will use from A-10 into a table.

|  | **Reactants** | | $\rightarrow$ | **Products** | |
|---|---|---|---|---|---|
| **Value** | **Fe$_2$O$_3$** | **2Al** | | **2 Fe** | **Al$_2$O$_3$** |
| $\Delta H_f^\circ$ (kJ/mol) | ? | 0 | | 0 | −1670 |
| $\Delta G_f^\circ$ (kJ/mol) | −741 | 0 | | 0 | −1580 |
| $\Delta S^\circ$ (J/mol K) | 90.0 | 28.3 | | 32.7 | 51.0 |

**b.** To find $\Delta G^\circ$ use the following equation.

$$\Delta G^\circ_{\text{(reaction)}} = \Sigma \Delta G^\circ_{\text{f (products)}} - \Sigma \Delta G^\circ_{\text{f (reactants)}}$$

It is important to use the balanced chemical equation. Multiply each $\Delta G_f^\circ$ by the number of moles from the balanced equation. Substitute these values into the equation used to determine $\Delta G^\circ$(reaction).

$$\Delta G^\circ = \left[ 1\,\text{mol Al}_2\text{O}_3 \middle| \frac{-1580\text{ kJ}}{1\,\text{mol Al}_2\text{O}_3} + 2\,\text{mol Fe} \middle| \frac{0\text{ kJ}}{1\,\text{mol Fe}} \right] -$$

$$\left[ 2\,\text{mol Al} \middle| \frac{0\text{ kJ}}{1\,\text{mol Al}} + 1\,\text{mol Fe}_2\text{O}_3 \middle| \frac{-741\text{ kJ}}{1\,\text{mol Fe}_2\text{O}_3} \right]$$

$$= -839\text{ kJ/mol}$$

**c.** To find $\Delta S^\circ$ use the equation

$$\Delta S^\circ_{\text{(reaction)}} = \Sigma S^\circ_{\text{(products)}} - \Sigma S^\circ_{\text{(reactants)}}$$

$$= \left[ 2\,\text{mol Fe} \middle| \frac{32.7\text{ J/mol·K}}{1\,\text{mol Fe}} + 1\,\text{mol Al}_2\text{O}_3 \middle| \frac{51.0\text{ J/mol·K}}{1\,\text{mol Al}_2\text{O}_3} \right] -$$

$$\left[ 1\,\text{mol Fe}_2\text{O}_3 \middle| \frac{90.0\text{ J/mol·K}}{1\,\text{mol Fe}_2\text{O}_3} + 2\,\text{mol Al} \middle| \frac{28.3\text{ J/mol·K}}{1\,\text{mol Al}} \right]$$

$$= -30.2\text{ J/mol·K}$$

**d.** To find $\Delta H^\circ$ for this reaction, use $\Delta G^\circ = \Delta H^\circ - T\Delta S^\circ$ and solve for $\Delta H^\circ$. ($T = 298$ K)

$$\Delta H^\circ = \Delta G^\circ + T\Delta S^\circ$$

$$= -839\text{ kJ} + \left( 298\,\text{K} \middle| \frac{-30.2\text{ J}}{\text{mol·K}} \middle| \frac{1\text{ kJ}}{1000\text{ J}} \right)$$

$$= -848\text{ kJ/mol}$$

**e.** To find $\Delta H_f^\circ$ for $Fe_2O_3$, substitute the $\Delta H^\circ_{(reaction)}$ into the equation

$$\Delta H^\circ_{(reaction)} = \Delta H^\circ_{f\,(products)} - \Delta H^\circ_{f\,(reactants)}$$

$$-848 \,\frac{kJ}{mol} = \left[\begin{array}{c|c} 2\,\text{mol Fe} & 0\ kJ \\ \hline & 1\,\text{mol Fe} \end{array} + \begin{array}{c|c} 1\,\text{mol Al}_2\text{O}_3 & -1670\ kJ \\ \hline & 1\,\text{mol Al}_2\text{O}_3 \end{array}\right] -$$

$$\left[\begin{array}{c|c} 1\,\text{mol Fe}_2\text{O}_3 & \Delta H_f^\circ \\ \hline & 1\,\text{mol Fe}_2\text{O}_3 \end{array} + \begin{array}{c|c} 2\,\text{mol Al} & 0\ kJ \\ \hline & 1\,\text{mol Al} \end{array}\right]$$

$$= \left(-1670 \,\frac{kJ}{mol}\right) - \Delta H_f^\circ$$

$$\Delta H_f^\circ = -821\ kJ/mol$$

---

## Example 5

For the reaction

$$P_4O_{10}(cr) + 6H_2O(l) \rightarrow 4H_3PO_4(aq)$$
$$\Delta H^\circ = -424\ kJ$$
$$\Delta S^\circ = -209\ J/K$$

Is the reaction spontaneous?

**Solving Process:**

The spontaneity of a reaction is indicated by $\Delta G^\circ$ and $\Delta G^\circ = \Delta H^\circ - T\Delta S^\circ$.

$$\Delta G^\circ = -424\ kJ - [(298\ K)(-209\ J/K)]$$
$$\Delta G^\circ = -424\ kJ + 62282\ J = -424\ kJ + 62.3\ kJ$$
$$\Delta G^\circ = -362\ kJ$$

The reaction is spontaneous.

---

## PROBLEMS

3. Find $\Delta G^\circ$ for the following reactions and predict the spontaneity at standard conditions.
   **a.** $Ca(OH)_2(cr) + 2NH_4Cl(aq) \rightarrow CaCl_2(aq) + 2NH_3(g) + 2H_2O(l)$
   **b.** $2NaCl(cr) + H_2SO_4(l) \rightarrow Na_2SO_4(l) + 2HCl(g)$
   **c.** $CaCl_2(aq) + 2NaOH(aq) \rightarrow Ca(OH)_2(cr) + 2NaCl(aq)$
4. Predict the spontaneity of the following reactions at 298 K.
   **a.** $Sn(cr) + 4HNO_3(aq) \rightarrow SnO_2(cr) + 4NO_2(g) + 2H_2O(l)$, ($\Delta H^\circ = -192\ kJ$, $\Delta S^\circ = 887\ J/K$)
   **b.** $2N_2O_5(g) \rightarrow 4NO_2(g) + O_2(g)$, ($\Delta H^\circ = 110\ kJ$, $\Delta S^\circ = 839\ J/K$)
   **c.** $Mn(cr) + 2HCl(aq) \rightarrow MnCl_2(aq) + H_2(g)$, ($\Delta H^\circ = -221\ kJ$, $\Delta S^\circ = 79.7\ J/K$)
5. Calculate $S^\circ$ for $H_2O$ (g) from the reaction that occurs when methane gas burns. $CH_4(g) + 2O_2(g) \rightarrow CO_2(g) + 2H_2O(g)$

6. Calculate $\Delta G_f^\circ$ for $H_2SO_4$ from the neutralization reaction between the base, NaOH, and sulfuric acid, $H_2SO_4$. $2NaOH(aq) + H_2SO_4(aq) \rightarrow Na_2SO_4(aq) + 2H_2O(l)$

# 20:3   HESS'S LAW

Some reactions may be too slow, explosive, or have many side re-actions making it impractical to measure directly the enthalpy of reaction. **Hess's Law** enables chemists to measure the enthalpy of a reaction that cannot be measured directly in the laboratory.

Enthalpy is a state function because it is independent of the reaction pathway. *The enthalpy change for a reaction is the sum of the enthalpy changes for a series of reactions that add up to the overall reaction.*

## Example 6

What is the enthalpy of reaction for the oxidation of ethanol to acetic acid?

$$CH_3CH_2OH(l) + O_2(g) \rightarrow CH_3COOH(l) + H_2O(l)$$

The standard enthalpy of combustion of ethanol is measured in a calorim-eter and found to be $-1370$ kJ/mol.

(reaction 1) $CH_3CH_2OH(l) + 3O_2(g) \rightarrow 2CO_2(g) + 3H_2O(g)$

The standard enthalpy of combustion of acetic acid is $-874$ kJ/mol.

(reaction 2) $CH_3COOH(l) + 2O_2(g) \rightarrow 2CO_2(g) + 2H_2O(g)$

**Solving Process:**

Since the desired reaction has $CH_3CH_2OH$ on the left, leave reaction one as it is. The desired reaction has $CH_3COOH$ on the right. Reaction 2 must be reversed before adding it to reaction 1.

(1) $CH_3CH_2OH + 3O_2 \rightarrow 2CO_2 + 3H_2O \quad \Delta H = -1370$ kJ/mol

(2) $2CO_2 + 2H_2O \rightarrow CH_3COOH + 2O_2 \quad \Delta H = +874$ kJ/mol

Note that the sign on the enthalpy for the reversed equation has been changed. Now the two equations can be simplified and their enthalpies can be added to give

$$CH_3CH_2OH + O_2 \rightarrow CH_3COOH + H_2O \quad \Delta H = -496 \text{ kJ/mol}$$

## PROBLEM

7. Calculate the enthalpy for the reaction given below.

$C_2H_4(g) + H_2(g) \rightarrow C_2H_6(g)$

Use the following data:

$$C_2H_6(g) + \tfrac{7}{2}O_2(g) \rightarrow 2CO_2(g) + 3H_2O(l) \quad \Delta H = -1560 \text{ kJ}$$
$$H_2(g) + \tfrac{1}{2}O_2(g) \rightarrow H_2O(l) \quad\quad\quad\quad\quad \Delta H = -286 \text{ kJ}$$
$$2CO_2(g) + 2H_2O(l) \rightarrow C_2H_4(g) + 3O_2(g) \quad \Delta H = +1411 \text{ kJ}$$

## CHAPTER REVIEW PROBLEMS

*Use Table A-10 in the Appendix for thermodynamic data.*

1. Find $\Delta G°$ for the following reactions and predict the spontaneity at standard conditions.
   a. $3Mg(cr) + N_2(g) \rightarrow Mg_3N_2(cr)$
   b. $3Cu(cr) + 8HNO_3(aq) \rightarrow 3Cu(NO_3)_2(aq) + 4H_2O(l) + 2NO(g)$
2. Find $\Delta H°$ for the following reactions.
   a. $2NO(g) + O_2(g) \rightarrow 2NO_2(g)$
   b. $4Zn(cr) + 9HNO_3(aq) \rightarrow 4Zn(NO_3)_2(aq) + NH_3(g) + 3H_2O(l)$
3. Find $\Delta S°$ for the following reactions.
   a. $4HBr(g) + O_2(g) \rightarrow 2H_2O(l) + 2Br_2(l)$
   b. $Cu(cr) + Ag_2SO_4(aq) \rightarrow CuSO_4(aq) + 2Ag(cr)$
4. Predict the spontaneity of the following reactions at 298 K using $\Delta G = \Delta H - T\Delta S$.
   a. $I_2(cr) + Cl_2(g) \rightarrow 2ICl(l)$ ($\Delta H° = -47.8$ kJ, $\Delta S° = -16.45$ J/K)
   b. $Na_2O(cr) + SiO_2(cr) \rightarrow Na_2SiO_3(cr)$ ($\Delta H° = -192$ kJ, $\Delta S° = -0.837$ J/K)
5. Calculate the enthalpy of reaction for the equation listed below.
$$CuCl_2(cr) + Cu(cr) \rightarrow 2CuCl(cr)$$
   Use the following data.
   $$Cu(cr) + Cl_2(g) \rightarrow CuCl_2(cr) \quad \Delta H = -206 \text{ kJ}$$
   $$2Cu(cr) + Cl_2(g) \rightarrow 2CuCl(cr) \quad \Delta H = -136 \text{ kJ}$$
6. Calculate the enthalpy of formation of carbon dioxide from its elements.
$$C(g) + 2O(g) \rightarrow CO_2(g)$$
   Use the following data.
   $$2O(g) \rightarrow O_2(g) \quad\quad\quad\quad\quad \Delta H = -250 \text{ kJ}$$
   $$C(cr) \rightarrow C(g) \quad\quad\quad\quad\quad\quad \Delta H = +720 \text{ kJ}$$
   $$CO_2(g) \rightarrow C(cr) + O_2(g) \quad \Delta H = +390 \text{ kJ}$$
7. If $\Delta H = +66$ kJ for the reaction $Ca(OH)_2(cr) \rightarrow CaO(cr) + H_2O(l)$ what is $\Delta H_f°$ for CaO(cr)?
8. Calculate $\Delta H_f°$ for 1 mol of butane gas, $C_4H_{10}$, from the reaction that occurs when a butane gas lighter is used.
$$2C_4H_{10}(g) + 13O_2(g) \rightarrow 8CO_2(g) + 10H_2O(g)$$

# SOLUTIONS 21

## 21:1 SOLUTE—SOLVENT

A solution consists of a dissolved substance, the **solute,** and a dissolving medium, the **solvent.** A solution is a homogeneous mixture (has a constant composition throughout). A solute need not be a solid. It can be a gas, such as HCl in hydrochloric acid, or a liquid, such as the ethylene glycol in a car's cooling system. If the solution contains two liquids, the liquid that is in the greater amount is called the solvent. The most common solvent is water.

Knowing the actual strength of a solution is more useful than knowing in general terms that it is dilute or concentrated. The concentration of solutions can be described quantitatively in many ways. Molarity, molality, and mole fraction are discussed in this chapter.

## 21:2 MOLARITY

A solution for which a precise concentration is known is called a **standard solution.** Its strength is often expressed in terms of **molarity.** A 1 molar solution contains 1 mole of solute dissolved in enough solvent (usually water) to make 1 cubic decimeter of solution.

$$molarity\ (M) = \frac{number\ of\ moles\ of\ solute}{cubic\ decimeters\ of\ solution}$$

Chemists express concentration in terms of molarity because they are interested in measuring a certain number of particles. One mole of sodium chloride, NaCl, is 58.5 grams. If 58.5 grams of NaCl are dissolved in enough water to make 1 cubic decimeter of solution, the solution is a 1*M* solution of NaCl. Similarly, if 2 moles of NaCl (117.0 grams) are dissolved in enough water to make 1 cubic decimeter of solution, the solution is a 2*M* solution. Fifty cubic centimeters of a solution with a 2*M* concentration and 500 cubic centimeters of the same solution will have the same concentration, 2*M*. The total number of particles changes when the volume is changed but the concentration of particles (the number of particles per unit volume) does not change.

## Example 1

Calculate the molarity of a 1500 cubic centimeter solution that contains 200.0 g of $MgCl_2$.

**Solving Process:**

The problem requires the calculation of molarity. Molarity is moles of solute per (divided by) $dm^3$ of solution. Therefore, the data concerning solute is placed in the numerator, and the data concerning the solution in the denominator. The solute data in the numerator is then converted to moles, and the solution data in the denominator to $dm^3$.

$$\text{molarity} = \frac{200.0 \text{ g } MgCl_2}{1500 \text{ cm}^3} \left| \frac{1 \text{ mol } MgCl_2}{95.3 \text{ g } MgCl_2} \right| \frac{1000 \text{ cm}^3}{1 \text{ dm}^3}$$

$$= 1.4 \text{ mol/dm}^3 = 1.4M$$

## Example 2

How many cubic centimeters of a $1.50M$ sulfuric acid solution can be made using 36.0 g of sulfuric acid?

**Solving Process:**

Convert grams of sulfuric acid to moles of sulfuric acid. The moles of $H_2SO_4$ can be converted to $dm^3$ of $H_2SO_4$ using the concentration. Finally, volume is converted to cubic centimeters.

$$\frac{\text{volume of}}{\text{solution}} = \frac{36.0 \text{ g } H_2SO_4}{} \left| \frac{1 \text{ mol } H_2SO_4}{98.1 \text{ g } H_2SO_4} \right| \frac{1 \text{ dm}^3}{1.50 \text{ mol } H_2SO_4} \right|$$

$$\frac{1000 \text{ cm}^3}{1 \text{ dm}^3} = 245 \text{ cm}^3$$

## Example 3

Calculate the mass of solute required to make 750 cubic centimeters of a $2.50M$ sodium chloride solution.

**Solving Process:**

Convert the volume of solution to moles using the given concentration. The $2.50M$ solution contains 2.50 mol $NaCl/dm^3$ solution. Convert the moles of $NaCl$ to grams of $NaCl$, using the formula mass of $NaCl$.

$$\frac{\text{grams of}}{\text{solute}} = \frac{750 \text{ cm}^3}{} \left| \frac{1 \text{ dm}^3}{1000 \text{ cm}^3} \right| \frac{2.50 \text{ mol } NaCl}{1 \text{ dm}^3} \right| \frac{58.5 \text{ g } NaCl}{1 \text{ mol } NaCl}$$

$$= 110 \text{ g } NaCl$$

## PROBLEMS

1. Calculate the molarity of the following solutions.
   a. 825 cm$^3$ that contains 30.0 g of acetic acid (CH$_3$COOH)
   b. 2050 cm$^3$ that contains 49.0 g of phosphoric acid (H$_3$PO$_4$)
   c. 1.50 dm$^3$ that contains 102 g of potassium hydroxide
2. How many cubic decimeters of solution can be made from each of the following?
   a. a 2.00$M$ solution using 80.0 g sodium hydroxide
   b. a 0.500$M$ solution using 80.0 g sodium hydroxide
   c. a 6.00$M$ solution using 126 g nitric acid
3. Calculate the mass of solute in the following solutions.
   a. 750.0 cm$^3$ of CaCl$_2$ solution that is 0.500$M$
   b. 3000.0 cm$^3$ of a KOH solution that is 2.50$M$
   c. 250.0 cm$^3$ of a Na$_2$SO$_4$ solution that is 2.00$M$

# 21:3  MOLALITY

Some properties of a solution depend only on the number of particles, not on the type of particles. These properties are called **colligative properties.** The number of particles in a mass of solvent can affect the boiling or freezing point of the solvent. Molality is used in place of molarity when dealing with colligative properties. **Molality (m)** is the number of moles of solute per 1000 grams or 1 kilogram of solvent. A one molal (1$m$) solution contains one mole of solute in each 1 kilogram of solvent. A two molal (2$m$) solution contains two moles of solute dissolved in each kilogram of solvent.

## Example 4

Calculate the molality of a solution made by dissolving 45.0 g of glucose, C$_6$H$_{12}$O$_6$, in 500.0 g of water.

**Solving Process:**

Convert grams of glucose to moles of glucose. The molality expression gives the number of moles of solute per kilogram of solvent (water). The molecular mass of glucose is 180.0 g.

$$\text{molality} = \frac{45.0\ \text{g C}_6\text{H}_{12}\text{O}_6}{500.0\ \text{g H}_2\text{O}} \left|\ \frac{1000\ \text{g H}_2\text{O}}{1\ \text{kg H}_2\text{O}}\ \right|\ \frac{1\ \text{mol C}_6\text{H}_{12}\text{O}_6}{180.0\ \text{g C}_6\text{H}_{12}\text{O}_6}$$

$$= \frac{0.500\ \text{mol}}{1\ \text{kg H}_2\text{O}} = 0.500m$$

## Example 5

Calculate the mass of ethanol that must be dissolved in 750.0 g of water to make a 2.00$m$ solution.

**Solving Process:**

The concentration unit 2.00$m$ can be written as

$$\frac{2.00 \text{ mol CH}_3\text{CH}_2\text{OH}}{1000 \text{ g H}_2\text{O}}$$

To obtain the mass of $CH_3CH_2OH$, multiply the mass of water by the concentration unit and then convert to grams of ethanol by using the molecular mass of the solute, 46.1 grams.

$$\frac{\text{mass of}}{\text{solute}} = \frac{750.0 \text{ g H}_2\text{O}}{} \left| \frac{2.00 \text{ mol CH}_3\text{CH}_2\text{OH}}{1000 \text{ g H}_2\text{O}} \right| \frac{46.1 \text{ g CH}_3\text{CH}_2\text{OH}}{1 \text{ mol CH}_3\text{CH}_2\text{OH}}$$

$$= 69.2 \text{ g CH}_3\text{CH}_2\text{OH}$$

## PROBLEMS

4. Calculate the molality of the following solutions.
   a. 1.50 mol $NaCH_3COO$ dissolved in 750.0 g of water
   b. 3.00 mol $H_2SO_4$ dissolved in 1250.0 g of water
   c. 50.0 g acetic acid, $CH_3COOH$, dissolved in 500.0 g of water
5. Determine the grams of solute required to prepare the following solutions.
   a. 3.00$m$ solution of KOH containing 1500.0 g of water
   b. 0.500$m$ solution $CH_3COOH$ containing 750.0 g of water
6. Calculate the grams of water required to make a 0.500$m$ solution that contains 20.0 g of NaCl.

## 21:4   MOLE FRACTION

Another way to express solution concentration is mole fraction. The mole fraction ($X$) of a substance in a solution is defined as the moles of substance divided by the moles of solution (sum of moles of solute + moles of solvent).

$$X = \frac{moles\ solute}{(moles\ of\ solute + moles\ of\ solvent)}$$

The sum of the mole fractions of all the components of a solution equals one.

## Example 6

What are the mole fractions of glucose and water in a solution made of 7.59 g of glucose, $C_6H_{12}O_6$, dissolved in 125 g of water?

**Solving Process:**

The molecular mass of glucose is 180.0 g. Find the moles of glucose.

$$\text{mol glucose} = \frac{7.59 \text{ g } C_6H_{12}O_6}{} \left| \frac{1 \text{ mol } C_6H_{12}O_6}{180.0 \text{ g } C_6H_{12}O_6} \right| = 0.0422 \text{ mol}$$

The molecular mass of $H_2O$ is 18.0 u. Find the moles of water.

$$\text{mol } H_2O = \frac{125 \text{ g } H_2O}{} \left| \frac{1 \text{ mol } H_2O}{18.0 \text{ g } H_2O} \right| = 6.94 \text{ mol}$$

Determine the mole fraction of $C_6H_{12}O_6$.

$$\text{mol fraction} = \frac{\text{mol solute}}{(\text{mol solute} + \text{mol solvent})}$$

$$= \frac{0.0422 \text{ mol}}{(0.0422 + 6.94) \text{ mol}} = \frac{0.0422}{6.98} = 0.006 \ 05$$

Determine the mole fraction of $H_2O$.

$$\text{mol fraction} = \frac{6.94}{6.98} = 0.994$$

If one multiplies the mole fraction by 100, you have the mole percent. In the above problem 99.4% of the molecules in the solution are $H_2O$.

## PROBLEMS

*Calculate the mole fraction for each component in the following solutions.*

**7.** 22.5 g $CH_3CH_2OH$ in $1.00 \times 10^2$ g $H_2O$

**8.** 39.5 g $C_6H_5CH_3$, toluene, in $1.5 \times 10^2$ g $C_6H_6$, benzene

## CHAPTER REVIEW PROBLEMS

**1.** Calculate the molarity of the following solutions.
   **a.** 500.0 cm$^3$ that contains 82.0 g calcium nitrate
   **b.** 250.0 cm$^3$ that contains 50.0 g copper(II) sulfate pentahydrate
   **c.** 1000.0 cm$^3$ that contains 116 g sodium carbonate heptahydrate
**2.** Calculate the mass of solute in the following solutions.
   **a.** 250.0 cm$^3$ of $Na_2SO_4 \cdot 7H_2O$ solution that is 2.00$M$
   **b.** 1.500 dm$^3$ of $KH_2PO_4$ solution that is 0.240$M$
   **c.** 2500.0 cm$^3$ of a $HNO_3$ solution that is 4.00$M$

3. How many cubic decimeters of solution can be made from each of the following?

   **a.** a 0.100$M$ solution using 117 g sodium chloride
   **b.** a 1.00$M$ solution using 50.0 g copper(II) sulfate pentahydrate
   **c.** a 0.200$M$ solution using 200.0 g sodium sulfide

4. How many grams of lead(II) acetate, $Pb(CH_3COO)_2$, must be used to make 500.0 $cm^3$ of a solution that is to contain 10.0 $mg/cm^3$ of lead ion? What is the molarity of this solution?

5. Calculate the molality of the following solutions.

   **a.** 15.0 g ethanol dissolved in 250.0 g water
   **b.** 10.0 g glucose, $C_6H_{12}O_6$, dissolved in 500.0 g water
   **c.** $1.204 \times 10^{24}$ molecules $CH_3COOH$ dissolved in 1500.0 g water

6. Determine the grams of solute required to prepare each of the following solutions.

   **a.** 2.50$m$ solution of $C_6H_{12}O_6$ containing 2000.0 g water
   **b.** 1.25$m$ solution of NaCl containing 250.0 g water

7. Determine the mass of ethylene glycol, $C_2H_4(OH)_2$, which must be dissolved in 2500.0 g water to make a 4.00$m$ solution.

8. Calculate the mole fraction of methanol, $CH_3OH$, when 3.20 g of methanol are dissolved in 4.61 g of ethanol, $CH_3CH_2OH$.

9. A laboratory experiment requires 0.100$M$ $Pb(NO_3)_2$. How many grams of $Pb(NO_3)_2$ are needed to make 175 $cm^3$ of the solution?

10. A teacher needs to prepare 15 sets of solutions for a chemistry lab. Each set must have 70.0 $cm^3$ of 0.200$M$ $FeSO_4 \cdot 7H_2O$. What mass of $FeSO_4 \cdot 7H_2O$ is required to prepare enough solution for the class?

# COLLIGATIVE AND COLLOIDAL PROPERTIES 22

## 22:1 MOLES OF SOLUTE

When a solute is dissolved in a solvent, the vapor pressure of the solvent is reduced. The amount of the reduction depends upon the number of solute particles in a given amount of solvent. Since both the freezing point and boiling point of a liquid depend on its vapor pressure, introduction of a solute into a solvent will change the solvent's freezing and boiling points. The freezing point of the solvent is lowered by the addition of the solute. The addition of a solute also increases the boiling point of a solvent.

The change in freezing point and boiling point varies directly as the concentration of solute particles. One mole or $6.02 \times 10^{23}$ particles of a molecular solute dissolved in 1000 grams of water (a 1 molal solution) lowers the freezing point of the water by 1.86 C°. This temperature interval (1.86 C°) is the **molal freezing point constant** for water. One mole of the ionic solute, NaCl, contains 2 moles of solute particles (1 mole $Na^+$ and 1 mole $Cl^-$). The freezing point of the water is lowered by $2 \times 1.86$ C°.

One mole of a molecular solute dissolved in 1000 grams of water (a 1 molal solution) raises the boiling point of the water by 0.512 C°. This temperature interval is called the **molal boiling point constant** for water. One mole of the ionic substance $BaCl_2$ contains 3 moles of solute particles (1 mole $Ba^{2+}$ and 2 moles $Cl^-$). The boiling point of the water is raised by $3 \times 0.512$ C°.

Both neutral molecules and electrically charged ions change the boiling and freezing points of a solution. Pure substances that act as solvents have fixed boiling and freezing points. Unless otherwise stated, the solvent used is water. Other solvents can be used, but each solvent has a different and characteristic molal freezing point depression constant and molal boiling point elevation constant. See Table A-12 in the Appendix for other values.

Boiling point and freezing point constants for water can be used to calculate

1. the freezing point of the solution
2. the boiling point of the solution
3. the molecular mass of the solute from the freezing point or the boiling point

## 22:2    FREEZING POINT CALCULATIONS

The freezing point of a solution can be calculated from the mass or the moles of the solute dissolved in a known mass of water. Or, if the freezing point is known, the concentration of the solution can be calculated. The conversion ratio used is

$$\frac{1m \text{ concentration}}{1.86 \text{ C}°}$$

This constant relates the freezing point depression for water to the molal concentration.

### Example 1

Calculate the freezing point of a solution containing 5.70 g of sugar, $C_{12}H_{22}O_{11}$, in 50.0 g water.

**Solving Process:**

Convert grams of solute per gram of water to moles of solute per kilogram of water (molality). Then multiply by the conversion ratio to obtain the change in freezing point.

$$\text{change in freezing point} = \frac{5.70 \text{ g } C_{12}H_{22}O_{11}}{50.0 \text{ g } H_2O} \left| \frac{1000 \text{ g } H_2O}{1 \text{ kg } H_2O} \right|$$

$$\left| \frac{1 \text{ mol}}{342 \text{ g } C_{12}H_{22}O_{11}} \right| \frac{1.86 \text{ C}°}{1 m} = 0.620 \text{ C}°$$

To determine the freezing point of the solution, subtract the change in freezing point from 0°C, the freezing point of water.

$$\text{freezing point} = 0°C - 0.620 \text{ C}° = -0.620°C$$

### PROBLEMS

1. Calculate the freezing point of a solution that contains 30.0 g sodium acetate, $NaCH_3COO$, dissolved in 250.0 g water.
2. Calculate the freezing point if 46.0 g glycerol, $C_3H_5(OH)_3$, are dissolved in 500.0 g water.

## 22:3    BOILING POINT CALCULATIONS

These calculations are similar to the calculations involving the freezing point of water solutions. The ratio used is $1m$ concentration/0.512 C°.

### Example 2

Calculate the boiling point of a solution containing 5.70 g sugar, $C_{12}H_{22}O_{11}$, dissolved in 50.0 g water.

**Solving Process:**

Use the molal boiling point constant of 0.512 C° to calculate the change in boiling point.

$$\text{change in boiling point} = \frac{5.70\ g\ C_{12}H_{22}O_{11}}{50.0\ g\ H_2O} \left| \frac{1000\ g\ H_2O}{1\ kg\ H_2O} \right| \frac{1\ mol}{342\ g\ C_{12}H_{22}O_{11}}$$

$$\frac{0.512\ C°}{1\ m} = 0.171\ C°$$

Add the change in boiling point to the boiling point of water 100°C.

$$\text{boiling point} = 100°C + 0.171\ C° = 100.171°C$$

## Example 3

How many grams of a molecular substance (molecular mass 50.0) must be added to 500.0 g water to have a boiling point of 101.56°C?

**Solving Process:**

Start with the change in boiling point (1.56 C°) and convert to molal concentration.

$$\text{molality} = \frac{1.56\ C°}{} \left| \frac{1\ m}{0.512\ C°} \right. = 3.05\ m$$

Convert to grams of solute.

$$\text{mass of solute} = \frac{500.0\ g\ H_2O}{} \left| \frac{3.05\ mol}{1000\ g\ H_2O} \right| \frac{50.0\ g}{1\ mol} = 76.3\ g$$

## PROBLEMS

3. Determine the boiling points of the following solutions.
   a. 16.0 g calcium chloride, $CaCl_2$, dissolved in 250.0 g $H_2O$
   b. 23.0 g copper(II) sulfate, $CuSO_4$, dissolved in 250.0 g $H_2O$
   c. 30.0 g silver nitrate, $AgNO_3$, dissolved in 250.0 g $H_2O$
4. How many grams of NaCl must be dissolved in 500.0 g water to raise the boiling point to 101.51°C?
5. How many grams of ethylene glycol, $C_2H_4(OH)_2$, must be dissolved in 2000.0 g $H_2O$ to lower the freezing point to −29.75°C?

# 22:4 MOLECULAR MASS CALCULATIONS

The molecular mass of a solute can be determined by changes in the freezing point or boiling point. The freezing point method is more practical because of the greater temperature interval involved. It also can be more accurately measured since the boiling point is changed more by atmospheric pressure than the freezing point.

First, determine the molality of the solute from the freezing or boiling point data. Second, determine the grams per mole (molecular mass) from the calculated molality and the concentration given.

## Example 4

If 3.25 g of a molecular substance are dissolved in 125.0 g $H_2O$, what is the molecular mass of the solute if the solution freezes at $-0.930°C$?

**Solving Process:**

Calculate the molality of the solution using the freezing point change.

$$\text{molality} = \frac{0.93\,\cancel{C°}}{} \left| \frac{1m}{1.86\,\cancel{C°}} \right. = 0.50m$$

Convert from grams solute per grams water to grams per mole by using the concentration determined in the first step.

$$\text{molecular mass} = \frac{3.25 \text{ g solute}}{125.0\,\cancel{\text{g } H_2O}} \left| \frac{1000\,\cancel{\text{g } H_2O}}{0.50 \text{ mol solute}} \right. = 52 \text{ g/mol}$$

## PROBLEMS

6. What is the molecular mass of glucose if 22.5 g gives a freezing point of $-0.93°C$ when dissolved in 250.0 g $H_2O$?

7. If 21.3 g of sodium nitrate, $NaNO_3$, are dissolved in $1.00 \times 10^3$ g $H_2O$, the freezing point is $-0.93°C$. What is the molecular mass of the solute?

8. When 92.0 g of a molecular compound were dissolved in 1000.0 g $H_2O$, the freezing point of the solution was lowered to $-3.72°C$. Determine the molecular mass of this compound.

# 22:5   OSMOTIC PRESSURE

Semipermeable membranes will allow solvent molecules to pass through them, but not larger solute molecules. When two solutions having the same solvent are separated by such a membrane, the solvent will move from the higher solvent concentration to the lower solvent concentration through the membrane. The pressure required to stop the flow is called the **osmotic pressure.** Since osmotic pressure depends on the solute concentration, not on the nature of the substance, it is a colligative property.

A solution's osmotic pressure $\Pi$ (pi) is related to the molar concentration. This relationship is expressed in the equation

$$\Pi = MRT.$$

Where $\Pi$ is the osmotic pressure, $M$ is the molarity of the solution, $R$ is the ideal gas constant, and $T$ is the kelvin temperature.

## Example 5

What osmotic pressure would be exerted by a solution that is 1.67$M$ at 22.0°C?

**Solving Process:**

Since the units of $R$ are dm$^3$·kPa/mol·K, we will express our molarity as 1.67 mol/1.00 dm$^3$.

$$\Pi = MRT$$

$$= \frac{1.67\ \cancel{mol}}{1.00\ \cancel{dm^3}} \left| \frac{8.31\ \cancel{dm^3}\text{·kPa}}{\cancel{mol\text{·}K}} \right| \frac{295\ \cancel{K}}{} = 4.09 \times 10^3\ \text{kPa}$$

## PROBLEMS

9. What osmotic pressure would be exerted by a solution that is 2.75$M$ at 30.5°C?

10. What is the osmotic pressure of the solution in which 75.9 g of solute with molecular mass of 3722 g/mol are dissolved in enough water to make 1.10 dm$^3$ of solution at 25°C?

## CHAPTER REVIEW PROBLEMS

*Use the constants from Table A-12 to solve the following.*

1. What are the freezing and boiling points of a solution that contains 10.0 g naphthalene, $C_{10}H_8$, dissolved in 50.0 g benzene?

2. What are the freezing and boiling points of a solution that contains 23.0 g $MgSO_4$ dissolved in 250.0 g $H_2O$?

3. How many grams of an organic compound (molecular mass 75.0) must be dissolved in 500.0 g acetic acid to lower the freezing point of the solution to 0.00°C?

4. Determine the grams of an organic compound (molecular mass 125) which must be dissolved in 750.0 g cyclohexane to raise the boiling point of the resulting solution to 88.46°C.

5. If the freezing point of a solution containing 0.258 g of a substance dissolved in 40.0 g benzene is 5.20°C, what is the molecular mass of the substance?

6. What is the molecular mass of an organic compound if 16.0 g of the compound when dissolved in 225.0 g nitrobenzene increased the boiling point by 8.56 C°?

7. Calculate the osmotic pressure at 30.0°C of an aqueous solution containing 12.7 g of sucrose, $C_{12}H_{22}O_{11}$, in 150.0 cm$^3$ of solution.

8. What osmotic pressure would be exerted by a 5.75 × 10$^{-2}M$ solution at 25.0°C?

**9.** Chemical analysis of an organic compound gives the following results: C 69.50%, H 7.25%, O 23.25%. When 1.58 grams of this compound were dissolved in 30.0 g benzene, it gave a freezing point depression of 1.95 C°. What is the molecular mass and the molecular formula of this compound?

**10.** Chemical analysis of an organic compound gave the following results: C 55.00%, H 2.75%, N 12.80%, O 29.40%. When 1.270 grams of this compound were dissolved in 35.00 g cyclohexane the boiling point was elevated by 0.464 C°. What are the molecular mass and the molecular formula of this compound?

# REACTION RATE AND CHEMICAL EQUILIBRIUM 23

In the previous chapters we have assumed that the reactions have gone to completion. Reactions tend to go to completion because of the formation of a gas (e.g., $CO_2$, $SO_2$), a precipitate (e.g., $AgCl$, $PbSO_4$), or a slightly ionized substance (e.g., $H_2O$, $HF$). Formation of these or similar species causes the ions from the initial reactants to be removed from the reaction.

$$2KClO_3(cr) \rightarrow 2KCl(cr) + 3O_2(g)$$
(formation of a gas)

$$Na^+(aq) + F^-(aq) + H^+(aq) + Cl^-(aq) \rightarrow Na^+(aq) + Cl^-(aq) + HF(aq)$$
(formation of a slightly ionized substance, hydrofluoric acid)

$$AgNO_3(aq) + NaCl(aq) \rightarrow NaNO_3(aq) + AgCl(cr)$$
(formation of a precipitate)

## 23:1 REVERSIBLE REACTIONS

It has been determined experimentally that the conversion of some reactants to products is incomplete, regardless of the reaction time. Initially the reactants are present at a definite concentration. As the reaction proceeds, the reactant concentration decreases as the product is produced. However, a point is reached at which the reactant concentration levels off and becomes constant. The concentration levels for the reactants and products no longer change. A state of **chemical equilibrium** is established.

An example of a reaction that can proceed in either direction is the equilibrium system involving nitrogen, hydrogen, and ammonia gases. The reversible reaction is written as

$$N_2(g) + 3H_2(g) \underset{\text{reverse}}{\overset{\text{forward}}{\rightleftharpoons}} 2NH_3(g) + energy$$

A reversible chemical reaction is in chemical equilibrium when the rates of the opposing reactions are equal and the overall concentrations remain constant. Thus a state of chemical equilibrium is considered to be dynamic.

# 23:2   REACTION RATE

The study of chemical kinetics involves the variables that affect reaction rates. The **reaction rate** is a measurement of the increase of product or decrease of reactant in $mol/dm^3 \cdot s$. The factors that can change the rate at which product is produced are reactant concentration, temperature, surface area, catalyst, and nature of reactants.

The rate can be calculated by using the rate law expression. The rate law expression relates rate of a chemical reaction to concentration of reactants. For the reaction $A + B \rightarrow$ products, the general form of the rate law is

$$rate = k[A]^x [B]^y$$

The **specific rate constant,** $k$, is a proportionality constant that relates rate and concentration. The exponents $x$ and $y$ give the reaction order with respect to that reactant. These exponents must be determined experimentally. The sum of the exponents in a rate law expression gives the overall order of a reaction.

The rate law expression is determined experimentally. A series of reactions is run in which the concentration of one reactant is varied while the other reactant's concentration remains fixed. The effect can be seen by observing any change in the rate of product formation. The concentration is expressed in $mol/dm^3$ and is indicated by brackets [ ].

## Example 1

Nitrogen(II) oxide reacts with oxygen gas to produce nitrogen(IV) oxide. What is the rate law expression?

$$2NO(g) + O_2(g) \rightarrow 2NO_2(g)$$

| Trial | Initial [NO] | Initial [$O_2$] | Initial rate of formation of $NO_2$ |
|-------|------|------|------|
| 1 | 0.015 | 0.010 | 0.0041 $mol/dm^3 \cdot s$ |
| 2 | 0.030 | 0.010 | 0.0164 $mol/dm^3 \cdot s$ |
| 3 | 0.015 | 0.020 | 0.0082 $mol/dm^3 \cdot s$ |

**Solving Process:**

By comparing Trial 1 with Trial 2 we observe that the concentration of NO has doubled while the concentration of $O_2$ remains constant. The rate increases four times. The rate law is second order with respect to NO. In the same way, compare Trial 1 to Trial 3. The concentration of NO remains constant while the concentration of $O_2$ doubles. The rate doubles, indicating that the rate law is first order with respect to $O_2$. The rate law expression is predicted to be

$$rate = k[NO]^2[O_2]$$

## PROBLEMS

Use the following data to answer questions 1-3 for the reaction

$$NO_2(g) + O_2(g) \rightarrow 2N_2O_5(g)$$

| Trial | Initial [NO$_2$] | Initial [O$_2$] | Initial rate of formation of N$_2$O$_5$ |
|-------|------------------|------------------|------------------------------------------|
| 1 | 0.025 | 0.011 | $3.1 \times 10^{-4}$ mol/dm$^3$·s |
| 2 | 0.025 | 0.022 | $6.2 \times 10^{-4}$ mol/dm$^3$·s |
| 3 | 0.050 | 0.011 | $6.2 \times 10^{-4}$ mol/dm$^3$·s |

1. Write the rate law expression for the reaction.
2. Calculate the rate constant.
3. Use the rate law expression and calculated value of $k$ to compute the initial rate of formation of N$_2$O$_5$ if the initial concentrations of NO$_2$ and O$_2$ were each 0.030$M$.

# 23:3  LE CHATELIER'S PRINCIPLE AND REACTANTS

Sometimes, systems initially at equilibrium are subjected to an outside influence or stress. Concentration, pressure, and temperature changes affect equilibrium because they produce a stress. **Le Chatelier's principle** states: *If a system in equilibrium is subjected to a stress, the equilibrium will shift in an attempt to reduce the stress.* To see how these variables affect the equilibrium, consider the reaction between nitrogen and hydrogen to form ammonia.

If more reactant is added to the system in equilibrium, the reaction shifts to the right (the product side) and more product is formed. For example, in the ammonia equation

$$N_2(g) + 3H_2(g) \rightleftarrows 2NH_3(g) + energy$$

the addition of N$_2$ puts a stress on the system. The system can relieve the stress by consuming N$_2$. The system shifts to the right to consume N$_2$, and in the process, produces more NH$_3$. If a reactant is removed, the reaction shifts to the left. In the ammonia synthesis, if we remove some H$_2$, the system can relieve the stress by producing H$_2$. When the system shifts left to replace the missing H$_2$, it also produces more N$_2$ and consumes NH$_3$.

Pressure affects only gaseous equilibrium systems. As pressure on the reactant gases is increased, the reaction shifts toward the side with the least volume. In the ammonia synthesis, an increase of pressure would shift the equilibrium to the right. In the process of shifting, four particles (N$_2$ + 3H$_2$) are converted to two particles (2NH$_3$). The number of particles colliding is thereby reduced, which also reduces the pressure. Lowering the pressure relieves the stress.

If temperature is increased, the reaction shifts in such a way that the endothermic reaction is favored. In the ammonia synthesis, the reaction from left to right is exothermic, while the reaction from right to left is endothermic. Consequently, a rise in temperature will shift the reaction to the left.

## PROBLEM

4. For the following gaseous equilibrium reactions, indicate what happens to the equilibrium position (shift to right or left) when the indicated stress or condition change occurs.

   **a.** remove $NH_3$ gas          **b.** decrease pressure

$$N_2 + 3H_2 \rightleftarrows 2NH_3 + energy$$

   **c.** decrease temperature      **d.** add a catalyst

$$CO_2 + H_2 + energy \rightleftarrows CO + H_2O$$

   **e.** increase $SO_2$ concentration   **f.** increase temperature

$$2SO_2 + O_2 \rightleftarrows 2SO_3 + energy$$

   **g.** increase temperature      **h.** increase CO concentration

$$CO_2 + C + energy \rightleftarrows 2CO$$

   **i.** decrease pressure          **j.** remove $N_2O_4$ .

$$N_2O_4 + energy \rightleftarrows 2NO_2$$

   **k.** increase $H_2$ concentration   **l.** increase pressure

$$H_2 + Cl_2 \rightleftarrows 2HCl + energy$$

   **m.** decrease $O_2$ concentration   **n.** add catalyst

$$N_2 + O_2 + energy \rightleftarrows 2NO$$

# 23:4  EQUILIBRIUM CONSTANT

Consider the reaction

$$N_2 + 3H_2 \rightleftarrows 2NH_3$$

The rate law expressions for the forward and reverse reactions obtained from experimental data are

$$\text{the rate of forward reaction} = k_f[N_2][H_2]^3$$
$$\text{the rate of reverse reaction} = k_r[NH_3]^2$$

At equilibrium, the two rates are equal.

$$k_f[N_2][H_2]^3 = k_r[NH_3]^2$$

Solving for the constants, $k_f/k_r$, gives a new constant termed the equilibrium constant, $K_{eq}$.

$$K_{eq} = \frac{[products]}{[reactants]} = \frac{[NH_3]^2}{[N_2][H_2]^3}$$

Note that the coefficients from the balanced equation are used as exponents in the expression for the equilibrium constant. Remember that for rate law expressions, the exponents must be determined experimentally.

There is a unique value of $K_{eq}$ for each reaction and for each temperature. At equilibrium, if $K_{eq}$ is much greater than 1, the products are favored. If the $K_{eq}$ is much less than 1, the reactants are favored.

## Example 2

What is the equilibrium constant, $K_{eq}$, for the following reaction if the equilibrium concentrations at 25°C are $[N_2O_4] = 0.0450M$ and $[NO_2] = 0.0161M$?

$$N_2O_4(g) \rightleftarrows 2NO_2(g)$$

**Solving Process:**

$$K_{eq} = \frac{[NO_2]^2}{[N_2O_4]} = \frac{[0.0161]^2}{[0.0450]}$$

$$= 0.005\ 76$$

The low value indicates that at equilibrium most of the oxygen and nitrogen will be in the form $N_2O_4$.

## Example 3

What is the equilibrium concentration of NO in the following reaction if the equilibrium concentration of $N_2$ and $O_2$ are each $0.72M$ and at 25°C $K_{eq} = 4.6 \times 10^{-31}$? The equation for the reaction is

$$N_2(g) + O_2(g) \rightleftarrows 2NO(g)$$

**Solving Process:**

$$K_{eq} = \frac{[NO]^2}{[N_2][O_2]}$$

$$4.6 \times 10^{-31} = \frac{[x]^2}{[0.72][0.72]}$$

$$x^2 = 2.4 \times 10^{-31}$$

$$x = 4.9 \times 10^{-16}M$$

## PROBLEMS

5. Determine the equilibrium constant for the following reaction if the equilibrium concentrations of $[N_2O_4] = 1.50 \times 10^{-3}$ and $[NO_2] = 0.571$.

$$N_2O_4(g) \rightleftarrows 2NO_2(g)$$

6. For the reaction $2SO_2(g) + O_2(g) \rightleftarrows 2SO_3(g)$, the equilibrium concentrations of the sulfur oxides are $[SO_2] = 2.00$ and $[SO_3] = 10.0$. What is the concentration of the oxygen when the $K_{eq}$ is 800.0 for the reaction?

7. Write the equilibrium constant expression for the following reactions.
   a. $CO(g) + 2H_2(g) \rightleftarrows CH_3OH(g)$
   b. $CO(g) + 3H_2(g) \rightleftarrows CH_4(g) + H_2O(g)$
   c. $4NH_3(g) + 3O_2(g) \rightleftarrows 2N_2(g) + 6H_2O(g)$
   d. $2CO(g) + O_2(g) \rightleftarrows 2CO_2(g)$

**8.** Bromine, $Br_2$, reacts with nitrogen(II) oxide, NO, to form nitrosyl bromide, NOBr, according to the equation

$$Br_2(g) + 2NO(g) \rightleftarrows 2NOBr(g)$$

At equilibrium, the concentration of $[Br_2] = 0.214M$, $[NOBr] = 0.0667M$, and $[NO] = 0.428M$. Calculate the value of $K_{eq}$ at 68°C.

**9.** The equilibrium constant for the reaction

$$4H_2(g) + CS_2(g) \rightleftarrows CH_4(g) + 2H_2S(g)$$

at 755°C is 0.246. What is the equilibrium concentration of $H_2S$ if at equilibrium the concentration of $[CH_4] = 0.001\ 08M$, $[H_2] = 0.0316M$, and $[CS_2] = 0.0898M$?

## 23:5   FREE ENERGY AND EQUILIBRIUM

The free energy change, $\Delta G$, of a reaction was used in Chapter 20 to predict if a reaction would be spontaneous ($\Delta G < 0$). A spontaneous reaction would be expected to go to completion. The reactants would be almost completely converted to products. We would expect the value of the equilibrium constant to be large. The mathematical relationship between $\Delta G$ and $K_{eq}$ is

$$\Delta G = -RT(\ln K_{eq})$$

In the expression, $R$ is the universal gas constant, $T$ is the absolute temperature, and $\ln$ is the base of natural logarithms.* Natural logarithms can be found using any scientific calculator.

### Example 4

For the reaction $2NO(g) + Br_2(g) \rightleftarrows 2NOBr(g)$ at 115.5°C the equilibrium constant is 1.774. What is the $\Delta G$ for this reaction? $R = 0.008\ 31$ kJ/mol·K
**Solving Process:**

$$\Delta G = -RT(\ln K_{eq})$$
$$= -(0.008\ 31)(388.5)(\ln 1.774)$$
$$= -1.85\ \text{kJ/mol}$$

### Example 5

What is the value of the equilibrium constant for the reaction $PCl_3(g) + Cl_2(g) \rightleftarrows PCl_5(g)$ at 27.8°C when $\Delta G = -55.1$ kJ?
**Solving Process:**

Solving the equation $\Delta G = -RT(\ln K_{eq})$ for $K_{eq}$ we find that

$$\ln K_{eq} = \frac{\Delta G}{-RT}$$

$$= \frac{-55.1\ \text{kJ}}{-(0.008\ 31)(300.8)}$$

*Expressed in terms of common logarithms the equation becomes $\Delta G = -2.30RT (\log K_{eq})$.

Use the $\boxed{e^x}$ key or $\boxed{INV}$ $\boxed{lnx}$ to take the antiln of 22.0.

$$K_{eq} = 3.74 \times 10^9$$

The equilibrium constant is so large that we assume all the reactant has been converted to product.

## PROBLEMS

10. Calculate the $\Delta G$ at 727°C for the reaction $2SO_2(g) + O_2(g) \rightleftarrows 2SO_3(g)$. The $K_{eq}$ is $4.17 \times 10^{-2}$.

11. At 188°C, $\Delta G$ for the reaction $PCl_5(g) \rightleftarrows PCl_3(g) + Cl_2(g)$ is 2.97 kJ/mol. Calculate the value of the equilibrium constant.

## CHAPTER REVIEW PROBLEMS

1. Write equilibrium constant expressions, $K_{eq}$, for each of the following reactions.
   a. $2NO_2(g) \rightleftarrows N_2O_4(g)$
   b. $2H_2(g) + CO(g) \rightleftarrows CH_3OH(g)$
   c. $4NO(g) + 6H_2O(g) \rightleftarrows 5O_2(g) + 4NH_3(g)$
   d. $2H_2S(g) + CH_4(g) \rightleftarrows 4H_2(g) + CS_2(g)$

2. The following initial rate data for the reaction $A + B \rightarrow C$ were obtained. Write the rate law for the reaction.

| Trial | [A] in mol/dm$^3$ | [B] in mol/dm$^3$ | Initial rate in mol/dm$^3$·s |
|---|---|---|---|
| 1 | 0.15 | 0.15 | $3 \times 10^{-2}$ |
| 2 | 0.15 | 0.30 | $3 \times 10^{-2}$ |
| 3 | 0.30 | 0.30 | $1.2 \times 10^{-1}$ |

3. A reaction has the rate law, $Rate = k[A][B]^2$. If the numerical value of $k = 2.5 \times 10^{-2}(dm^3)^2/mol^2 \cdot s$, what is the rate when the concentration of A is $0.20M$ and the concentration of B is $0.30M$?

4. The thermal decomposition of ethylene oxide, $C_2H_4O$, produces methane, $CH_4$, and carbon monoxide, CO.

$$C_2H_4O(g) \rightleftarrows CH_4(g) + CO(g)$$

The following data was collected at 725 K.

| Trial | Initial [C$_2$H$_4$O] in mol/dm$^3$ | Initial rate in mol/dm$^3$·s |
|---|---|---|
| 1 | 0.001 412 | $3.451 \times 10^{-5}$ |
| 2 | 0.002 824 | $6.902 \times 10^{-5}$ |

   a. Write the rate law for the reaction.
   b. Calculate the value of the specific rate constant.

5. Ammonia can be converted to the high nitrogen content fertilizer urea, $NH_2CONH_2$, according to the equation

$$CO_2(aq) + 2NH_3(aq) \rightleftarrows NH_2CONH_2(aq) + H_2O(l) + energy$$

Indicate whether the equilibrium shifts left or right when the indicated stress or condition change occurs.

**a.** remove urea, $NH_2CONH_2$
**b.** increase $CO_2$ concentration
**c.** increase temperature
**d.** add catalyst

6. Industries manufacture methanol, $CH_3OH$, by the reaction

$$2H_2(g) + CO(g) \rightleftarrows CH_3OH(g)$$

The equilibrium constant is 10.42 at 479.0 K. What is the equilibrium concentration of methanol vapor if the equilibrium concentration of $[H_2] = 0.4578M$ and $[CO] = 0.2289M$?

7. What is the equilibrium constant, $K_{eq}$, for the reaction $H_2(g) + Br_2(g) \rightleftarrows 2HBr(g)$ if the equilibrium concentrations at 381°C are $[H_2] = 0.0821M$, $[Br_2] = 0.0433M$, and $[HBr] = 0.357M$?

8. What is the value of the equilibrium constant for the catalyzed reaction $2SO_2(g) + O_2(g) \rightleftarrows 2SO_3(g)$ at 25.0°C when $\Delta G$ for the reaction is $-142$ kJ?

9. Calculate $\Delta G$ for the reaction $Ag(NH_3)_2{}^+(aq) \rightleftarrows Ag^+(aq) + 2NH_3(aq)$ at 325 K. The $K_{eq}$ is $5.29 \times 10^{-16}$.

# ACIDS, BASES, AND SALTS  24

## 24:1  ACID-BASE THEORIES

Several definitions have been proposed for acids and bases. Depending upon the situation, each definition has its advantages and disadvantages. Three acid-base theories are Arrhenius, Brønsted-Lowry, and Lewis.

The **Arrhenius theory** is the oldest approach to acid-base theory. It is adequate for most introductory chemistry concepts. The theory explains acids and bases by the concept of ion formation. An acid ionizes in solution to produce hydrogen ions, $H^+$. For example, hydrochloric acid ionizes in one step.

$$HCl \rightarrow H^+ + Cl^-$$

Sulfuric acid, a polyprotic compound, ionizes in two steps.

$$H_2SO_4 \rightarrow H^+ + HSO_4^-$$
$$HSO_4^- \rightarrow H^+ + SO_4^{2-}$$

A base ionizes or dissociates in solution to produce hydroxide ions, $OH^-$.

$$NaOH \rightarrow Na^+ + OH^-$$

The Arrhenius theory accounts for the characteristic properties of acids and bases.

**Brønsted and Lowry** expanded the definition of a base to include any substance that would accept a proton. An acid is defined as a proton donor. The products that result from an acid-base reaction are called the conjugate acid and the conjugate base.

$$\underset{\text{acid}}{HF(aq)} + \underset{\text{base}}{HCO_3^-(aq)} \rightleftarrows \underset{\substack{\text{conjugate} \\ \text{acid}}}{H_2CO_3(aq)} + \underset{\substack{\text{conjugate} \\ \text{base}}}{F^-(aq)}$$

The conjugate base is the particle that remains after a proton is donated by an acid. The conjugate acid is formed when a base accepts a proton from an acid. The hydrogen carbonate ion, $HCO_3^-$, behaves as a base but does not contain ionizable hydroxide.

The **Lewis** definition of acids and bases is the broadest of the three theories. Lewis defined an acid as an electron-pair acceptor and a base as

**163**

an electron-pair donor. This definition includes reactions that contain neither hydrogen nor hydroxide ions. Molecules as well as ions can be treated as acids or bases. Consider the reaction

$$Na_2O + SO_3 \rightarrow Na_2SO_4$$

Sodium is a spectator ion. Using the Lewis electron dot symbols

|        | base            | acid            |
|        | electron-pair   | electron-pair   |
|        | donor           | acceptor        |

The oxide ion can donate the electron pair to the $SO_3$ molecule.

## PROBLEMS

1. Identify the acid, base, conjugate acid, and conjugate base in the following reactions.
   a. $HCN(aq) + SO_4^{2-}(aq) \rightarrow HSO_4^-(aq) + CN^-(aq)$
   b. $CH_3COO^-(aq) + H_2S(aq) \rightarrow CH_3COOH(aq) + HS^-(aq)$
2. Identify the Lewis acid and Lewis base in the following reactions.
   a. $Al^{3+} + 6H_2O \rightarrow Al(H_2O)_6^{3+}$
   b. $2NH_3 + Ag^+ \rightarrow Ag(NH_3)_2^+$

## 24:2  NAMING ACIDS AND SALTS

Water solutions of binary hydrides form acids. The stem derived from the hydride is given a prefix *hydro-* and a suffix *-ic* and is followed by the word *acid*. The binary hydride HCl is called hydrogen chloride as a gas, but as an aqueous solution it is called hydrochloric acid.

**Table 24-1**

| Binary Acids | | |
|---|---|---|
| Formula | Name | Anion |
| HF(aq) | hydrofluoric acid | $F^-$, fluoride ion |
| HCl(aq) | hydrochloric acid | $Cl^-$, chloride ion |
| HBr(aq) | hydrobromic acid | $Br^-$, bromide ion |
| $H_2S$(aq) | hydrosulfuric acid | $S^{2-}$, sulfide ion |

Many common acids contain only oxygen, hydrogen, and a nonmetallic ion or a polyatomic ion. Such acids are called **oxyacids**. The suffixes *-ous* and *-ic* indicate the oxidation state of the atom bound to the oxygen and hydrogen. The *-ous* suffix indicates a lower oxidation state. Table 24-2 lists common acids and anions.

**Table 24-2**

| Acids Containing Oxygen | | | |
|---|---|---|---|
| **Formula** | **Name** | **Anion** | |
| $HClO_4$ | perchloric acid | $ClO_4^-$ | perchlorate |
| $HClO_3$ | chloric acid⁻ | $ClO_3^-$ | chlorate |
| $HClO_2$ | chlorous acid | $ClO_2^-$ | chlorite |
| $HClO$ | hypochlorous acid | $ClO^-$ | hypochlorite |
| $HNO_3$ | nitric acid | $NO_3^-$ | nitrate |
| $HNO_2$ | nitrous acid | $NO_2^-$ | nitrite |
| $H_2SO_4$ | sulfuric acid | $SO_4^{2-}$ | sulfate |
| $H_2SO_3$ | sulfurous acid | $SO_3^{2-}$ | sulfite |
| $CH_3COOH$ | acetic acid | $CH_3COO^-$ | acetate |
| $H_2CO_3$ | carbonic acid | $CO_3^{2-}$ | carbonate |
| $H_3PO_4$ | phosphoric acid | $PO_4^{3-}$ | phosphate |
| $H_2C_2O_4$ | oxalic acid | $C_2O_4^{2-}$ | oxalate |

In a neutralization reaction an acid reacts with a base to form a salt and $H_2O$. The reaction goes to completion since a molecular compound (water) is formed. The water is only slightly ionized. For practical purposes, the water does not react again.

$$H_2SO_4 + 2NaOH \rightarrow Na_2SO_4 + 2H_2O$$
Acid      Base      Salt      Water

The other compound formed is called a salt. **Salts** are crystalline solids. A salt contains the positive ion of a base and the negative ion of an acid. In addition to common salts such as NaCl and $Na_2SO_4$, another group of salts, termed acid salts, contain hydrogen, $NaHSO_4$, sodium hydrogen sulfate; $K_2HPO_4$, potassium monohydrogen phosphate; $KH_2PO_4$, potassium dihydrogen phosphate.

Salts may be soluble or insoluble in water. The common solubility rules are indicated in Table A-11 in the Appendix.

## PROBLEMS

3. Name the following acids.
   a. HCl
   b. $HNO_3$
   c. $H_2SO_4$
   d. $H_3PO_4$
   e. $HClO_3$
   f. $CH_3COOH$
   g. $HNO_2$
   h. $HClO$
   i. $H_2SO_3$
   j. $H_2CO_3$
   k. $HClO_2$
   l. $HClO_4$

4. Name the following salts. Include the name of the acid from which the salt is obtained.
   a. $NaClO_3$
   b. $Fe(ClO_4)_2$
   c. $NH_4BrO_3$
   d. $Mg(IO_3)_2$
   e. $MnI_2$
   f. $Ba(NO_3)_2$
   g. $PbCl_2$
   h. $Hg(BrO_3)_2$
   i. $ZnSO_4$
   j. $Ca(ClO)_2$

**5.** Write formulas for each salt and write the formula of the acid from which the salt can be obtained.

**a.** ammonium sulfate
**b.** barium hypochlorite
**c.** lithium chlorate
**d.** cobalt(II) sulfite

**e.** mercury(I) bromate
**f.** chromium(III) nitrate
**g.** magnesium chloride
**h.** potassium perchlorate

## 24:3   STRENGTHS OF ACIDS AND BASES

A strong acid such as hydrochloric acid exists in solution as ions.

$$H_2O(l) + HCl(g) \rightarrow H_3O^+(aq) + Cl^-(aq)$$

The concentration of $H_3O^+$ ions determines the strength of an Arrhenius acid. When a weak acid dissolves in water, an equilibrium is established between the molecular form and the ionic form of the substance.

$$H_2O(l) + CH_3COOH(l) \rightleftarrows H_3O^+(aq) + CH_3COO^-(aq)$$

The reverse reaction is favored. As a result, there is a small concentration of ions. The amount of ionization is directly related to acid strength.

Strong bases, such as sodium hydroxide, also dissolve in water to form ions.

$$NaOH(cr) \rightarrow Na^+(aq) + OH^-(aq)$$

When $NH_3(g)$, a weak base, dissolves in water, few ions are produced.

$$H_2O(l) + NH_3(g) \rightleftarrows NH_4^+(aq) + OH^-(aq)$$

About 99% of the $NH_3(g)$ remains in the molecular form. As with acids, the amount of ionization is directly related to base strength.

## 24:4   NET IONIC EQUATIONS

When an aqueous solution of silver nitrate is added to an aqueous solution of zinc chloride, a white precipitate, silver chloride, forms.

$$2AgNO_3(aq) + ZnCl_2(aq) \rightarrow 2AgCl(cr) + Zn(NO_3)_2(aq)$$

The equation above shows all the substances as molecules even though three of them are actually existing as ions in solution. The equation would be more accurate if it were written in ionic form.

$$2Ag^+(aq) + 2NO_3^-(aq) + Zn^{2+}(aq) + 2Cl^-(aq) \rightarrow$$
$$2AgCl(cr) + Zn^{2+}(aq) + 2NO_3^-(aq)$$

You will notice that some ions appear in the same form on both the reactant and product sides. These ions, called **spectator ions,** do not take part in the reaction. Spectator ions can be subtracted from both sides of the equation to leave the **net ionic equation.**

$$2Ag^+(aq) + 2Cl^-(aq) \rightarrow 2AgCl(cr)$$

We divide each coefficient by two to reduce the net ionic equation to its final form.

$$Ag^+(aq) + Cl^-(aq) \rightarrow AgCl(cr)$$

The net ionic equation shows that mixing any solution of silver ions with any solution of chloride ions will produce the precipitate AgCl.

The following rules are used to write net ionic equations.

**Rule 1.** The binary acids HCl, HBr, and HI are strong and are written in ionic form. All others are weak, and are written in molecular form.

**Rule 2.** The number of oxygen atoms in a strong ternary acid exceeds the number of hydrogen atoms by two or more. Strong acids are written in ionic form.

**Rule 3.** The second and subsequent ionizations of polyprotic acids are always weak, even if the original acid is strong. Weak acids are written in molecular form.

**Rule 4.** Group IA (1) and IIA (2) metal hydroxides are strong bases and are written in ionic form. All other hydroxides are written in molecular form.

**Rule 5.** Soluble salts are written in ionic form. Insoluble salts are written in molecular form. Use Table A-11 to determine the solubility of a salt.

**Rule 6.** Oxides are written in molecular form.

**Rule 7.** Gases are written in molecular form.

## Example 1

Write the net ionic equation for the following reaction.

zinc metal + hydrochloric acid $\rightarrow$ zinc chloride + hydrogen gas

**Solving Process:**

**Rule 1:** HCl is a strong acid (ionic).

**Rule 5:** $ZnCl_2$ is soluble (ionic).

**Rule 7:** $H_2$ gas is molecular.

**(a)** Write the balanced molecular equation.

$$Zn(cr) + 2HCl(aq) \rightarrow ZnCl_2(aq) + H_2(g)$$

**(b)** Write the ionic equation.

$$Zn(cr) + 2H^+(aq) + 2Cl^-(aq) \rightarrow Zn^{2+}(aq) + 2Cl^-(aq) + H_2(g)$$

**(c)** Determine the net ionic equation by subtracting out any spectator ions.

$$Zn(cr) + 2H^+(aq) \rightarrow Zn^{2+}(aq) + H_2(g)$$

## PROBLEM

**6.** Write the net ionic equation for each word equation.

**a.** sodium + water $\rightarrow$ sodium hydroxide + hydrogen

   **b.** phosphoric acid + magnesium hydroxide →
                        magnesium phosphate + water
   **c.** barium chloride + sodium sulfate →
                        sodium chloride + barium sulfate
   **d.** magnesium hydroxide + ammonium phosphate →
                        magnesium phosphate + ammonia + water
   **e.** iron(III) bromide + ammonium sulfide →
                        iron(III) sulfide + ammonium bromide

# 24:5   IONIZATION CONSTANT

   When ionic compounds are dissolved in water the ions separate from each other in a process called **dissociation.** Many molecular compounds, when dissolved in water, react with the water to produce ions in a process called **ionization.**

   It is assumed that strong electrolytes dissociate completely. A $0.1M$ solution of a strong acid, such as HCl, contains $0.1M$ hydronium ions. Similarly, a $0.5M$ solution of a strong base, such as NaOH, contains $0.5M$ hydroxide ions. However, the ionization of weak electrolytes, such as the weak acids $CH_3COOH$, $HNO_2$, $H_2SO_3$, and the only common weak base, $NH_3(aq)$, is not complete.

   Weak acids and weak bases ionize, in general, as follows (HA represents a weak acid and B represents a weak base)

$$HA + H_2O \rightleftarrows H_3O^+ + A^-    B + H_2O \rightleftarrows BH^+ + OH^-$$

The ionization of weak electrolytes occurs only to a small extent before equilibrium is established. An equation that allows you to determine the concentration of each substance at equilibrium is called an equilibrium expression.

   The equilibrium expression for ionization involves the concentration of the products multiplied together and divided by the concentration of the reactants. All of these concentrations are in moles per $dm^3$ and are thus placed in brackets [ ]. Assuming the reaction $A + 2B \rightleftarrows C + 3D$, the constant $K$ is

$$K_{eq} = \frac{[products]}{[reactants]} = \frac{[C][D]^3}{[A][B]^2}$$

   Note that the individual concentrations of B and D are raised to the second and third powers. The numbers 2 and 3 come from the coefficients in front of B and D, respectively, in the balanced equation. The equilibrium expression for the ionization equation of a weak acid or a weak base is

$$K_{eq} = \frac{[H_3O^+][A^-]}{[HA][H_2O]}    K_{eq} = \frac{[BH^+][OH^-]}{[B][H_2O]}$$

The concentration of the water is essentially constant (55.6$M$). Multiplying both sides of the equation by [$H_2O$] produces a new constant expression called an **ionization constant.** The expression for the weak acid ionization constant is

$$K_a = \frac{[H_3O^+][A^-]}{[HA]}$$

The expression for the weak base ionization constant is

$$K_b = \frac{[BH^+][OH^-]}{[B]}$$

## Example 2

Calculate the [$OH^-$] of a 0.500$M$ solution of aqueous ammonia. The $K_b$ of $NH_3$ is 1.77 × 10$^{-5}$.

**Solving Process:**

From the ionization equation, $NH_3 + H_2O \rightleftarrows NH_4^+ + OH^-$, write the ionization constant expression of ammonium hydroxide.

$$K_b = \frac{[NH_4^+][OH^-]}{[NH_3]}$$

Let [$NH_4^+$] = [$OH^-$] = $x$. [$NH_3$] is slightly less than the 0.500$M$ by the concentration of the [$NH_4^+$].

$$1.77 \times 10^{-5} = \frac{x^2}{0.500 - x}$$

Because $K_a$ is 10$^{-5}$ and [$NH_3$] is 5 × 10$^{-1}M$, the difference is greater than three orders of magnitude. Thus, $0.500 - x \approx 0.500$.

$$1.77 \times 10^{-5} = \frac{x^2}{0.500}$$

$$x^2 = (1.77 \times 10^{-5})(0.500) = 8.85 \times 10^{-6}$$

$$x = \sqrt{8.85 \times 10^{-6}} = 2.97 \times 10^{-3}$$

Therefore, $x$ = [$NH_4^+$] = [$OH^-$] = 2.97 × 10$^{-3}M$.

To check your answer you can use a process called iteration. To iterate, substitute your value for $x$, 2.97 × 10$^{-3}$, to obtain the value for [$NH_3$]. Then solve for [$NH_4^+$] and [$OH^-$].

$$x^2 = (1.77 \times 10^{-5})(0.500 - 2.97 \times 10^{-3})$$
$$x^2 = 8.80 \times 10^{-6}$$
$$x = 2.97 \times 10^{-3}M$$

The answer for $x$ is the same for both processes and can be considered correct.

## Example 3

Determine the experimental ionization constant of an acetic acid solution if 0.100 mole of acetic acid is dissolved in enough water to make 1.00 $dm^3$ of solution in which $[H_3O^+]$ equals 0.001 35 mol/$dm^3$.

**Solving Process:**

The ionization equation is

$$CH_3COOH + H_2O \rightleftarrows H_3O^+ + CH_3COO^-$$

The ionization constant, $K_a$, for the acetic acid is

$$K_a = \frac{[H_3O^+][CH_3COO^-]}{[CH_3COOH]}$$

The concentration of the hydronium ion and the acetate ion both equal 0.001 35$M$. The molecular acetic acid has a concentration of [0.100 − 0.001 35$M$]. Substitute the value into the $K_a$ expression and solve.

$$K_a = \frac{[0.001\ 35][0.001\ 35]}{[0.100 - 0.001\ 35M]} = 1.85 \times 10^{-5}$$

## PROBLEMS

7. Determine the ionization constant for each of the weak electrolytes.
   a. a 0.001 00$M$ acetic acid solution with $[H_3O^+]$ = 1.27 × $10^{-4}M$.
   b. a 0.0070$M$ aqueous ammonia solution with $[OH^-]$ = 3.46 × $10^{-4}M$.
   c. a 0.100$M$ hydrogen cyanide solution with $[H_3O^+]$ = 7.85 × $10^{-6}M$.
8. Determine the concentration of all substances in a flask that contains 1.00$M$ CH$_3$COOH. The $K_a$ is 1.76 × $10^{-5}$.

# 24:6  PERCENT OF IONIZATION

When weak acids or bases dissolve in water, they ionize slightly. Most of the acid or base remains in the molecular form. The amount of original acid or base that ionizes is expressed as the percent of ionization.

$$\% \ ionization = \frac{[amount\ ionized]}{[original\ acid\ or\ base]} \times 100$$

The percent of ionization is used as an indicator of acid or base strength. The stronger acids usually have a higher percent of ionization.

If the percent ionization of the weak electrolyte is known, the $K_a$ or the $K_b$ can be calculated if the concentration of the solution is given.

## Example 4

If an acetic acid solution has an initial concentration of 0.0800$M$ and is 1.50% ionized, determine the experimental $K_a$ of the CH$_3$COOH.

**Solving Process:**

If the initial $[CH_3COOH]$ concentration is 0.0800, the $[H_3O^+]$ and the $[CH_3COO^-]$ can be obtained by multiplying the concentration by the percent ionization.

$$[H_3O^+] = [CH_3COO^-] = (0.0800)(0.0150) = 0.001\ 20M$$

At equilibrium $[CH_3COOH] = 0.0800 - 0.001\ 20 = 0.0788M$.

From the ionization equation $CH_3COOH + H_2O \rightleftarrows H_3O^+ + CH_3COO^-$ write the $K_a$ expression. Substitute and solve for $K_a$.

$$K_a = \frac{[H_3O^+][CH_3COO^-]}{[CH_3COOH]} = \frac{[1.20 \times 10^{-3}]^2}{[7.88 \times 10^{-2}]} = \frac{1.44 \times 10^{-6}}{7.88 \times 10^{-2}} = 1.83 \times 10^{-5}$$

## Example 5

If the $K_a$ of hydrofluoric acid is $3.53 \times 10^{-4}$ and the HF solution has an initial concentration of $0.150M$, calculate the percent of ionization.

**Solving Process:**

From the ionization equation determine the amount ionized by solving the $K_a$ expression for $x$.

$$HF + H_2O \rightleftarrows H_3O^+ + F^-$$

$$K_a = \frac{[H_3O^+][F^-]}{[HF]} = \frac{[x][x]}{[0.150]}$$

The [HF] is assumed to be 0.150 instead of $0.150 - x$, as $x$ is a very small number. Substitute the $K_a$ value and solve for $x$:

$$3.53 \times 10^{-4} = \frac{[x][x]}{[0.150]}$$

$$x^2 = 5.30 \times 10^{-5}$$

$$x = 7.28 \times 10^{-3}M$$

Check your answer using iteration.

$$x^2 = (3.53 \times 10^{-4})(0.150 - 7.28 \times 10^{-3})$$
$$x^2 = 5.04 \times 10^{-5}$$
$$x = 7.10 \times 10^{-3}$$

Since there is a difference between your two values for $x$, continue to iterate until your value for $x$ does not change.

$$x = (3.53 \times 10^{-4})(0.150 - 7.10 \times 10^{-3})$$
$$x = 7.10 \times 10^{-3}$$

Now that you have a corrected value for $x$, continue to solve for percent of ionization.

$$\% \; ionization = \frac{[amount\;ionized]}{[original\;acid]} \times 100$$

$$= \frac{7.10 \times 10^{-3}M}{0.150M} \times 100 = 4.73\%$$

## PROBLEMS

9. Find the experimental ionization constants of the following weak electrolytes.

    **a.** 0.100M HF                     8.50% ionized
    **b.** 0.500$M$ $CH_3COOH$         1.88% ionized
    **c.** 0.0130$M$ $CH_3CH_2COOH$  3.70% ionized
    **d.** 0.200$M$ $HAsO_2$            0.005 50% ionized

10. If the $K_a$ of chlorous acid, $HClO_2$, is $1.1 \times 10^{-2}$, calculate the percent of ionization of a 0.225$M$ solution.

11. Calculate the percent of ionization of a 0.125$M$ hypoiodous acid (HIO) solution. The $K_a$ is $2.30 \times 10^{-11}$.

## 24:7  COMMON ION EFFECT

In the previous problems it was assumed that the ionization process occurred in pure water. If, however, a common ion provided by an electrolyte is present, the calculations are slightly different.

Consider the ionization of acetic acid in pure water.

$$CH_3COOH + H_2O \rightleftarrows H_3O^+ + CH_3COO^-$$

The concentrations of the $[H_3O^+]$ and the $[CH_3COO^-]$ are the same, since both ions come from the same source that yields one ion of each when the acid ionizes.

If some sodium acetate is added, the concentration of the $[CH_3COO^-]$ increases because there are two sources of acetate ion, and one of the sources (the $NaCH_3COO$) is completely ionized. According to Le Chatelier's principle (an equilibrium reaction shifts so as to relieve a stress), the $[H_3O^+]$ decreases sharply as the reverse reaction toward the molecular acid occurs and the acetic acid concentration increases. The $K_a$ value remains constant.

## Example 6

Determine the $H_3O^+$ concentration in a solution of $CH_3COOH$ that is 0.100$M$ if enough $NaCH_3COO$ is added to make the solution 2.00$M$ with respect to the $CH_3COO^-$. The $K_a$ of $CH_3COOH$ is $1.76 \times 10^{-5}$.

**Solving Process:**

$$CH_3COOH + H_2O \rightleftarrows H_3O^+ + CH_3COO^-$$

Let $[H_3O^+] = x$ and we know $[CH_3COO^-] = 2.00$.
Also $[CH_3COOH] = 0.100 - x \cong 0.100$.

$$K_a = \frac{[H_3O^+][CH_3COO^-]}{[CH_3COOH]}$$

$$1.76 \times 10^{-5} = \frac{x(2.00)}{(0.100)}$$

$$= \frac{(1.76 \times 10^{-5})(0.100)}{(2.00)} = 8.80 \times 10^{-7} M$$

The $[H_3O^+]$ in a solution that is $2.00M$ in acetate ion and $0.100M$ in $CH_3COOH$ is $8.80 \times 10^{-7} M$. The $[H_3O^+]$ in a pure $0.100M$ $CH_3COOH$ solution is $1.32 \times 10^{-3} M$. The concentration of the $[H_3O^+]$ has decreased sharply after adding the sodium acetate.

## PROBLEMS

**12.** What is the hydronium ion concentration in a solution $0.0875M$ HClO and $0.0550M$ NaClO? Refer to Table A-13 for the $K_a$.

**13.** If it is necessary to reduce the concentration of the $[H_3O^+]$ to $2.00 \times 10^{-4} M$, what must be the concentration of the $[CH_3COO^-]$ in a $0.400M$ solution of acetic acid? The $K_a$ is $1.76 \times 10^{-5}$.

# 24:8 POLYPROTIC ACIDS

A number of polyprotic acids ionize to form one $H_3O^+$ ion in each step of the ionization. Thus a polyprotic acid has several ionization constants, with each constant relating to the ionization of that particular step.

Phosphoric acid ($H_3PO_4$), a triprotic acid, has three different ionization constants.

$$H_3PO_4 + H_2O \rightleftarrows H_3O^+ + H_2PO_4^- \quad K_1 = \frac{[H_3O^+][H_2PO_4^-]}{[H_3PO_4]}$$

$$= 7.52 \times 10^{-3}$$

$$H_2PO_4^- + H_2O \rightleftarrows H_3O^+ + HPO_4^{2-} \quad K_2 = \frac{[H_3O^+][HPO_4^{2-}]}{[H_2PO_4^-]}$$

$$= 6.23 \times 10^{-8}$$

$$HPO_4{}^{2-} + H_2O \rightleftarrows H_3O^+ + PO_4{}^{3-} \quad K_3 = \frac{[H_3O^+][PO_4{}^{3-}]}{[HPO_4{}^{2-}]}$$

$$= 2.20 \times 10^{-13}$$

The smaller the value of $K$, the weaker the acid. For any polyprotic acid, the first ionization constant is always considerably larger than the second; the second ionization constant is greater than the third. Each successive ionization leaves the negative polyatomic ion with greater attraction for the remaining hydrogen ion or ions and, therefore, each successive ionization is less likely to occur than the preceding ionizations.

For the previous problems in this chapter, it was assumed that the concentration of the ionized species was very small compared to the concentration of the molecular species. This assumption is correct for slightly ionized acids and bases in aqueous solution which are not too dilute. However, for medium strength electrolytes, this simplifying assumption cannot be made. For these electrolytes, it is necessary to use the quadratic equation or iteration.

## Example 7

Determine the hydronium ion concentration for the first ionization of a phosphoric acid, $H_3PO_4$, solution which is 0.0100$M$. The $K_a$ of $H_3PO_4$ is $7.52 \times 10^{-3}$.

**Solving Process:**

From the equation, $H_3PO_4 + H_2O \rightleftarrows H_3O^+ + H_2PO_4{}^-$, obtain the expression for the equilibrium constant.

$$K_a = \frac{[H_3O^+][H_2PO_4{}^-]}{[H_3PO_4]}$$

Since $[H_3O^+] = [H_2PO_4{}^-]$, both can equal $x$. Also, at equilibrium, $[H_3PO_4] = 0.0100 - x$. (In previous problems, $0.0100 - x$ was assumed to be 0.0100. This assumption cannot be made for medium strength electrolytes.) Substitute the values into the $K_a$ expression.

$$7.52 \times 10^{-3} = \frac{[x][x]}{[0.0100 - x]}$$

Rearrange and obtain

$$x^2 + 7.52 \times 10^{-3}\,x + (-7.52 \times 10^{-5}) = 0$$

The rearrangement has the quadratic form $ax^2 + bx + c = 0$. If $a$, $b$, and $c$ are coefficients, the roots can be obtained by substituting into the quadratic equation.

$$x = \frac{-b \pm \sqrt{b^2 - 4ac}}{2a}$$

where $a = 1$; $b = 7.52 \times 10^{-3}$; and $c = -7.52 \times 10^{-5}$.

$$x = \frac{-7.52 \times 10^{-3} \pm \sqrt{(7.52 \times 10^{-3})^2 - 4(1)(-7.52 \times 10^{-5})}}{2(1)}$$

$$= \frac{-7.52 \times 10^{-3} \pm 1.89 \times 10^{-2}}{2}$$

$$= +0.005\ 69 \text{ and } -0.0132 \text{ mol}/dm^3$$

A negative concentration ($-0.0132$) has no meaning in chemistry. The correct answer is $0.005\ 69M$. Obviously $0.005\ 69M$ is not negligible compared to the original concentration of $0.0100M$. This problem can be solved using iteration. However, you would need to iterate 18 times to obtain your final answer. You should still check your answer using iteration.

$$x^2 = (7.52 \times 10^{-3})(0.0100 - 5.69 \times 10^{-3})$$
$$x = 5.69 \times 10^{-3}M$$

## PROBLEM

14. The second ionization of a $0.100M$ sulfuric acid solution is

$$HSO_4^- + H_2O \rightarrow H_3O^+ + SO_4^{2-}$$

The $K_a$ is $1.20 \times 10^{-2}$. Calculate the hydronium ion concentration by:
   a. making the false assumption that $x$ can be neglected compared to $0.100M$.
   b. solving by using the quadratic equation.

## CHAPTER REVIEW PROBLEMS

1. Define an acid according to the following theories.
   a. Arrhenius theory
   b. Brønsted-Lowry theory
   c. Lewis theory

2. Name the following acids.
   a. HBr
   b. $HNO_2$
   c. $H_2SO_4$
   d. $H_2S$
   e. $H_3PO_3$
   f. $HClO_3$
   g. HI
   h. $CH_3COOH$
   i. $H_3AsO_4$
   j. $HIO_3$
   k. $H_2SiO_3$
   l. $H_2CO_3$

3. Write formulas for the following. Identify each as acid, base, or salt.
   a. magnesium hydroxide
   b. hydrochloric acid
   c. zinc nitrate
   d. sulfurous acid
   e. sodium hypochlorite
   f. potassium hydroxide

4. Label the acid, base, conjugate acid, and conjugate base in the following reactions.
   a. $HSO_4^-(aq) + Cl^-(aq) \rightarrow SO_4^{2-}(aq) + HCl(aq)$
   b. $OH^-(aq) + CH_3COOH(aq) \rightarrow CH_3COO^-(aq) + H_2O(l)$

5. Identify the Lewis acid and Lewis base in the reaction of $Ni^{2+}$ with four water ligands.

$$Ni^{2+}(aq) + 4H_2O(l) \rightarrow Ni(H_2O)_4^{2+}(aq)$$

6. Apply the rules for writing the net ionic equations to these reactions.
   **a.** sodium hydroxide + hydrochloric acid $\rightarrow$ sodium chloride + water
   **b.** potassium metal + water $\rightarrow$ potassium hydroxide + hydrogen gas
   **c.** silver nitrate + sodium chloride $\rightarrow$ sodium nitrate + silver chloride

7. Using Table A-13, determine the molar concentration of all substances in a $1.000 \ dm^3$ volumetric flask filled with a water solution containing 1.750 moles of boric acid, $H_3BO_3$.

8. Calculate the hydronium ion concentration in a $0.045M$ HIO solution. Refer to Table A-13 for $K_a$.

9. What is the value of $K_b$ for $NH_3(aq)$ if a $0.1250M$ solution has the following equilibrium concentrations: $[NH_4^+] = [OH^-] = 1.478 \times 10^{-3}M$, $[NH_3] = 0.1235M$?

10. Determine the first ionization constant for $0.0285M \ H_2CO_3$ solution with $[H_3O^+] = 1.11 \times 10^{-4}M$.

11. Find the experimental ionization constant for a $0.0535M$ HClO solution that ionizes 2.35%.

12. Calculate the percent ionization of a $0.075M$ HCN solution. Refer to Table A-13 for $K_a$.

13. Calculate the $[H_3O^+]$ in a solution that is $1.125M \ CH_3COOH$ if enough $NaCH_3COO$ is added to make the solution $0.5005M$ with respect to the $CH_3COO^-$. Refer to Table A-13 for $K_a$.

14. Use the quadratic equation to calculate the $[H_3O^+]$ in a $0.750M$ $CH_2ClCOOH$ solution. Refer to Table A-13 for $K_a$.

$$CH_2ClCOOH(aq) + H_2O(l) \rightarrow H_3O^+(aq) + CH_2ClCOO^-(aq)$$

# SOLUTIONS OF ELECTROLYTES 25

## 25:1 SOLUBILITY PRODUCT CONSTANT

Most insoluble ionic solids are actually soluble in water to a limited extent. These solids dissociate slightly in water. The compound silver chloride dissociates slightly in water to give silver ions, $Ag^+$, and chloride ions, $Cl^-$. An equilibrium is established in the saturated solution between the solid and the ions in the solution. The equation for this equilibrium is

$$AgCl(cr) \rightleftarrows Ag^+(aq) + Cl^-(aq)$$

The above equation can be represented mathematically by a constant, $K_{eq}$, called the **equilibrium constant.** By definition, this constant is equal to the concentration of the products in moles per $dm^3$ divided by the concentration of the reactants in moles per $dm^3$. The concentration of each ion is raised to a power that is equal to the coefficient of the ion in the balanced equation. This constant can be expressed as follows.

$$K_{eq} = \frac{[\text{products}]}{[\text{reactants}]} = \frac{[Ag^+][Cl^-]}{[AgCl]}$$

The concentration of a pure solid such as AgCl is a constant. Since both terms, [AgCl] and $K_{eq}$, are constants, they can be multiplied together to form a new constant, which is termed the **solubility product constant,** $K_{sp}$.

$$[Ag^+][Cl^-] = K_{eq}[AgCl] = K_{sp}$$

The solubility product constant, $K_{sp}$, is the product of the concentrations of the ions in a saturated solution raised to the power of their coefficients in the balanced equation. For example, the expression of the solubility product for $PbCl_2$ would be

$$PbCl_2 \rightleftarrows Pb^{2+} + 2Cl^-$$

$$K_{sp} = [Pb^{2+}][Cl^-]^2$$
$$\text{ion product}$$

Using the equation for $K_{sp}$, it is possible to calculate the solubility of a salt if its $K_{sp}$ is known, or to calculate the $K_{sp}$ from the solubility. The $K_{sp}$ is an experimental value and depends on the temperature, as does $K_{eq}$. The solubility of a salt expressed in moles per cubic decimeter is the molar solubility of the salt.

## Example 1

A 1.00 dm³ saturated solution of AgCl is evaporated to dryness and the residue is equivalent to $1.34 \times 10^{-5}$ mole. What is the experimental $K_{sp}$ of the silver chloride?

**Solving Process:**

The equation for the system is $AgCl \rightleftarrows Ag^+ + Cl^-$. Therefore, in a saturated solution of AgCl, $1.34 \times 10^{-5}$ mole AgCl gives $1.34 \times 10^{-5}$ mole $Ag^+$ and $1.34 \times 10^{-5}$ mole $Cl^-$. The solubility product expression for AgCl is

$$K_{sp} = [Ag^+][Cl^-]$$

Since the concentration in moles per dm³ is given, substitute this value directly into the equation.

$$K_{sp} = [1.34 \times 10^{-5}][1.34 \times 10^{-5}] = 1.80 \times 10^{-10}$$

## Example 2

If the $K_{sp}$ of AgCl is $1.56 \times 10^{-10}$, determine the solubility of AgCl in grams per dm³.

**Solving Process:**

From the equation $AgCl \rightleftarrows Ag^+ + Cl^-$, note that the concentration of $Ag^+$ is equal to the concentration of $Cl^-$. Let the $Ag^+$ concentration be equal to $x$:

$$[Ag^+] = [Cl^-] = x$$

Substitute this value into the $K_{sp}$ equation:

$$[Ag^+][Cl^-] = x^2 = K_{sp} = 1.56 \times 10^{-10}$$

$$x^2 = 1.56 \times 10^{-10}$$

$$x = \sqrt{1.56 \times 10^{-10}} = 1.25 \times 10^{-5} M$$

The molar solubility, $x$, is $1.25 \times 10^{-5}$ mole per dm³. In grams per dm³ it is

$$\text{molar solubility} = \frac{1.25 \times 10^{-5} \text{ mol AgCl}}{1 \text{ dm}^3} \left| \frac{144 \text{ g AgCl}}{1 \text{ mol AgCl}} \right.$$

$$= 1.80 \times 10^{-3} \text{ g AgCl/dm}^3$$

A useful application of the $K_{sp}$ data is to determine if precipitation will occur when a salt and a solution or when two solutions are mixed. Precipitation takes place only when the ion product exceeds the $K_{sp}$.

$$\left.\begin{array}{l} \text{ion product} < K_{sp} \\ \text{ion product} = K_{sp} \end{array}\right\} \quad \text{no precipitate will form}$$

$$\text{ion product} > K_{sp} \qquad \text{precipitate will form}$$

Remember that if the final solution is formed by mixing two solutions it is necessary to consider dilution. Each solute is diluted when the other solution is added.

## Example 3

Will precipitation occur when 50.0 cm$^3$ of a $3.00 \times 10^{-2}M$ Pb(NO$_3$)$_2$ solution is added to 50.0 cm$^3$ of $2.00 \times 10^{-3}M$ KCl? The $K_{sp}$ of PbCl$_2$ is $1.62 \times 10^{-5}$.

**Solving Process:**

Assume that no change in volume occurs when the two solutions are mixed and that the final volume will be 100.0 cm$^3$. First calculate the concentration of ions in the mixture as if they do not react. The Pb$^{2+}$ concentration, because of a twofold dilution, is $1.50 \times 10^{-2}M$. The Cl$^-$ concentration, because of a twofold dilution, is $1.00 \times 10^{-3}M$. Use these new concentrations of Pb$^{2+}$ and Cl$^-$ to calculate the ion product and determine if it exceeds the $K_{sp}$.

The equation for equilibrium of a saturated solution is

$$PbCl_2 \rightleftarrows Pb^{2+} + 2Cl^-$$

Therefore, on substitution the ion product becomes

$$[Pb^{2+}][Cl^-]^2 = [1.50 \times 10^{-2}][1.00 \times 10^{-3}]^2 = 1.50 \times 10^{-8}$$

Since $1.50 \times 10^{-8}$ is smaller than the $K_{sp}$ of PbCl$_2$($1.62 \times 10^{-5}$), precipitation does not occur. The solution is unsaturated.

## PROBLEMS

From the solubilities, determine the experimental value of the $K_{sp}$ for each of the following compounds.

1. AgI      $2.88 \times 10^{-6}$ g/1.00 dm$^3$
2. BaCO$_3$      $7.00 \times 10^{-5}$ mol/dm$^3$
3. CaF$_2$      0.0170 g/1.00 dm$^3$
4. Pb(OH)$_2$      $4.20 \times 10^{-6}$ mol/dm$^3$
5. SrF$_2$      $1.22 \times 10^{-2}$ g/100 cm$^3$
6. Pb(IO$_3$)$_2$      2.30 mg/100 cm$^3$

Calculate the molar solubility of the following compounds from their $K_{sp}$ values.

7. CuS      $6.31 \times 10^{-36}$
8. SrC$_2$O$_4$      $1.58 \times 10^{-7}$
9. Al(OH)$_3$      $1.26 \times 10^{-33}$
10. PbI$_2$      $1.39 \times 10^{-8}$
11. Determine the solubility in g/dm$^3$ of the compounds listed in Problems 8 and 10.

*Determine if precipitation would occur in the following cases.* (Use Table A-15 for $K_{sp}$ values.)

**12.** $25.0 \text{ cm}^3$ of $6.00 \times 10^{-6}M$ $Sr(NO_3)_2$ is mixed with $25.0 \text{ cm}^3$ of $4.00 \times 10^{-7}M$ $H_3PO_4$. $K_{sp}$ of $Sr_3(PO_4)_2$ is $4.07 \times 10^{-28}$.

**13.** $100.0 \text{ cm}^3$ of a $5.00 \times 10^{-3}M$ $Ba(NO_3)_2$ is mixed with $100.0 \text{ cm}^3$ of $2.00 \times 10^{-2}M$ NaF.

**14.** $50.0 \text{ cm}^3$ of $6.0 \times 10^{-4}M$ $AgNO_3$ is mixed with $50.0 \text{ cm}^3$ of $5.0 \times 10^{-4}M$ $K_2CrO_4$.

# 25:2   IONIZATION OF WATER: THE pH SCALE

Pure water ionizes slightly into hydronium and hydroxide ions:

$$H_2O(l) + H_2O(l) \rightleftarrows H_3O^+(aq) + OH^-(aq)$$

It has been found by experiment that one $dm^3$ of pure water contains only one ten millionth of a mole of hydronium ions and one ten millionth of a mole of hydroxide ions. A substance that contains more hydronium ions than hydroxide ions is acidic; a substance that contains more hydroxide ions than hydronium ions is basic. A neutral substance such as pure water contains an equal number of hydronium ions and hydroxide ions. The ions are in equilibrium in pure water when the concentration of hydronium ions is $1.00 \times 10^{-7} \text{ mol/dm}^3$ and the hydroxide ion concentration is also $1.00 \times 10^{-7} \text{ mol/dm}^3$.

| $H_2O + H_2O$ | $\rightleftarrows$ | $H_3O^+$ | $+$ | $OH^-$ |
|---|---|---|---|---|
| *1 dm³ water* | *at equilibrium* | *1.00 × 10⁻⁷ mol* | | *1.00 × 10⁻⁷ mol* |
| *(55.6 mol)* | *contains* | *hydronium ions* | | *hydroxide ions* |

We can now write the equilibrium expression for water with the information just given and find an equilibrium constant for water.

$$2H_2O \rightleftarrows H_3O^+ + OH^-$$

$$K_{eq} = \frac{[H_3O^+][OH^-]}{[H_2O][H_2O]}$$

Since the ionization of water is very small in comparison with the total concentration of water ($55.6M$)*, the concentration of water can be assumed to remain constant. If the concentration of water is constant, we can multiply both sides of the equation by this constant without destroying the relationship.

$$[H_2O]^2 \times (K_{eq}) = [H_2O]^2 \times \left( \frac{[H_3O^+][OH^-]}{[H_2O]^2} \right)$$

---

*You may wonder where the $55.6M$ came from. We are working with one $dm^3$ of water that has a mass of 1000 g. You know that one mole of water has a mass of 18.0 g. Therefore, one $dm^3$ of water must contain

$$\frac{1000 \text{ g}}{18.0 \text{ g/mol}} = 55.6 \text{ mol water.}$$

Since both $[H_2O]$ and $K_{eq}$ are constants, their product will also be constant. We call this constant the ion product constant of water and denote it by the symbol $K_w$. The ion product constant for water has been found to be $1.00 \times 10^{-14}$ at room temperature.

$$K_w = [H_3O^+][OH^-] = 1.00 \times 10^{-14}$$

Note that when

$$[H_3O^+] = 1.00 \times 10^{-1}, \text{ the } [OH^-] = 1.00 \times 10^{-13}$$
$$[H_3O^+] = 1.00 \times 10^{-13}, \text{ the } [OH^-] = 1.00 \times 10^{-1}$$
$$[H_3O^+] = 1.00 \times 10^{-7}, \text{ the } [OH^-] = 1.00 \times 10^{-7}$$

This simple relationship has been used to construct the pH scale, which is used to indicate how acidic or basic a solution is. The pH scale ranges from 0 to 14. A pH of 7 is neutral; a pH below 7 is acidic; and a pH above 7 is basic.

The pH scale indicates the hydronium ion concentration. Another related scale, the pOH scale, is used to indicate the hydroxide ion concentration. Note that as the pH increases, the pOH decreases and the product, $[H_3O^+] \times [OH^-]$, is always $1.00 \times 10^{-14}$. If you know the pH, simply subtract the pH value from 14 to change to the pOH scale.

$$pH + pOH = 14$$

$K_w$ is a constant for all dilute aqueous solutions. Although the concentrations of $H_3O^+$ and $OH^-$ may change when substances are added to water, the product of $[H_3O^+]$ and $[OH^-]$ remains the same.

$$K_w = [H_3O^+][OH^-] = 1.00 \times 10^{-14}$$

If an acid is added to a solution, the $[H_3O^+]$ increases and the $[OH^-]$ decreases. If a base is added, the $[OH^-]$ increases and $[H_3O^+]$ decreases. Even in solutions that are acidic and contain a very large number of hydronium ions, a very small number of hydroxide ions exist.

To work problems involving pH and pOH, you must translate from these two scales back to concentration of moles per $dm^3$. If you wish to prepare a solution of a specific pH, you must also know how many moles of hydronium ion must be present per $dm^3$. For the simpler problems, you will have no difficulty if you thoroughly understand the definitions of pH, pOH, $[H_3O^+]$ and $[OH^-]$. For the more complex problems, you must be able to manipulate logarithms and exponents using a scientific calculator.

We will use a neutral solution to show the relationship between the symbols and their relation to exponents and logarithms. A neutral solution contains $1.00 \times 10^{-7}$ moles of hydronium ions per $dm^3$ and $1.00 \times 10^{-7}$ moles of hydroxide ions per $dm^3$.

$$[H_3O^+] = 1.00 \times 10^{-7} \qquad pH = 7$$
$$[OH^-] = 1.00 \times 10^{-7} \qquad pOH = 7$$

Note that the pH and pOH are simply the exponents of the ion concentrations without the negative signs. To translate into mathematical form, we must introduce logarithms because we are dealing with exponents.

$$pH = -\log [H_3O^+] \qquad pOH = -\log [OH^-]$$

Logs are used because they are exponents of ten and it is convenient to deal with hydronium ion concentrations in terms of powers of ten and scientific notation. (See the Appendix B for a discussion on logs.)

## Example 4

What is the pH of a solution that contains $1.00 \times 10^{-4}$ mol $H_3O^+/dm^3$?
**Solving Process:**

$$
\begin{aligned}
pH &= -\log [H_3O^+] \\
&= -\log (1.00 \times 10^{-4}) = -(\log 1.00 + \log 10^{-4}) \\
&= -[0.0000 + (-4)] = 4.00
\end{aligned}
$$

## Example 5

Find the pH and pOH of a solution that contains 0.003 50 mol $H_3O^+/dm^3$.
**Solving Process:**
**Method I: Using Log Tables**

$$
\begin{aligned}
pH &= -\log [H_3O^+] \\
&= -\log (3.50 \times 10^{-3}) = -(\log 3.50 + \log 10^{-3}) \\
&= -[0.5441 + (-3)] = 2.46
\end{aligned}
$$

**Method II: Using a Calculator**

$$
\begin{aligned}
pH &= -\log [H_3O^+] \\
&= -\log (3.50 \times 10^{-3})
\end{aligned}
$$

Enter the concentration into the display of a scientific calculator. Press the key labeled $\boxed{LOG}$ .
Press $\boxed{+/-}$ to change the sign.

$$pH = 2.46$$

Solve for the pOH:

$$
\begin{aligned}
pH + pOH &= 14.00 \\
pOH &= 14.00 - 2.46 = 11.54
\end{aligned}
$$

## Example 6

Calculate the $[H_3O^+]$ of a solution that has a pH of 3.70.
**Solving Process:**
**Method I: Using Log Tables**

$$
\begin{aligned}
pH &= -\log [H_3O^+] \\
-3.70 &= \log [H_3O^+]
\end{aligned}
$$

Because the logarithm table does not give the mantissa for negative numbers, $-3.70$ is expressed as a positive mantissa and a negative characteristic, $0.3000 - 4$. From the log table, the antilog of $0.3000$ is $2.00$. The antilog of $-4$ is $10^{-4}$.

$$0.3000 - 4 = \log [H_3O^+]$$
$$2.00 \times 10^{-4}M = [H_3O^+]$$

## Method II: Using a Calculator

Enter the pH into the calculator's display. Change its sign by pressing $\boxed{+/-}$ .

Take the antilog by pressing $\boxed{INV}$ then $\boxed{LOG}$ , or use the $\boxed{Y^x}$ by entering 10 $\boxed{Y^x}$ with $x = -pH$.

$$2.00 \times 10^{-4}M = [H_3O^+]$$

## Example 7

What is the $[OH^-]$ and the $[H_3O^+]$ of a solution if the pOH is 4.40?

**Solving Process:**

$$pOH = -\log [OH^-]$$
$$-4.40 = \log [OH^-]$$

## Method I: Using Log Tables

Because the logarithm table does not give the mantissa for negative numbers, $-4.4$ is expressed as $0.6000 - 5$. From the log table, antilog $0.6000 = 3.98$.

$$0.6000 - 5 = \log [OH^-]$$
$$3.98 \times 10^{-5} = [OH^-]$$

## Method II: Using a Calculator

Enter the pOH into the calculator's display. Change its sign by pressing $\boxed{+/-}$ .

Take the antilog by pressing $\boxed{INV}$ then $\boxed{LOG}$ , or use the $\boxed{Y^x}$ by entering 10 $\boxed{Y^x}$ with $x = -pOH$.

$$3.98 \times 10^{-5}M = [OH^-]$$

To solve for the $[H_3O^+]$, substitute into the equation.

$$[H_3O^+] \times [OH^-] = 1.00 \times 10^{-14}$$
$$[H_3O^+] = \frac{1.00 \times 10^{-14}}{[OH^-]}$$
$$= \frac{1.00 \times 10^{-14}}{3.98 \times 10^{-5}}$$
$$= 2.51 \times 10^{-10}M$$

## PROBLEMS

**15.** Calculate the pH and pOH of solutions with these concentrations.
  **a.** 0.000 10 mole $H_3O^+$ per $dm^3$
  **b.** 0.018 mole $OH^-$ per $dm^3$
  **c.** $1.62 \times 10^{-5}$ mole $OH^-$ per $dm^3$
  **d.** $4.09 \times 10^{-2}$ mole $H_3O^+$ per $dm^3$

**16.** Calculate the $[H_3O^+]$ of the following solutions.
  **a.** pH = 3.72    **b.** pH = 6.65    **c.** pOH = 12.0    **d.** pH = 8.2

**17.** Calculate the $[OH^-]$ of the following solutions.
  **a.** pOH = 11.0    **b.** pH = 4.25    **c.** pOH = 8.5    **d.** pH = 2.9

**18.** Calculate the pH and the pOH of solutions having the following concentrations. Assume 100% ionization. Remember that 1 mole of $H_2SO_4$ produces 2 moles of $H_3O^+$ ion.
  **a.** 0.0025$M$ NaOH            **d.** 0.048$M$ HCl
  **b.** 0.0025$M$ $H_2SO_4$       **e.** 0.032$M$ KOH
  **c.** 0.075$M$ $H_2SO_4$        **f.** 0.000 17$M$ NaOH

**19.** The pH of human blood is 7.4. What is the $[H_3O^+]$?

**20.** What is the $[H_3O^+]$ in a ripe red tomato that has a pH of 4.2?

# 25:3  BUFFERS

One use of the common ion effect (Chapter 24) is in buffering a solution. A solution is buffered if it resists change in its hydronium or hydroxide ion concentration when either of these ions is added.

A solution containing a weak acid or base and its completely ionized salt will act as a buffer. An example is a solution of acetic acid, $CH_3COOH$ and sodium acetate, $NaCH_3COO$. Another example is aqueous ammonia, $NH_3(aq)$ and ammonium chloride, $NH_4Cl$.

In a solution of $CH_3COOH$ and $NaCH_3COO$ there are a large quantity of $CH_3COO^-$ ions, a large quantity of $CH_3COOH$ molecules, and a small quantity of $H_3O^+$ ions. The $Na^+$ is a spectator ion and does not take part in the buffering. Any completely ionized acetate salt, such as $KCH_3COO$ would work just as well. If an acid such as $HNO_3$ were added to the buffer, the $H_3O^+$ of the acid reacts with part of the $CH_3COO^-$ to form more $CH_3COOH$. The following equation indicates only those ions actually involved in the reaction.

$$\underset{\substack{\text{from the}\\ \text{acid}}}{H_3O^+} + \underset{\substack{\text{from the}\\ \text{salt}}}{CH_3COO^-} \rightarrow CH_3COOH + H_2O$$

The reaction tends to restore the original $H_3O^+$ concentration.

If a base, such as KOH, is added, the $OH^-$ reacts with the $CH_3COOH$ in a neutralization reaction.

$$CH_3COOH + OH^- \rightarrow H_2O + CH_3COO^-$$

from the acid     from the base

If the concentrations of the weak acid and its salt or the weak base and its salt are varied, the $H_3O^+$ concentration of the solution can be fixed within broad limits. The calculations are the same as those illustrated in Section 24:7.

Consider a buffer solution consisting of sodium acetate and acetic acid. Most of the acetate ion is furnished by the soluble salt. The equation for $K_a$ can be modified to determine $[H_3O^+]$.

$$K_a = \frac{[H_3O^+][CH_3COO^-]}{[CH_3COOH]} = \frac{[H_3O^+][salt]}{[acid]}$$

$$[H_3O^+] = K_a \frac{[acid]}{[salt]}$$

The pH can be calculated using $[H_3O^+]$, as in the following example.

## Example 8

A buffer solution contains 0.500 mole per $dm^3$ each of acetic acid and sodium acetate. Determine the pH of the solution. The $K_a$ of the acetic acid is $1.76 \times 10^{-5}$.

**Solving Process:**

**Method I: Using Log Tables**

$$[H_3O^+] = K_a \frac{[acid]}{[salt]} = \frac{[1.76 \times 10^{-5}][0.500]}{[0.500]} = 1.76 \times 10^{-5} M$$

$$pH = -\log H_3O^+ = -\log (1.76 \times 10^{-5})$$

$$= -(\log 1.76 + \log 10^{-5})$$

$$= -[0.2455 + (-5)]$$

$$pH = 4.75$$

**Method II: Using the Calculator**

Enter the concentration into the display of a scientific calculator. Press the key labeled $\boxed{LOG}$. Press $\boxed{+/-}$ to change the sign.

$$pH = 4.75$$

## PROBLEMS

21. A buffer solution contains 0.133 $mol/dm^3$ of acetic acid and 0.215 $mol/dm^3$ sodium acetate. Determine the pH of the solution. The $K_a$ of acetic acid is $1.76 \times 10^{-5}$.

22. Blood contains the $H_2CO_3$, $NaHCO_3$ buffer system. Calculate the pH of a blood sample that contains 0.001 34$M$ $H_2CO_3$ and 0.0250$M$

$NaHCO_3$. The $K_a$ for the first ionization of $H_2CO_3$ is $4.30 \times 10^{-7}$.

$$H_2O(l) + H_2CO_3(aq) \rightleftarrows H_3O^+(aq) + HCO_3^-(aq)$$

## 25:4  TITRATIONS

**Titration** is an experimental procedure in which a standard solution is used to determine the concentration of an unknown solution. A **standard solution** is one of known concentration. The titration involves the gradual addition of one solution to another until the solute in the first solution has completely reacted with the solute in the second solution. This point is called the equivalence point (same as stoichiometric point). The equivalence point is detected using an indicator. The point at which the indicator changes color is called the endpoint of the titration.

The most common titrations involve the reaction of an acid solution with a basic solution. The reaction of the acid and base is termed a **neutralization.** The products of this reaction are a salt and water.

acid + base → salt + water

The three types of titration reactions are: (1) an acid with a base to give a soluble salt and water, (2) a soluble salt with a second soluble salt to give a precipitate, and (3) an oxidizing material with a reducing material.

The reaction between a strong acid (e.g., HCl or $HNO_3$) and a strong base (e.g., NaOH) gives salts (e.g., NaCl or $NaNO_3$). Since these salts are products of strong acids and strong bases, the resulting solution is neutral.

For a strong acid/strong base titration, the pH at the equivalence point is 7; but only a small amount of reagent causes a major pH change. The titration curve for the neutralization reaction is shown in Figure 25-1a. Curves can be produced using a pH meter connected to a chart recorder. The indicator selected should change color in the pH range from about 4 to 10. Phenolphthalein is usually used since it is easy to detect visually a slight pink color from a colorless liquid.

Reaction between a strong acid (HCl, $HNO_3$, or $H_2SO_4$) and a weak base ($NH_3$) also produces salts ($NH_4Cl$, $NH_4NO_3$, or $(NH_4)_2SO_4$). These salts hydrolyze to form slightly acidic solutions. The titration curve for this reaction is shown in Figure 25-1b. Methyl orange can be used as an indicator because of the low pH region in which it changes color.

The reaction between a weak acid ($CH_3COOH$) and a strong base (NaOH) gives a salt ($NaCH_3COO$). Such salts hydrolyze to give a slightly basic solution. The titration curve for this reaction is shown in Figure 25-1c. Any indicator changing color in the higher pH ranges could be used, but phenolphthalein is most frequently used.

The concentration of the acid and basic solutions will change the position of the curves only slightly (especially at the start and completion of the titration) in relation to the pH.

## Example 9

If 20.0 cm$^3$ of a 0.300$M$ solution of NaOH is required to neutralize completely 30.0 cm$^3$ of a sulfuric acid solution, what is the molarity of the $H_2SO_4$ solution?

**Solving Process:**

(a) First write the balanced equation.

$$2NaOH + H_2SO_4 \rightarrow Na_2SO_4 + 2H_2O$$

(b) Since the concentration of the base is given, determine the moles of NaOH.

$$\text{number of moles} = \frac{20.0 \text{ cm}^3}{} \left| \frac{0.300 \text{ mol NaOH}}{1.00 \text{ dm}^3} \right| \frac{1 \text{ dm}^3}{1000 \text{ cm}^3}$$

$$= 0.006\ 00 \text{ mol NaOH}$$

(c) From the coefficients of the balanced equation, 2 moles of base are required for reaction with 1 mole of acid.

$$\text{number of moles} = \frac{0.006\ 00 \text{ mol NaOH}}{} \left| \frac{1 \text{ mol } H_2SO_4}{2 \text{ mol NaOH}} \right.$$

$$= 0.003\ 00 \text{ mol } H_2SO_4$$

(d) Determine the molarity of the acid.

$$\text{molarity} = \frac{0.003\ 00 \text{ mol } H_2SO_4}{30.0 \text{ cm}^3} \left| \frac{1000 \text{ cm}^3}{1 \text{ dm}^3} \right.$$

$$= 0.100 \text{ mol } H_2SO_4/\text{dm}^3$$

## Example 10

What volume of 0.500$M$ $HNO_3$ is required to neutralize 25.0 cm$^3$ of a 0.200$M$ NaOH solution?

**Solving Process:**

(a) The balanced equation is

$$HNO_3 + NaOH \rightarrow NaNO_3 + H_2O$$

(b) Since the concentration of the base is given, determine the moles of NaOH.

$$\text{mol NaOH} = \frac{25.0 \text{ cm}^3 \text{ soln}}{} \left| \frac{0.200 \text{ mol NaOH}}{1.00 \text{ dm}^3 \text{ soln}} \right| \frac{1 \text{ dm}^3}{1000 \text{ cm}^3}$$

$$= 0.005\ 00 \text{ mol}$$

(c) From the coefficients of the balanced equation, 1 mole of acid will react completely with 1 mole of base.

$$0.005\ 00 \text{ mol NaOH} = 0.005\ 00 \text{ mol } HNO_3$$

**(d)** Therefore

$$\text{volume} = \frac{0.005\ 00\ \cancel{\text{mol HNO}_3}}{} \left| \frac{1.00\ \cancel{\text{dm}^3\ \text{soln}}}{0.500\ \cancel{\text{mol HNO}_3}} \right| \frac{1000\ \text{cm}^3}{\cancel{1\ \text{dm}^3}}$$

$$= 10.0\ \text{cm}^3\ \text{soln}$$

## PROBLEMS

**23.** Calculate the unknown quantity for the complete neutralization of the following.

| Acid | | Base | |
|---|---|---|---|
| concentration | volume | concentration | volume |
| **a.** 0.250$M$ HCl | 30.00 cm$^3$ | ? NaOH | 25.00 cm$^3$ |
| **b.** 0.500$M$ H$_2$SO$_4$ | ? | 0.750$M$ KOH | 20.00 cm$^3$ |
| **c.** ? HNO$_3$ | 15.00 cm$^3$ | 1.50$M$ NH$_3$ | 25.00 cm$^3$ |
| **d.** 0.400$M$ HNO$_3$ | 35.00 cm$^3$ | 0.800$M$ NaOH | ? |

**24.** What is the molarity of a NaOH solution if 25.00 cm$^3$ is required to completely neutralize 40.00 cm$^3$ of a 1.50$M$ solution of H$_2$SO$_4$?

**25.** Calculate the cm$^3$ of a 0.600$M$ solution of HNO$_3$ necessary to neutralize 28.55 cm$^3$ of a 0.450$M$ solution of KOH.

**26.** A titration of 15.00 cm$^3$ of household ammonia, NH$_3$(aq), required 38.57 cm$^3$ of 0.780$M$ HCl. Calculate the molarity of the ammonia.

# 25:5 TITRATIONS WITH NORMAL SOLUTIONS

Another quantitative expression for the concentration of solutions is **normality.** A 1$N$ solution contains one equivalent mass of solute per dm$^3$ of solution.

$$\text{normality } (N) = \frac{\text{number of equivalents of solute}}{\text{dm}^3 \text{ of solution}}$$

An equivalent is that quantity of a substance that provides 1 mole of charge. Consider these three substances.

$$\text{NaNO}_3 \rightarrow \text{Na}^+ + \text{NO}_3^-$$
$$\text{Na}_2\text{SO}_4 \rightarrow 2\text{Na}^+ + \text{SO}_4^{2-}$$
$$\text{Na}_3\text{PO}_4 \rightarrow 3\text{Na}^+ + \text{PO}_4^{3-}$$

NaNO$_3$ contains 1 equivalent per mole; Na$_2$SO$_4$ contains 2 equivalents; and Na$_3$PO$_4$ contains 3 equivalents. The equivalent masses of these substances are

$$\text{NaNO}_3 \qquad \frac{85.0\ \text{g}}{1\ \text{mol}} \times \frac{1\ \text{mol}}{1\ \text{eq}} = 85.0\ \text{g/eq}$$

$$\text{Na}_2\text{SO}_4 \qquad \frac{142.1\ \text{g}}{1\ \text{mol}} \times \frac{1\ \text{mol}}{2\ \text{eq}} = 71.05\ \text{g/eq}$$

$$Na_3PO_4 \quad \frac{164.0 \text{ g}}{1 \text{ mol}} \times \frac{1 \text{ mol}}{3 \text{ eq}} = 54.67 \text{ g/eq}$$

Titration problems can also be solved using the concentration expression normality and substituting into a mathematical equation.

Consider a reaction between a 1.00$N$ HCl solution and a 1.00$N$ NaOH solution. It is necessary to add equal volumes of the acid and base to have a complete reaction. An equal number of $H_3O^+$ ions and $OH^-$ ions react to produce water. The other product, NaCl, is a salt of a strong acid and a strong base. The resulting solution is neutral.

The equivalent mass of a substance is that mass of material that will produce one mole of charge. One equivalent mass of hydrogen ions will react with one equivalent mass of hydroxide ions. An equal number of equivalents of acid and equivalents of base will react completely to form a salt.

$$normality = \frac{number \text{ of equivalents of solute}}{1 \text{ } dm^3 \text{ of solution}}$$

$$\frac{eq \text{ acid}}{1 \text{ } dm^3 \text{ solution}} \left| \begin{array}{c} dm^3 \text{ acid} \end{array} \right. = \frac{eq \text{ base}}{1 \text{ } dm^3 \text{ solution}} \left| \begin{array}{c} dm^3 \text{ base} \end{array} \right.$$

On substitution:

$$normality \text{ } acid \times volume \text{ } acid = normality \text{ } base \times volume \text{ } base$$

or

$$N_a \times V_a = N_b \times V_b$$

If any three values are known, the fourth value can be calculated. For the factors to be equivalent, both volume terms must be in the same unit.

Acids or bases with one reacting hydrogen ion or hydroxide ion per formula unit contain 1 equivalent per mole. Acids or bases with two reacting hydrogen ions or hydroxide ions contain 2 equivalents per mole. Examples of the relationship between molarity and normality are

| one reacting ion | HCl | 2.00$M$ HCl | = 2.00$N$ HCl |
|---|---|---|---|
| (1 eq = 1 mol) | NaOH | 0.300$M$ NaOH | = 0.300$N$ NaOH |
| two reacting ions | $H_2SO_4$ | 0.750$M$ $H_2SO_4$ | = 1.50$N$ $H_2SO_4$ |
| (2 eq = 1 mol) | | | |

## Example 11

If 20.0 cm$^3$ of a 3.00$N$ solution of NaOH are required to neutralize 30.0 cm$^3$ of a sulfuric acid solution, what is the normality of the $H_2SO_4$?

**Solving Process:**

$$equivalents \text{ of } acid = equivalents \text{ of } base$$
$$N_a \times V_a = N_b \times V_b$$

Change cm$^3$ to dm$^3$ and then substitute:

$$N_a = \frac{3.00N}{} \frac{0.0200\,dm^3}{0.0300\,dm^3}$$

$$= 2.00N$$

## Example 12

How many grams of KOH are required to neutralize completely 200.0 cm$^3$ of a 4.00$N$ solution of HNO$_3$?

**Solving Process:**

For neutralization to be complete, the number of equivalents of acid must be equal to the number of equivalents of base. First, calculate the number of equivalents of acid. Then convert this answer to grams of KOH.

$$\text{equivalents HNO}_3 = \frac{4.00 \text{ eq HNO}_3}{1\,dm^3} \frac{0.200\,dm^3}{} = 0.800 \text{ eq}$$

equivalents acid = equivalents base

$$\text{mass KOH} = \frac{0.800\,eq\,KOH}{} \frac{1\,mol\,KOH}{1\,eq\,KOH} \frac{56.1 \text{ g KOH}}{1\,mol\,KOH} = 44.9 \text{ g}$$

## PROBLEMS

27. What is the normality and the molarity of a phosphoric acid solution if 25.00 cm$^3$ of the solution is necessary to completely react with 30.00 cm$^3$ of a 0.500$N$ KOH solution?

28. In a laboratory experiment involving the neutralization of vinegar using 0.500$N$ NaOH, the following data was collected.

|  | **Volume of vinegar** | **Volume of base** |
|---|---|---|
| Trial 1 | 10.00 cm$^3$ | 17.59 cm$^3$ |
| Trial 2 | 15.27 cm$^3$ | 28.39 cm$^3$ |
| Trial 3 | 20.14 cm$^3$ | 36.58 cm$^3$ |

Calculate:

a. the normality of the vinegar in each trial
b. the grams of acetic acid per dm$^3$ of vinegar

## CHAPTER REVIEW PROBLEMS

1. Given the following solubilities, determine the $K_{sp}$ for each compound.
   a. Bi$_2$S$_3$ $\quad$ 1.70 $\times$ 10$^{-15}$ mol/dm$^3$
   b. Ca$_3$(PO$_4$)$_2$ $\quad$ 3.92 $\times$ 10$^{-6}$ mol/dm$^3$

2. Calculate the molar solubility for the following compounds using the $K_{sp}$ values given.
   a. Ag$_2$S $\quad$ 6.31 $\times$ 10$^{-50}$
   b. BaCrO$_4$ $\quad$ 2.00 $\times$ 10$^{-10}$

3. Determine the mass of calcium fluoride, CaF$_2$, that will dissolve in 100.0 dm$^3$ of water. Assume that there is no volume change. $K_{sp}$ of CaF$_2$ is 2.69 $\times$ 10$^{-11}$.

4. Determine if a precipitate of silver chromate, $Ag_2CrO_4$, will form when 100.0 $cm^3$ of 0.100$M$ $AgNO_3$ are added to 100.0 $cm^3$ of 0.350$M$ $K_2CrO_4$. $K_{sp}$ of $Ag_2CrO_4$ is 9.00 × $10^{-12}$.

5. If a solution contains 1.00 × $10^{-2}M$ chloride ions and 1.00 × $10^{-3}M$ iodide ions, which will precipitate first, AgCl or AgI, if a solution of $AgNO_3$ is added one drop at a time? The $K_{sp}$ of AgCl is 1.56 × $10^{-10}$; $K_{sp}$ of AgI is 1.50 × $10^{-16}$.

6. The approximate pH of some common substances is listed. Calculate the pOH, the $[H_3O^+]$, and the $[OH^-]$.

   a. vinegar     2.9         e. soft drink          3.0
   b. orange      3.5         f. tomato              4.2
   c. rainwater   6.2         g. egg                 7.8
   d. seawater    8.5         h. milk of magnesia   10.5

7. The approximate pH of some common chemical solutions is listed. Calculate the pOH, the $[H_3O^+]$, and the $[OH^-]$.

   a. 0.1$M$ HCl              1.00     d. 0.1$M$ $H_2SO_4$       1.20
   b. 0.1$M$ $CH_3COOH$       2.90     e. 0.1$M$ $NaHCO_3$       8.40
   c. 0.1$M$ $NH_3$(aq)      11.10     f. 0.1$M$ NaOH           13.00

8. What is the pH of a buffer solution that contains 0.159 mol/$dm^3$ acetic acid and 0.195 mol/$dm^3$ sodium acetate? The $K_a$ for acetic acid is 1.76 × $10^{-5}$.

9. How many $cm^3$ of 0.500$M$ NaOH are necessary to neutralize completely 20.00 $cm^3$ of each of the following acids?

   a. 0.150$M$ $HNO_3$        c. 0.220$M$ HCl
   b. 0.250$M$ $H_2SO_4$      d. 0.450$M$ $H_3PO_4$

10. In a laboratory experiment, 20.00 $cm^3$ of $NH_3$(aq) solution is titrated to the methyl orange endpoint using 15.65 $cm^3$ of a 0.200$M$ HCl solution. What is the concentration of the aqueous ammonia solution?

11. How many $cm^3$ of 0.750$M$ sulfuric acid are needed to neutralize completely 20.00 $cm^3$ of 0.427$M$ NaOH solution?

12. What volume of 0.250$N$ $H_3PO_4$ is required to neutralize 30.00 $cm^3$ of a 0.0500$N$ $Ba(OH)_2$ solution?

13. Determine the normality and the molarity of a sulfuric acid solution if 30.00 $cm^3$ is used to neutralize 40.00 $cm^3$ of a 0.500$N$ KOH solution.

14. If 1.25 grams of pure $CaCO_3$ required 25.50 $cm^3$ of a hydrochloric acid solution for complete reaction, calculate the normality of the acid.

15. A common constituent of the "hardness" of water is calcium carbonate. The amount of $CaCO_3$ is determined in the laboratory by titration with a standard acid such as HCl, producing water and $CO_2$. A laboratory technician titrated a 100.0 $cm^3$ sample of water containing $CaCO_3$ with 0.100$N$ HCl and found that 15.20 $cm^3$ of acid were needed to reach the endpoint. Calculate the mass of $CaCO_3$ contained in exactly one $dm^3$ of the water.

# OXIDATION-REDUCTION

# 26

## 26:1 OXIDATION NUMBERS

In most of the equations considered in previous chapters one species displaces another species that is similarly charged. Double displacement reactions such as the neutralizations are common examples. The species are ionic and retain the same charge as reactants and products.

$$2NaOH(aq) + H_2SO_4(aq) \rightarrow Na_2SO_4(aq) + 2HOH(l)$$

$$2Na^+(aq) + 2OH^-(aq) + 2H^+(aq) + SO_4^{2-}(aq)$$
$$\rightarrow 2Na^+(aq) + SO_4^{2-}(aq) + 2H_2O(l)$$

An oxidation-reduction reaction or **redox reaction** involves a change in the charges of the ions. Reactions such as synthesis and single displacement are oxidation-reduction reactions since there have been changes in the charges.

**Oxidation number** is the charge that an atom *appears* to have when both electrons in a bond are assigned to the more electronegative atom. Without knowledge of electron bond formulas, the oxidation states of an atom may be assigned from the following rules.

1. All free elements are assigned an oxidation number of zero. Thus, hydrogen in $H_2$, oxygen in $O_2$, and phosphorus in $P_4$, all have an oxidation number of zero.

2. The oxidation number of a monatomic ion is equal to the charge on the ion.
   a. Group IA (1) elements form only 1+ ions.
   b. Group IIA (2) elements form only 2+ ions.
   c. Halogen elements have a 1− oxidation number except in interhalogen compounds.

3. In practically all hydrogen-containing compounds, the oxidation number of hydrogen is 1+. The exception occurs with the metal hydrides, in which the oxidation number of hydrogen is 1−.

4. The oxidation number of oxygen in compounds is generally 2−. The exceptions are the peroxides, in which the oxidation number is 1−, and in oxygen difluoride, $OF_2$, where oxygen has an oxidation number of 2+.

**193**

**5.** All oxidation numbers that are assigned must be consistent with the conservation of charge. For neutral particles, the oxidation numbers of all atoms must add up to zero. For a polyatomic ion, the oxidation numbers of the atoms must add up to the charge on the polyatomic ion. Review the following examples.

|  | hydrogen | oxygen | sulfur | Total Charge |
|---|---|---|---|---|
| sulfuric acid | $2(1+)$ + | $4(2-)$ + | ? | = 0 |
| $H_2SO_4$ | oxidation number of S = $6+$ | | | |
| sulfite ion | | $3(2-)$ + | ? | = $2-$ |
| $SO_3^{2-}$ | oxidation number of S = $4+$ | | | |

## PROBLEM

**1.** In the following, give the oxidation number for the indicated atoms.

**a.** Al in $Al_2O_3$               **e.** Fe in $FeCl_3$
**b.** S in $Na_2S_2O_3$             **f.** Cr in $Cr_2O_7^{2-}$
**c.** Mn in $MnO_4^-$               **g.** C in $K_2CO_3$
**d.** Cl in $ClO_3^-$               **h.** N in $NO_3^-$

# 26:2  HALF-REACTIONS

**Oxidation** is the process by which electrons are removed from atoms or ions. **Reduction** is the process by which electrons are added to atoms or ions. Oxidation and reduction must occur at the same time in a reaction, and the number of electrons lost must equal the number gained.

A redox equation can be separated into an oxidation half-reaction and a reduction half-reaction. The method of balancing oxidation-reduction equations is to balance separately the oxidation half-reaction and the reduction half-reaction. The two half-reactions are added to obtain the balanced equation for the total reaction.

Use the following general approach to balance redox reactions.

**1.** Write the separate half-reactions.
**2.** Balance the electrons using oxidation numbers.
**3.** Balance the atoms in each half-reaction as follows:
   **a.** Balance all atoms with the use of coefficients, except hydrogen and oxygen atoms.
   **b.** Add enough water ($H_2O$) to the side deficient in oxygen to balance the oxygen.
   **c.** Add sufficient hydrogen ion ($H^+$) to the side deficient in hydrogen to balance the hydrogen.
**4.** Multiply the half-reactions by small whole numbers to balance the electrons.
**5.** Add the two half-reactions and subtract any duplications on either side of the equation.

## Example 1

Write a balanced oxidation-reduction equation for the following reaction.

$$MnO_4^- + H_2SO_3 \rightarrow Mn^{2+} + HSO_4^- + H_2O$$

**Solving Process:**

Separate the reaction into two half-reactions. Balance the half-reactions separately. The reduction half-reaction is

$$MnO_4^- \rightarrow Mn^{2+}$$

The first step in balancing the half-reaction is to indicate the number of electrons gained or lost. In the reduction half-reaction being considered here, the manganese has an oxidation number 7+ before the reaction and 2+ after the reaction. Thus manganese must gain 5 electrons.

$$MnO_4^- + 5e^- \rightarrow Mn^{2+}$$

The next step is to balance all elements other than oxygen and hydrogen. In the reaction above, one manganese atom appears on each side of the equation. The equation is balanced with respect to maganese atoms, the only element present in addition to oxygen. No change is needed to balance the manganese.

Next oxygen should be balanced. You may assume that all the oxidation-reduction reactions in this book take place in water solution. Thus, oxygen atoms are always available in the form of water molecules.

$$MnO_4^- + 5e^- \rightarrow Mn^{2+} + 4H_2O$$

Finally the hydrogen atoms must be balanced. Hydrogen is available in water molecules but using water to balance hydrogen atoms would throw the oxygen atoms out of balance. If you note that the solution is acidic ($H_2SO_3$ is one of the reactants) then you will realize that $H^+$ ions will be abundant in the solution and can be used to balance the hydrogen atoms.

$$MnO_4^- + 8H^+ + 5e^- \rightarrow Mn^{2+} + 4H_2O$$

The reduction half-reaction is now balanced.

The oxidation half-reaction must now be balanced. The sulfur atoms change oxidation number from 4+ to 6+, and they lose two electrons each.

$$H_2SO_3 \rightarrow HSO_4^- + 2e^-$$

Again use the available $H_2O$ and $H^+$ to balance the half-reaction with respect to oxygen and hydrogen.

$$H_2SO_3 + H_2O \rightarrow HSO_4^- + 2e^- + 3H^+$$

Before the two half-reactions can be combined to give the overall equation, the coefficients of the electrons must be adjusted so that the same number of electrons are lost as are gained. The manganese half-reaction requires five electrons while the sulfur half-reaction produces two. The least common multiple of five and two is ten, so the reduction half-reaction is multiplied by two and the oxidation half-reaction by five.

Reduction half-reaction $\times$ 2

$$2MnO_4^- + 16H^+ + 10e^- \rightarrow 2Mn^{2+} + 8H_2O$$

Oxidation half-reaction $\times$ 5

$$5H_2SO_3 + 5H_2O \rightarrow 5HSO_4^- + 10e^- + 15H^+$$

Adding the two half-reactions and eliminating the electrons that appear in equal numbers on both sides gives

$$2MnO_4^- + H^+ + 5H_2SO_3 \rightarrow 2Mn^{2+} + 5HSO_4^- + 3H_2O$$

Reactions of the oxidation-reduction type can also take place in basic solution. Balance these just as you would an acidic reaction and then add sufficient hydroxide ions ($OH^-$) to each side to change all $H^+$ ions to $H_2O$ molecules. Remember that the same number of hydroxide ions must be added to each side of the reaction.

## Example 2

Write a balanced oxidation-reduction equation for the following reaction.

$$NO_2 + OH^- \rightarrow NO_2^- + NO_3^-$$

**Solving Process:**

Note that nitrogen is both oxidized and reduced in this reaction.

| Reduction | Oxidation |
|---|---|

Skeleton

$NO_2 \rightarrow NO_2^-$ $\qquad$ $NO_2 \rightarrow NO_3^-$

Balance electrons

$NO_2 + e^- \rightarrow NO_2^-$ $\qquad$ $NO_2 \rightarrow NO_3^- + e^-$

Nitrogen atoms are balanced

Balance oxygen

$NO_2 + e^- \rightarrow NO_2^-$ $\qquad$ $H_2O + NO_2 \rightarrow NO_3^- + e^-$

Balance hydrogen

(same) $\qquad$ $H_2O + NO_2 \rightarrow NO_3^- + 2H^+ + e^-$

Convert to basic solution

(same) $\qquad$ $H_2O + NO_2 + 2OH^- \rightarrow NO_3^- + 2H_2O + e^-$

Eliminate the excess water molecules on both sides

$$NO_2 + 2OH^- \rightarrow NO_3^- + H_2O + e^-$$

The number of electrons in each half-reaction is the same, so they may be added directly. The nitrogen dioxide molecules appearing in each half-reaction are combined in the final equation just as the electrons appearing on each side are eliminated.

$$2NO_2 + 2OH^- \rightarrow NO_2^- + NO_3^- + H_2O$$

## PROBLEMS

*Balance the following oxidation-reduction equations. All reactions take place in an acidic solution unless otherwise indicated.*

2. $Cr(cr) + Sn^{4+}(aq) \rightarrow Cr^{3+}(aq) + Sn^{2+}(aq)$

3. $Al(cr) + H^+(aq) \rightarrow Al^{3+}(aq) + H_2(g)$

4. $Zn(cr) + Ag^+(aq) \rightarrow Zn^{2+}(aq) + Ag(cr)$

5. $NO_3^-(aq) + S(cr) \rightarrow NO_2(g) + H_2SO_4(aq)$

6. $Br_2(l) + SO_3^{2-}(aq) \rightarrow Br^-(aq) + SO_4^{2-}(aq)(basic)$

7. $Fe^{2+}(aq) + MnO_4^-(aq) \rightarrow Mn^{2+}(aq) + Fe^{3+}(aq)$

8. $Cu(cr) + SO_4^{2-}(aq) \rightarrow Cu^{2+}(aq) + SO_2(g)$

9. $Cu(cr) + NO_3^-(aq) \rightarrow Cu^{2+}(aq) + NO(g)$

10. $MnO_4^-(aq) + S^{2-}(aq) \rightarrow Mn^{2+}(aq) + S(cr)$

11. $CuS(cr) + NO_3^-(aq) \rightarrow Cu^{2+}(aq) + NO_2(g) + S(cr)$

12. $NO_2(g) + ClO^-(aq) \rightarrow NO_3^-(aq) + Cl^-(aq)(basic)$

13. $Fe^{2+}(aq) + Cr_2O_7^{2-}(aq) \rightarrow Fe^{3+}(aq) + Cr^{3+}(aq)$

14. $MnO_4^-(aq) + Cl^-(aq) \rightarrow Mn^{2+}(aq) + Cl_2(g)$

15. $IO_3^-(aq) + H_2S(g) \rightarrow I_2(g) + SO_3^{2-}(aq)(basic)$

16. $H_2SeO_3(aq) + Br^-(aq) \rightarrow Se(cr) + Br_2(g)$

17. $BrO_3^-(aq) + MnO_2(cr) \rightarrow Br^-(aq) + MnO_4^-(aq)(basic)$

18. $H_2S(g) + NO_3^-(aq) \rightarrow S(cr) + NO(g)$

## CHAPTER REVIEW PROBLEMS

1. Give the oxidation number for the following.
   a. Te in $TeO_2$      d. P in $PO_4^{3-}$
   b. Cl in $HClO_2$      e. Sb in $Sb_2O_5$
   c. N in $N_2O$      f. I in $IO_3^-$

*Balance the following oxidation-reduction equations. All reactions take place in an acidic solution unless otherwise indicated.*

2. $AsH_3(g) + ClO_3^-(aq) \rightarrow H_3AsO_4(aq) + Cl^-(aq)$

3. $HNO_2(aq) + I^-(aq) \rightarrow NO(g) + I_2(g)$

4. $MnO_4^-(aq) + H_2O_2(aq) \rightarrow Mn^{2+}(aq) + O_2(g)$

5. $MnO_2(cr) + ClO_3^-(aq) \rightarrow MnO_4^-(aq) + Cl^-(aq)(basic)$

6. $Br_2(l) \rightarrow Br^-(aq) + BrO_3^-(aq)(basic)$

7. $N_2O_4(aq) + Br^-(aq) \rightarrow NO_2^-(aq) + BrO_3^-(aq)(basic)$

8. $H_2PO_2^-(aq) + SbO_2^-(aq) \rightarrow HPO_3^{2-}(aq) + Sb(cr)(basic)$

9. $CrO_2^-(aq) + ClO^-(aq) \rightarrow CrO_4^{2-}(aq) + Cl^-(aq)(basic)$

10. $Cu(OH)_2(cr) + HPO_3^{2-}(aq) \rightarrow Cu_2O(cr) + PO_4^{3-}(aq)$

11. $HS^-(aq) + IO_3^-(aq) \rightarrow I^-(aq) + S(cr)$

12. $N_2O(g) + ClO^-(aq) \rightarrow Cl^-(aq) + NO_2^-(aq)(basic)$

**13.** $H_2SO_3(aq) + MnO_2(cr) \rightarrow SO_4{}^{2-}(aq) + Mn^{2+}(aq)$

**14.** $IO_4{}^-(aq) + I^-(aq) \rightarrow I_2(g)$

**15.** $CrO_4{}^{2-}(aq) + I^-(aq) \rightarrow Cr^{3+}(aq) + I_2(g)$

# ELECTRO-CHEMISTRY 27

## 27:1 REDUCTION POTENTIAL AND REACTION PREDICTION

Redox reactions can be used to generate electricity or can be produced by electricity. The study of these electrochemical changes is called **electrochemistry.**

Oxidation is the loss of electrons. A substance that acquires electrons from other substances easily is called an oxidizing agent. It is an oxidizing agent because it causes other substances to be oxidized. By convention, a series of half-reactions, termed the standard reduction potential table, is set up with the best oxidizing agent at the bottom left position. (See Table A-16 in the Appendix.) Each half-reaction has a characteristic reduction potential ($E°$) that is compared to a standard reference half-reaction.

$$2H^+(aq) + 2_e^- \rightarrow H_2(g)$$

This reaction is assumed to have a reduction potential of 0.000 volt (V) at 25°C, 101.325 kPa pressure and 1 molar $H^+$. Fluorine, $F_2$, is at the bottom of the list because it shows the greatest tendency to acquire electrons and become the fluoride ion. The fluoride ion is a very weak reducing agent since $F^-$ does not readily give up its electrons.

The lithium ion, $Li^+$, is a weak oxidizing agent, as it does not readily gain electrons. However, the lithium atom easily gives up electrons, so it is a strong reducing agent.

A large positive potential indicates a great tendency for the reaction to occur. Fluorine gas will proceed readily to fluoride ion, since the potential is +2.87 volts. For all practical purposes, fluoride ion will not go to fluorine gas. Lithium ion will not proceed spontaneously to lithium metal since the potential is negative, −3.05 volts.

The potentials given in Table A-16 apply when the half-reaction takes place in the forward direction. In the reverse direction, the sign of the voltage is reversed. The E° values do not depend upon the number of electrons transferred.

Use the table to see if two half-reactions will react by adding the half-reaction potentials. It is necessary to balance the chemical quantities and the number of electrons, but no adjustment need be made in potential values. The potential is the ease with which certain electrons per atom or

**199**

ion are lost. Potentials are dependent on temperature, pressure, and concentration. Keep in mind that the given potential applies to the forward reaction. For the reverse direction, the sign of the potential is reversed.

## Example 1

The following equation represents copper metal placed in a colorless silver ion solution.

$$Cu(cr) + 2Ag^+(aq) \rightarrow Cu^{2+}(aq) + 2Ag(cr)$$

**Solving Process:**

Write the half-reactions and obtain each voltage from the reduction potential table. Remember that the sign of the voltage may be reversed. Balance the electrons and add.

$$
\begin{array}{ll}
Cu \rightarrow Cu^{2+} + 2e^- & -0.34 \text{ V} \\
\underline{2Ag^+ + 2e^- \rightarrow 2Ag} & \underline{+0.80 \text{ V}} \\
Cu + 2Ag^+ \rightarrow Cu^{2+} + 2Ag & +0.46 \text{ V}
\end{array}
$$

Since the voltage is positive, this reaction should occur spontaneously. Spontaneous does not mean instantaneous. A reaction occurs spontaneously when it occurs without additional energy such as heat or light. Note that the reverse reaction does not take place.

$$
\begin{array}{ll}
Cu^{2+} \, 2_e^- \rightarrow Cu & -0.34 \text{ V} \\
\underline{2Ag \rightarrow 2Ag^+ + 2e^-} & \underline{+0.80 \text{ V}} \\
\text{No reaction} & +0.46 \text{ V}
\end{array}
$$

This reaction does not occur spontaneously since the voltage is negative.

## PROBLEM

1. Calculate the potential in volts for each of the following reactions.
    **a.** $Cr(cr) + Ni^{2+}(aq) \rightarrow Cr^{2+}(aq) + Ni(cr)$
    **b.** $Al(cr) + H^+(aq) \rightarrow Al^{3+}(aq) + H_2(g)$
    **c.** $Br_2(l) + I^-(aq) \rightarrow Br^-(aq) + I_2(cr)$
    **d.** $Fe^{2+}(aq) + MnO_4^-(aq) \rightarrow Fe^{3+}(aq) + Mn^{2+}(aq)$
    **e.** $Cl_2(g) + Sn^{2+}(aq) \rightarrow Cl^-(aq) + Sn^{4+}(aq)$
    **f.** $Hg(l) + Hg^{2+}(aq) \rightarrow Hg_2^{2+}(aq)$

## 27:2  VOLTAIC CELLS

Chemists refer to a battery as an electrochemical cell. It consists of electrodes in contact with an electrolyte. An electric current is produced when the two half-cells are physically separated but electrically connected and electrons move through an external circuit. This process occurs spontaneously in a **voltaic** or **galvanic cell.** The voltaic cell is usually made of two half-cells connected by a salt bridge. The salt bridge completes the internal circuit by allowing ions to migrate between the cells. A porous ceramic cup can serve the same purpose as the salt bridge.

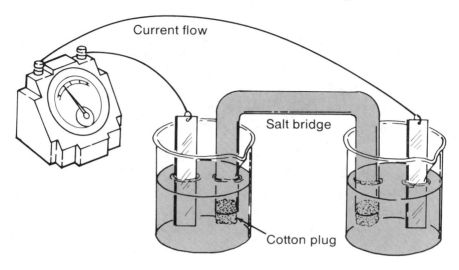

A convenient notation is used to represent a particular voltaic cell. The nickel-cadmium cell pictured above is represented by $Cd|Cd^{2+}||Ni^{2+}|Ni$. In this form the anode (oxidation half-cell) is written on the left. The cathode (reduction half-cell) is written on the right. The salt bridge connecting the two half-cells is represented by the two parallel vertical lines. The single line between Cd and $Cd^{2+}$ represents the phase boundary between the solid Cd electrode and the solution (electrolyte).

## Example 2

Consider the following electrochemical cell.

$$Li|Li^+||Ag^+|Ag$$

Use Table A-16 in the Appendix to help you analyze the cell.

**Solving Process:**

From Table A-16 find the two reduction half-reactions, and their $E°$ value.

$$Li^+ + e^- \rightarrow Li, \ -3.05 \ V$$
$$Ag^+ + e^- \rightarrow Ag, \ +0.80 \ V$$

The lower positive voltage indicates which half-reaction is written in reverse order. The sign on the voltage is also changed. The oxidation half-reaction is

$$Li \rightarrow Li^+ + e^-, \ +3.05 \ V$$

This reaction occurs at the anode. Here the Li electrode loses both electrons and mass as it dissolves to form the $Li^+$ cation. Lithium metal is the reducing agent. The electrons leave the Li electrode and travel through the external circuit to the Ag electrode.

The reduction half-reaction is

$$Ag^+ + e^- \rightarrow Ag, \quad +0.80 \text{ V}$$

This reaction occurs at the cathode. The cathode gains both electrons and mass. The silver cations migrate to the cathode, gain an electron, and plate out as silver metal. The $Ag^+$ is the oxidizing agent. The theoretical voltage on the meter would be

$$3.05 \text{ V} + 0.80 \text{ V} = +3.85 \text{ V}$$

## PROBLEMS

*Use Table A-16 to help you answer questions 2 and 3.*

2. Refer to the electrochemical cell below to answer each of the following questions.

$$Zn|Zn^{2+}||Pb^{2+}|Pb$$

   a. At which electrode does oxidation occur?
   b. Which electrode is the cathode?
   c. Electrons will flow from which electrode?
   d. Which electrode will gain in mass?
   e. What is the oxidizing agent?
   f. Write the half-reaction for the zinc half-cell.
   g. What is the theoretical voltage on the meter?

3. Refer to the electrochemical cell below to answer each of the following questions.

$$Al|Al^{3+}||Au^{3+}|Au$$

   a. At which electrode does reduction occur?
   b. Which electrode is the anode?
   c. Which electrode will lose in mass?
   d. To which electrode will the cations migrate?
   e. What is the reducing agent?
   f. Write the half-reaction for the gold half-cell.
   g. What is the theoretical voltage on the meter?

# 27:3  FARADAY'S LAWS

Electrochemistry is the study of the relationship between chemical change and electric energy. Michael Faraday experimented extensively to determine the relationship between electric charge and chemical energy. The following statements are known as Faraday's laws.

1. The mass of an element released at the electrode during electrolysis varies directly as the quantity of electricity that is passed through a solution.

2. The quantity of different elements that can be deposited by the same amount of electricity depends on the equivalent masses of these elements. Chemists measure the quantity of electrons in moles. Electricity is measured in coulombs (C). One coulomb is the quantity of electricity in one ampere (A) flowing for one second. The relationship of all these quantities is

$$1 \text{ mole } e^- = 96\ 500 \text{ coulomb} = 1 \text{ ampere·second}$$

Thus 96 500 coulombs passing through molten $Al_2O_3$ will liberate 1/3 of an equivalent mass of aluminum (27.0 g) and 1/2 of an equivalent mass of oxygen (16.0 g).

$$96\ 500 \text{ C} = 9.0 \text{ g Al} = 1/3 \text{ mol Al} = 6.02 \times 10^{23} \ e^-$$
$$96\ 500 \text{ C} = 8.0 \text{ g O} = 1/2 \text{ mol O} = 6.02 \times 10^{23} \ e^-$$

## Example 3

How many grams of aluminum will be deposited if 31 500 coulombs of electricity pass through an aluminum nitrate solution?

**Solving Process:**

Begin with the balanced equation for the reaction.

$$Al^{3+} + 3e^- \rightarrow Al$$

Convert coulombs to moles of electrons, to moles, to grams.

$$\text{grams Al} = \frac{31\ 500\ \cancel{C}}{} \left| \frac{1\ \cancel{mole\ e^-}}{96\ 500\ \cancel{C}} \right| \frac{1\ \cancel{mol\ Al}}{3\ \cancel{mole\ e^-}} \left| \frac{27.0 \text{ g Al}}{1\ \cancel{mol\ Al}} \right. = 2.94 \text{ g}$$

## Example 4

If 10.0 amperes of current flow for 20.0 minutes through a solution of copper(II) nitrate, how many moles of copper are deposited?

**Solving Process:**

$$Cu^{2+} + 2e^- \rightarrow Cu$$

$$\text{mol Cu} = \frac{10.0\ \cancel{A}}{} \left| \frac{20.0\ \cancel{min}}{1\ \cancel{min}} \right| \frac{60\ \cancel{s}}{} \left| \frac{1\ \cancel{C}}{\cancel{A\cdot s}} \right| \frac{1\ \cancel{mole\ e^-}}{96\ 500\ \cancel{C}} \left| \frac{1 \text{ mol Cu}}{2\ \cancel{mol\ e^-}} \right.$$

$$= 0.0622 \text{ mol Cu}$$

## Example 5

Calculate the mass of silver metal that can be deposited if a 5.12 A current is passed through a silver nitrate solution for 2.00 hours. The equation for the reaction is $Ag^+ + e^- \rightarrow Ag$.

**Solving Process:**

Obtain ampere·seconds by converting hours to seconds and multiplying by the number of amperes given. Convert ampere·seconds to coulombs. Finally change to moles of electrons, to moles, to grams.

$$\text{grams Ag} = \frac{5.12\,A \mid 2.00\,h \mid 60\,min \mid 60\,s \mid 1\,C}{1\,h \mid 1\,min \mid A \cdot s}$$

$$\frac{1\,mol\,e^- \mid 1\,mol\,Ag \mid 108\,g\,Ag}{96\,500\,C \mid 1\,mol\,e^- \mid 1\,mol\,Ag} = 41.3\,g$$

## Example 6

How many cubic decimeters of chlorine gas measured at STP are released by the passage of 8.12 amperes for 2.00 hours through molten magnesium chloride?

**Solving Process:**

The equation would be $2Cl^- \rightarrow Cl_2 + 2e^-$.

$$\text{volume Cl}_2 = \frac{8.12\,A \mid 2.00\,h \mid 60\,min \mid 60\,s \mid 1\,C}{1\,h \mid 1\,min \mid A \cdot s}$$

$$\frac{1\,mol\,e^- \mid 1\,mol\,Cl_2 \mid 22.4\,dm^3\,Cl_2}{96\,500\,C \mid 2\,mol\,e^- \mid 1\,mol\,Cl_2} = 6.79\,dm^3\,Cl_2$$

## PROBLEMS

4. How many seconds are required to deposit 2.51 g Fe on an object using 15.4 A of current passing through an iron(III) nitrate solution? The equation for the reaction is $Fe^{3+} + 3e^- \rightarrow Fe$.

5. How many amperes are required to deposit 0.504 g Fe in 40.0 minutes by passing a current through a solution of iron(II) acetate?

6. Calculate the current required to liberate 5.60 dm³ $Cl_2$ at STP in 2.00 hours in the electrolysis of molten NaCl.

7. During the operation of a lead storage battery, the reaction at the two electrodes is as follows:

cathode    $PbO_2 + 4H^+ + SO_4^{2-} + 2e^- \rightarrow PbSO_4 + 2H_2O$

anode      $Pb + SO_4^{2-} \rightarrow PbSO_4 + 2e^-$

How much $PbO_2$ (in grams) is used when a current of 50.0 A in 1 hour is withdrawn from the battery?

## CHAPTER REVIEW PROBLEMS

1. Calculate the positive or negative potential for each equation. Determine if the reactions will occur.

   a. $Ni(cr) + Cu^{2+}(aq) \rightarrow Ni^{2+}(aq) + Cu(cr)$
   b. $Cl^-(aq) + Br_2(l) \rightarrow Cl_2(g) + Br^-(aq)$
   c. $Cu(cr) + H^+(aq) \rightarrow Cu^{2+}(aq) + H_2(g)$
   d. $Mn(cr) + Co^{2+}(aq) \rightarrow Mn^{2+}(aq) + Co(cr)$
   e. $Zn^{2+}(aq) + Pb(cr) \rightarrow Zn(cr) + Pb^{2+}(aq)$

2. Determine the theoretical voltage for the following electrochemical cell.

$$Mn|Mn^{2+}||Fe^{2+}|Fe$$

3. Write the half-reaction that occurs at the anode in the following electrochemical cell.

$$Cr|Cr^{2+}||Sn^{2+}|Sn$$

4. How many moles of electrons are required to produce a 5.00 A current for 2.00 hours?

5. If 3.00 moles of electrons are required in producing 10.0 A of current, how many seconds are required?

6. What mass of copper is produced if 10 000.0 A·s pass through a copper(II) nitrate solution?

7. Calculate the grams of zinc deposited if 5.00 moles of electrons pass through a zinc acetate solution.

8. Using 2.50 moles of electrons how many grams of cadmium metal will be deposited from a cadmium sulfate solution?

9. If 193 000 coulombs of electricity pass through a silver nitrate solution, how many grams of silver metal are produced?

10. In the electrolysis of molten NaCl, how many moles of sodium metal are produced if 20.0 A of current flowing for 8.00 hours are used?

11. If it is necessary to deposit 1.50 g Ag on an object, how many seconds must 5.00 A of electricity flow through a solution of silver nitrate?

12. How many amperes of electricity flowing for 30.0 minutes are required to deposit 0.250 g Fe from an iron(III) nitrate solution?

# NUCLEAR CHEMISTRY      28

## 28:1    TYPES OF RADIATION

The reactions studied in preceding chapters involved alterations in the electronic structure of atoms. In chemical reactions, the atom's nucleus remains unchanged. In contrast, nuclear reactions change nuclei of atoms. The number of protons and/or neutrons in the nuclei may increase or decrease. One element may be converted into another element. Nuclear reactions are accompanied by a change in energy. The amount of energy involved is many times greater than the energy associated with chemical reactions.

Radioactive elements such as uranium, radium, and polonium have unstable nuclei. Particles are emitted from unstable nuclei as they undergo a process called **radioactive decay.** The decay process continues until a stable element is formed. Stable nuclei do not give off particles of radiation.

Radioactive elements may occur naturally in the earth, as in the case of uranium, radium, and polonium. Normally stable elements can be made radioactive in the laboratory by bombarding them with high speed neutrons or charged particles.

Naturally occurring radioactive material produces three types of radiation. Alpha and beta radiation are made up of particles. Gamma rays are quanta of energy.

**Alpha particles** ($\alpha$) are positively charged helium nuclei, each consisting of 2 protons and 2 neutrons. Each particle can be represented by the symbol $_2^4He$, in which the 2 represents the number of protons and the 4 represents the mass number.

**Beta particles** ($\beta$) are electrons represented by the symbol $_{-1}^0e$. The atomic number of each particle is $-1$ and the mass number is zero. Electrons do not exist in the nucleus as such but are produced when a neutron decays to form a proton.

$$_0^1n \rightarrow {}_1^1H + {}_{-1}^0e$$

When beta rays are emitted, the mass number of the nucleus remains the same, but the neutron/proton ratio is reduced.

**Gamma rays** ($\gamma$) possess neither mass nor charge but are quanta of energy similar to highly energetic X rays. Gamma rays are emitted when changes in the nucleus produce an excess of energy. Gamma radiation does not change the mass number or atomic number of the nucleus. The emission of excess energy brings the nucleus to a less excited, more stable state. Gamma rays travel at the speed of light.

Other types of radioactive particles can be emitted when nuclei are bombarded with charged particles or high-speed neutrons and made artificially radioactive. Examples of these particles include the following:

$^{1}_{1}H$    is a proton or hydrogen atom with $A = 1$ and $Z = 1$

$^{2}_{1}H$    is a deuteron or hydrogen isotope with $A = 2$ and $Z = 1$

$^{1}_{0}n$    is a neutron with $A = 1$ and $Z = 0$ (no electric charge)

$^{0}_{+1}e$    is a positron with $A = 0$ and $Z = 1$

$^{0}_{0}\upsilon$    is a neutrino with $A = 0$ and $Z = 0$

# 28:2  BALANCING NUCLEAR EQUATIONS

In balancing nuclear equations, two rules must be followed.

1. The sum of the mass numbers on the left side and the right side of the equation must be equal.
2. The sum of the electric charges on the left side and the right side of the equation must be equal.

Radioactive particles given off during nuclear reactions are included in these equations in order to balance them.

## Example 1

Complete the following nuclear equation.

$$^{208}_{84}Po \rightarrow ? + ^{4}_{2}He$$

**Solving Process:**

(a) Find the mass number of the unknown product. We know that the mass number is conserved in a nuclear reaction.

mass no. of 4 + mass no. of ? = 208
mass no. of ? = 208 − mass no. of 4
= 204

(b) Find the charge of the unknown product. We know that electric charge is conserved in a nuclear equation.

charge of 2 + charge of ? = 84
charge of ? = 84 − charge of 2
= 82

(c) Determine the identity of the unknown product and complete the nuclear equation. Turn to the periodic table and find which nuclide has an 82+ charge. This nuclide is lead, Pb. Thus, the completed nuclear equation is

$$^{208}_{84}Po \rightarrow ^{204}_{82}Pb + ^{4}_{2}He$$

## PROBLEMS

1. Using the periodic table, write nuclear symbols for the isotopes.
   a. lead-208
   b. lead-210
   c. uranium-235
   d. carbon-14
   e. helium-5
   f. potassium-40
   g. lithium-8
   h. uranium-238

2. Complete and balance the following equations.
   a. $^7_3\text{Li} + ^1_1\text{H} \rightarrow ^4_2\text{He} + ?$
   b. $^3_1\text{H} + ^2_1\text{H} \rightarrow ? + ^1_0n$
   c. $^{14}_6\text{C} \rightarrow ^{14}_7\text{N} + ?$
   d. $^9_4\text{Be} + ^4_2\text{He} \rightarrow ^{12}_6\text{C} + ?$
   e. $^{14}_7\text{N} + ^4_2\text{He} \rightarrow ? + ^0_{+1}e$
   f. $^{26}_{12}\text{Mg} + ^1_0n \rightarrow ? + ^0_{+1}e$
   g. $^{59}_{27}\text{Co} + ^2_1\text{H} \rightarrow ? + ^0_{+1}e$

3. In a portion of the uranium decay series, lead-214 decays to bismuth-214 by beta emission. The bismuth-214 decays to polonium-214 by beta emission. The polonium-214 decays to lead-210 by alpha emission. Write balanced nuclear equations to represent these three steps.

# 28:3  HALF-LIFE

In a nuclear reaction, one element is changed into another element when there is a change in the number of protons in the nucleus. This process, called **transmutation,** can be natural or artificial. Transmutation continues until a stable element, whose nucleus is not radioactive, is produced. The time required for half of a sample of a radioactive isotope to decay is termed its **half-life.** Half-lives of some isotopes are only a fraction of a second. For others, the half-life may be millions or billions of years.

**Table 28-1**

| Half-Life and Decay Mode of Selected Nuclides | | |
|---|---|---|
| **Nuclide** | **Half-Life** | **Decay Mode** |
| $^3_1\text{H}$ | 12.3 years | $\beta^-$ |
| $^6_2\text{He}$ | 0.802 seconds | $\beta^-$ |
| $^{14}_6\text{C}$ | 5730 years | $\beta^-$ |
| $^{19}_8\text{O}$ | 29.1 seconds | $\beta^-$ and $\gamma$ |
| $^{26}_{14}\text{Si}$ | 2.1 seconds | $\beta^+$ and $\gamma$ |
| $^{60}_{26}\text{Fe}$ | $3 \times 10^5$ years | $\beta^-$ |
| $^{71}_{30}\text{Zn}$ | 2.4 minutes | $\beta^-$ and $\gamma$ |
| $^{84}_{34}\text{Se}$ | 3.2 minutes | $\beta^-$ |
| $^{212}_{82}\text{Pb}$ | 10.6 hours | $\beta^-$ and $\gamma$ |
| $^{210}_{84}\text{Po}$ | 138 days | $\alpha$ |
| $^{227}_{92}\text{U}$ | 1.3 minutes | $\alpha$ and $\gamma$ |
| $^{235}_{92}\text{U}$ | $7.1 \times 10^8$ years | $\alpha$ and $\gamma$ |
| $^{238}_{92}\text{U}$ | $4.51 \times 10^9$ years | $\alpha$ and $\gamma$ |
| $^{236}_{94}\text{Pu}$ | 2.85 years | $\alpha$ and $\gamma$ |
| $^{242}_{94}\text{Pu}$ | $3.79 \times 10^5$ years | $\alpha$ |

The half-life of one isotope of zinc, $^{71}_{30}$Zn, is 2.4 minutes. Suppose we begin with 10.0 g of this isotope. At the end of 2.4 minutes, 5.0 g $^{71}_{30}$Zn would remain. The rest of the 10.0 g sample would have decayed to gallium. At the end of another 2.4 minutes, 2.5 g $^{71}_{30}$Zn would remain. After the third 2.4 minutes, the original 10.0 g sample would contain 1.25 g of the zinc isotope. The other 8.75 g $^{71}_{30}$Zn would have decayed to gallium.

## Example 2

Cobalt-60 is used in cancer radiation therapy. If you start with 4.516 × $10^8$ atoms of $^{60}_{27}$Co, how much time will pass before the amount is reduced to 1.764 × $10^6$ atoms? The half-life is 5.26 years.
**Solving Process:**
(a) Divide the original amount by the present amount to obtain a ratio of atoms.

$$\frac{4.516 \times 10^8 \text{ atoms}}{1.764 \times 10^6 \text{ atoms}} = \frac{256 \text{ original atoms}}{1 \text{ remaining atom}}$$

(b) Determine the number of half-lives, where $n$ is the number of half-lives.

$$2^n = 256$$
$$n(\log 2) = \log 256$$
$$n = \frac{\log 256}{\log 2}$$
$$= 8 \text{ half-lives}$$

(c) Calculate the amount of time that will pass.

$$\text{elapsed time} = \frac{5.26 \text{ y}}{\text{half-life}} \left| \frac{8 \text{ half-lives}}{} \right. = 42.1 \text{ years}$$

## Example 3

Strontium-90 is present in nuclear fallout. Because it is in the same family as calcium, it can be found in milk and later, bones. If you start with 1.94 × $10^{17}$ atoms of $^{90}_{38}$Sr, how many atoms will remain after 140.5 years? The half-life of $^{90}_{38}$Sr is 28.1 years.
**Solving Process:**
number of remaining atoms = number of original atoms × $1/2^n$
(a) Divide 140.5 years by 28.1 years to find the number of half-lives.

$$\frac{140.5 \text{ y}}{28.1 \text{ y/half-life}} = 5.00 \text{ half-lives}$$

**(b)** To determine the ratio of remaining atoms to original atoms, use $1/2^n$ where $n$ is the number of half-lives.

$$\frac{\text{remaining atoms}}{\text{original atoms}} = \frac{1}{2^n} = \frac{1}{2^5} = \frac{1}{32}$$

Only one atom remains for every 32 original atoms.

**(c)** Multiply the original number of atoms by 1/32.

$$(1.94 \times 10^{17} \text{ atoms}) (1/32) = 6.06 \times 10^{15} \text{ atoms}$$

Thus after 140.5 years, $6.06 \times 10^{15}$ atoms of radioactive $^{90}_{38}\text{Sr}$ remain.

## PROBLEMS

4. The half-life of $^{71}_{30}\text{Zn}$ is 2.4 minutes. How long will it take for a sample of zinc-71 to decay to 1/16 its original mass?

5. A radioactive tracer, sodium-24, is used to study circulatory problems. If you start with $5.85 \times 10^{23}$ atoms, how many atoms will remain after 12.0 days? The half-life of $^{24}_{11}\text{Na}$ is 4.0 days.

6. Some patients with thyroid disorders receive radioactive iodine-131. The half-life of $^{131}_{53}\text{I}$ is 8.07 days. If you start with $7.73 \times 10^{12}$ atoms, how much time will pass before the amount is reduced to $7.55 \times 10^9$ atoms?

## CHAPTER REVIEW PROBLEMS

1. Complete the following nuclear equations. Indicate the new element formed during these reactions. Name the nuclear particle emitted.
   a. $^{22}_{11}\text{Na} \rightarrow ? + ^{0}_{-1}e$    c. $^{208}_{84}\text{Po} \rightarrow ? + ^{4}_{2}\text{He}$
   b. $^{66}_{29}\text{Cu} \rightarrow ? + ^{0}_{-1}e$    d. $^{27}_{14}\text{Si} \rightarrow ? + ^{0}_{+1}e$

2. Complete the following nuclear equations.
   a. $^{27}_{13}\text{Al} + ^{2}_{1}\text{H} \rightarrow ? + ^{4}_{2}\text{He}$
   b. $? + ^{1}_{0}n \rightarrow ^{42}_{19}\text{K} + ^{4}_{2}\text{He}$
   c. $^{63}_{29}\text{Cu} + ^{1}_{1}\text{H} \rightarrow ^{63}_{30}\text{Zn} + ?$
   d. $^{1}_{0}n + ? \rightarrow ^{136}_{53}\text{I} + ^{96}_{39}\text{Y} + 4^{1}_{0}n$

3. Batteries used in heart pacemakers contain plutonium-238. If your original sample contains $2.57 \times 10^9$ atoms of $^{238}_{94}\text{Pu}$, how much time will pass before the amount is reduced to $5.02 \times 10^6$ atoms. The half-life is 27.1 years.

4. Carbon-14 has a half-life of 5730 years and is used for radioactive dating. Assume we started with $2.18 \times 10^{17}$ atoms of $^{14}_{6}\text{C}$ in a wood sample obtained from a wooden beam from an ancient tomb. There are $1.21 \times 10^{17}$ atoms remaining. How old can we assume the wooden beam to be?

5. Promethium-147 has a half-life of 2.5 years and is used to paint luminous dials. If a sample originally contains $9.72 \times 10^{23}$ atoms of $^{147}_{61}Pm$, how many atoms will remain after 10.0 years?

# CLASSES OF ORGANIC COMPOUNDS  29

## 29:1  HYDROCARBONS

**Organic compounds** are compounds that contain carbon atoms linked together in chains or rings. **Hydrocarbons** are compounds that contain carbon and hydrogen. They are the simplest organic compounds. Hydrocarbons may be grouped into families. In some of these families, all the carbon-carbon bonds are single bonds. These compounds are said to be **saturated.** In other families, the compounds contain double or triple bonds and are **unsaturated.**

## 29:2  ALKANES

**Alkanes** are saturated hydrocarbons conforming to the general formula $C_nH_{2n+2}$, where $n$ is a whole number equal to the number of carbon atoms. The alkane series is also termed the methane or paraffin series. The simplest alkanes are

$CH_4$
methane

$$H—\overset{\displaystyle H}{\underset{\displaystyle H}{\overset{|}{\underset{|}{C}}}}—H$$

$CH_3CH_3$
ethane

$$H—\overset{\displaystyle H}{\underset{\displaystyle H}{\overset{|}{\underset{|}{C}}}}—\overset{\displaystyle H}{\underset{\displaystyle H}{\overset{|}{\underset{|}{C}}}}—H$$

$CH_3CH_2CH_3$
propane

$$H—\overset{\displaystyle H}{\underset{\displaystyle H}{\overset{|}{\underset{|}{C}}}}—\overset{\displaystyle H}{\underset{\displaystyle H}{\overset{|}{\underset{|}{C}}}}—\overset{\displaystyle H}{\underset{\displaystyle H}{\overset{|}{\underset{|}{C}}}}—H$$

The first formula is a condensed structural formula. The second formula is an expanded structural formula.

Table 29-1 lists the stem name for each number of carbon atoms in a continuous chain or ring. It also gives some information about the alkanes of low molecular mass.

Table 29-1

| Alkanes | | | | |
|---|---|---|---|---|
| Stem Name | Alkane Name | Condensed Structural Formula (unbranched) | Chemical Formula | Number of Isomers |
| meth- | methane | $CH_4$ | $CH_4$ | 1 |
| eth- | ethane | $CH_3CH_3$ | $C_2H_6$ | 1 |
| prop- | propane | $CH_3CH_2CH_3$ | $C_3H_8$ | 1 |
| but- | butane | $CH_3(CH_2)_2CH_3$ | $C_4H_{10}$ | 2 |
| pent- | pentane | $CH_3(CH_2)_3CH_3$ | $C_5H_{12}$ | 3 |
| hex- | hexane | $CH_3(CH_2)_4CH_3$ | $C_6H_{14}$ | 5 |
| hept- | heptane | $CH_3(CH_2)_5CH_3$ | $C_7H_{16}$ | 9 |
| oct- | octane | $CH_3(CH_2)_6CH_3$ | $C_8H_{18}$ | 18 |
| non- | nonane | $CH_3(CH_2)_7CH_3$ | $C_9H_{20}$ | 35 |
| dec- | decane | $CH_3(CH_2)_8CH_3$ | $C_{10}H_{22}$ | 75 |

With $C_4H_{10}$, the carbon atoms may be connected to give two different structural formulas. These two arrangements are **isomers.** Isomers have the same chemical formula but different structural formulas.

# 29:3   RULES FOR NAMING HYDROCARBONS

The following rules are used to name hydrocarbons.

1. Pick the longest continuous chain of carbon atoms and determine its name.
2. Number the carbon atoms in the chain beginning at the end that will give the lowest possible numbers for the different attached hydrocarbon groups.
3. Name the hydrocarbon groups attached to the longest chain by adding -*yl* to the stem name. Indicate the point of attachment by the number of the carbon atom to which the group is attached. Common group names are meth*yl*, —$CH_3$, and eth*yl*, —$CH_2CH_3$.

For example, consider the following compound.

$$CH_3\overline{\rule{0pt}{1em}}CH-CH_2-CH_2-CH_3$$
$$\phantom{CH_3}\underset{\displaystyle CH_3}{\underset{|}{\overline{\rule{0pt}{1em}CH_2}}}$$

The longest chain, which consists of six carbon atoms, is enclosed in a box. A chain of six carbon atoms is termed *hexane*. The carbon atoms in the longest chain are numbered in such a way as to give the lowest number possible to the attached group. At position 3 the attached group is termed *methyl*. The name of the compound is 3-methylhexane. Note that position numbers are separated from the name by hyphens.

The $C_4H_{10}$ isomers we discussed previously are named butane and 2-methylpropane. The following are the isomers of pentane.

$$CH_3CH_2CH_2CH_2CH_3 \qquad \underset{\text{2-methylbutane}}{CH_3\underset{|}{\overset{CH_3}{\overset{|}{C}}}HCH_2CH_3} \qquad \underset{\text{2,2-dimethylpropane}}{\overset{CH_3}{\underset{CH_3}{\underset{|}{CH_3\overset{|}{C}CH_3}}}}$$

pentane

Note that the position numbers are separated from each other by commas. The following are the isomers of hexane.

$$\underset{\text{hexane}}{CH_3CH_2CH_2CH_2CH_2CH_3} \qquad \underset{\text{2-methylpentane}}{CH_3\overset{\overset{\displaystyle CH_3}{|}}{C}HCH_2CH_2CH_3} \qquad \underset{\text{3-methylpentane}}{CH_3CH_2\overset{\overset{\displaystyle CH_3}{|}}{C}HCH_2CH_3}$$

$$\underset{\text{2,3-dimethylbutane}}{CH_3\overset{\overset{\displaystyle CH_3}{|}}{C}H-\overset{\overset{\displaystyle CH_3}{|}}{C}HCH_3} \qquad \underset{\text{2,2-dimethylbutane}}{\overset{\overset{\displaystyle CH_3}{|}}{\underset{\underset{\displaystyle CH_3}{|}}{CH_3CCH_2CH_3}}}$$

4. When two or more groups are attached to a compound, the groups are named in alphabetical order. Consider the following example.

$$CH_3-\overset{\overset{\displaystyle CH_3}{|}}{C}H-CH-CH_2-\overset{\overset{\displaystyle CH_3}{|}}{C}H-CH_2-CH_3$$
$$\phantom{CH_3-CH-}\underset{\displaystyle CH_3}{\underset{|}{CH_2}}$$

3-ethyl-2,5-dimethylheptane

The longest continuous chain of carbon atoms is named heptane. The branched groups are ethyl and methyl. Since there are two methyl groups the prefix *di-* is used to indicate this number.

## PROBLEMS

**1.** Name the following hydrocarbons.

a.
$$
\begin{array}{c}
\qquad\qquad CH_3 \\
\qquad\qquad | \\
CH_3-CH_2-CH-CH-CH_3 \\
\qquad\qquad\quad | \\
\qquad\qquad\quad CH_2 \\
\qquad\qquad\quad | \\
\qquad\qquad\quad CH_3
\end{array}
$$

b.
$$
\begin{array}{c}
\qquad\quad CH_3 \\
\qquad\quad | \\
CH_3\ \ CH_2 \\
\ \ |\qquad | \\
CH_3-C\!-\!-\!-CH-CH_3 \\
\ \ | \\
\ \ CH_3
\end{array}
$$

c.
$$
\begin{array}{c}
\quad CH_3 \\
\quad | \\
CH_3-C-CH_3 \\
\quad | \\
\quad CH_2 \\
\quad | \\
\quad CH_3
\end{array}
$$

d.
$$
\begin{array}{c}
\qquad\qquad\ CH_2-CH_2-CH_3 \\
\qquad\qquad\ | \\
CH_3-CH_2-C-CH_2-CH_3 \\
\qquad\qquad\ | \\
\qquad\qquad\ CH_2-CH_3
\end{array}
$$

e.
$$
\begin{array}{c}
\qquad\qquad\qquad CH_3 \\
\qquad\qquad\qquad | \\
CH_3\qquad\qquad CH_2 \\
\ \ |\qquad\qquad\quad | \\
CH_3-CH-CH-CH-CH_3 \\
\qquad\qquad\ | \\
\qquad\qquad\ CH_3
\end{array}
$$

f.
$$
\begin{array}{c}
\qquad\qquad\qquad\qquad CH_3 \\
\qquad\qquad\qquad\qquad | \\
\qquad\qquad CH_3\qquad\ CH_2 \\
\qquad\qquad\ |\qquad\qquad | \\
CH_3-CH_2-CH-CH-CH-CH_3 \\
\qquad\qquad\qquad\ | \\
\qquad\qquad\qquad\ CH_3
\end{array}
$$

g.
$$
\begin{array}{c}
\qquad\quad CH_3 \\
\qquad\quad | \\
\qquad\quad CH_2 \\
\qquad\quad | \\
CH_3-CH-CH-CH_3 \\
\qquad\qquad\ | \\
\qquad\qquad\ CH-CH_2-CH_3 \\
\qquad\qquad\ | \\
\qquad\qquad\ CH_3
\end{array}
$$

h.
$$
\begin{array}{c}
\qquad\qquad CH_2-CH_3 \\
\qquad\qquad | \\
CH_3-CH-CH-CH_3 \\
\ \ | \\
CH_3-CH-CH_3
\end{array}
$$

**2.** Name the following hydrocarbons.

a.
$$
\begin{array}{c}
\qquad\qquad\ CH_3 \\
\qquad\qquad\ | \\
CH_3CH_2CH_2CHCH_3
\end{array}
$$

b.
$$
\begin{array}{c}
\quad CH_3 \\
\quad | \\
CH_3CHCH_2CH_3
\end{array}
$$

c.
$$
\begin{array}{c}
\quad CH_3 \\
\quad | \\
CH_3CHCHCH_3 \\
\qquad\ | \\
\qquad\ CH_2CH_3
\end{array}
$$

d.
$$
\begin{array}{c}
CH_3CH_2CHCH_2CH_3 \\
\qquad\quad | \\
\qquad\quad CH_2 \\
\qquad\quad | \\
\qquad\quad CH_3
\end{array}
$$

e.
$$
\begin{array}{c}
\ \ CH_3\qquad CH_3 \\
\ \ |\qquad\qquad | \\
CH_3CHCH_2CHCH_3
\end{array}
$$

f.
$$
\begin{array}{c}
\qquad\ CH_3 \\
\qquad\ | \\
CH_3CH\ CHCH_2CH_3 \\
\qquad\quad | \\
\qquad\quad CH_3
\end{array}
$$

g. $CH_3CHCH_2CH_3$
   |
   $CH_2$
   |
   $CH_3$

$CH_3$
|
$CH_2$
|
h. $CH_3CHCHCH_3$
          |
          $CH_3$

3. Listed below are the condensed structural formulas or names of the nine isomers of heptane, $C_7H_{16}$. Write either the formula or name for each.

   a. $CH_3CH_2CH_2CH_2CH_2CH_2CH_3$

   b. $CH_3CHCH_2CHCH_3$
          |          |
          $CH_3$    $CH_3$

   c. $CH_3C$———$CHCH_3$
          |          |
          $CH_3$    $CH_3$

   d. 2,3-dimethylpentane

   e. 3,3-dimethylpentane

   f. $CH_3CH_2CHCH_2CH_2CH_3$
                |
                $CH_3$

   g. $CH_3CCH_2CH_2CH_3$
          |
          $CH_3$
          |
          $CH_3$

   h. 2-methylhexane

   i. 3-ethylpentane

# 29:4  CYCLOALKANES

The cycloalkanes are saturated ring compounds having the general formula $C_nH_{2n}$. The following are some examples of cycloalkanes:

$C_3H_6$
cyclopropane

$CH_2$—$CH_2$
   \     /
    $CH_2$

$C_5H_{10}$
methlyclobutane

$CH_2$—$CH$—$CH_3$
|          |
$CH_2$—$CH_2$

$C_4H_8$
cyclobutane

$CH_2$—$CH_2$
|          |
$CH_2$—$CH_2$

$C_4H_8$
methylcyclopropane

$CH_3$
|
$CH$
/    \
$CH_2$—$CH_2$

$C_5H_{10}$
cyclopentane

$CH_2$
/      \
$CH_2$  $CH_2$
|          |
$CH_2$— $CH_2$

$C_5H_{10}$
1,1-dimethylcyclopropane

$CH_2$—$CH_2$
   \     /
    $C$
   /   \
$CH_3$  $CH_3$

## 29:5  ALKENES

Alkenes are unsaturated compounds containing one double bond and having the general formula $C_nH_{2n}$. The -ene ending indicates a double bond. The position of the double bond is indicated by using the lower number of the two carbon atoms that the double bond joins. In compounds containing branched groups, the numbering of the double bond takes precedence. Note the following examples.

$$CH_2{=}CH_2 \qquad CH_3CH{=}CH_2 \qquad CH_3CH{=}CHCH_3$$
$$\text{ethene} \qquad\qquad \text{propene} \qquad\qquad \text{2-butene}$$

$$\begin{array}{c} CH_3 \\ | \\ CH_3CH_2C{=}CH_2 \end{array} \qquad \begin{array}{c} CH_3CHCH{=}CH_2 \\ | \\ CH_3 \end{array}$$
$$\text{2-methyl-1-butene} \qquad\qquad \text{3-methyl-1-butene}$$

If a compound contains more than one double bond, the numbers of double bonds are noted with a Greek prefix preceding the -ene ending. For example,

$$CH_2{=}CHCH_2CH{=}CH_2 \qquad CH_2{=}CHCH{=}CH_2 \qquad CH_2{=}C{=}CHCH_2CH_3$$
$$\text{1,4-pentadiene} \qquad\qquad \text{1,3-butadiene} \qquad\qquad \text{1,2-pentadiene}$$

## 29:6  ALKYNES

Alkynes contain a triple bond and have the general formula $C_nH_{2n-2}$. They are named by replacing the -ane of the corresponding saturated hydrocarbon with -yne, except for the first compound in the series, for which the common name is used.

$$HC{\equiv}CH \qquad\qquad CH_3{-}C{\equiv}C{-}CH_3$$
$$\text{acetylene} \qquad\qquad \text{2-butyne}$$
$$\text{(ethyne)}$$

**Table 29-2**

| Hydrocarbon Summary | | | |
|---|---|---|---|
| Family | Formula | Prefix or Suffix | Type of Compound |
| alkanes | $C_nH_{2n+2}$ | -ane | single bonds, saturated |
| cycloalkanes | $C_nH_{2n}$ | cyclo- | ring structure, saturated |
| alkenes | $C_nH_{2n}$ | -ene | double bond, unsaturated |
| alkynes | $C_nH_{2n-2}$ | -yne | triple bond, unsaturated |

## 29:7  AROMATIC HYDROCARBONS

All aromatic hydrocarbons contain one or more rings of carbon atoms held together by delocalized electrons. The compounds are named as derivatives of basic ring systems. Consider the ring structure of benzene. All positions on the benzene ring are equivalent.

benzene

Thus, only one monosubstituted compound is possible. The following are examples of monosubstituted aromatic hydrocarbons.

methylbenzene
(toluene)

ethylbenzene

propylbenzene

For two substituents on the benzene ring three positions are possible. These positions may be designated by numbers or names, although the use of numbers is more correct.

| position number | name |
|---|---|
| 1,2 | ortho- (o-) |
| 1,3 | meta- (m-) |
| 1,4 | para- (p-) |

Disubstituted aromatic hydrocarbons include the following.

| 1,2-dimethylbenzene | 1,3-dimethylbenzene | 1,4-dimethylbenzene |
|---|---|---|
| (ortho-dimethylbenzene) | (meta-dimethylbenzene) | (para-dimethylbenzene) |

Thousands of compounds are derived from benzene or other ring systems. These other rings may be considered to be fused benzene rings. Two examples of fused rings are naphthalene, $C_{10}H_8$, and anthracene, $C_{14}H_{10}$.

naphthalene

anthracene

The radical —$C_6H_5$, which is the benzene ring with one less hydrogen, is termed the **phenyl radical.** Note the following examples.

CH$_3$CHCH$_2$CH$_3$

phenyl radical

−CH$_2$CH$_3$

ethylbenzene
(phenylethane)

2-phenylbutane

2-acetyloxybenzoic acid
(acetylsalicyclic acid or aspirin)

styrene

2,4,6-trinitrotoluene
(TNT)

dichlorodiphenyltrichloroethane
(DDT)

## PROBLEMS

**4.** Name the compounds represented by the following formulas.

**a.** CH$_3$CH=CHCH$_2$CH$_3$    **c.**    **e.**

**b.**    −CH$_3$ −CH$_3$    **d.**    −C≡CH    **f.** CH≡CCH$_3$

**5.** Draw the structural formulas for the following:
**a.** 3-heptyne               **d.** 1,3-butadiene
**b.** cyclopentene            **e.** 1-ethyl-2-methylbenzene
**c.** 3-phenyl-2,2-dimethylhexane  **f.** 2,4-dimethyl-2-pentene

# 29:8   HALOGEN DERIVATIVES OF HYDROCARBONS

By replacing a hydrogen atom with a halogen atom (—F, *fluoro;* —Cl, *chloro;* —Br, *bromo;* and —I, *iodo*) on a hydrocarbon, additional isomers are possible. When naming these alkyl halides, the longest chain must contain the halogen-bearing carbon that is given the lowest possible number. For example,

$$CH_3CH_2CH_2Cl$$
1-chloropropane

$$\overset{\displaystyle Cl}{\underset{\displaystyle |}{}}\,\overset{\displaystyle CH_3}{\underset{\displaystyle |}{}}$$
$$CH_3CH_2CHCHCH_2CH_3$$
3-chloro-4-methylhexane

2,2-dibromo-3-ethylheptane

2,2-dichloro-5-ethyl-6-methylheptane

1,4-dibromobenzene

1,3-dichloronaphthalene

## PROBLEMS

6. Listed below are the condensed structural formulas or the names of the eight isomers of $C_5H_{11}Cl$. Write either the formula or the name for each.

a. $CH_3CH_2CH_2CH_2CH_2Cl$

b. $CH_3\overset{\displaystyle CH_3}{\underset{\displaystyle |}{C}}HCH_2CH_2Cl$

c. 2-chloropentane

d. 2-chloro-2-methylbutane

e. $CH_3CH_2\overset{\displaystyle Cl}{\underset{\displaystyle |}{C}}HCH_2CH_3$

f. $CH_3\overset{\displaystyle CH_3}{\underset{\displaystyle |}{C}}H—\overset{\displaystyle Cl}{\underset{\displaystyle |}{C}}HCH_3$

g. 1-chloro-2-methylbutane

h. 1-chloro-2,2-dimethylpropane

**7.** Name the following compounds.

a. $CH_3CH_2\overset{\overset{\displaystyle CH_3}{|}}{C}CH_2CH_2Br$
$\overset{\overset{\displaystyle }{|}}{CH_2}$
$\overset{\overset{\displaystyle }{|}}{CH_3}$

h. $CH_3\overset{\overset{\displaystyle CH_3}{|}}{C}HCH=CHCH_3$

i. $CH_3\overset{\overset{\displaystyle CH_3}{|}}{C}=\overset{\overset{\displaystyle CH_3}{|}}{C}CH_2CH_3$

b. $CH_2=CH\overset{\overset{\displaystyle CH_3}{|}}{C}HCH=CH_2$

j. $CH_2=\overset{\overset{\displaystyle CH_3}{|}}{C}CH_2\overset{\overset{\displaystyle CH_3}{|}}{C}=CH_2$

c. $CH_2=CH\overset{\overset{\displaystyle CH_3}{|}}{\underset{\underset{\displaystyle CH_3}{|}}{C}}CH_3$

k. $CH_2=\overset{\overset{\displaystyle CH_3}{|}}{C}-\overset{\overset{\displaystyle CH_3}{|}}{\underset{\underset{\displaystyle CH_3}{|}}{C}}-CH=CHCH_3$

d. $C_6H_5Cl$

e. $CH_3CH=CHCH_2CH_3$

f. $CH_3\overset{\overset{\displaystyle CH_3}{|}}{C}=CHCH_3$

g. $CH_3CH_2CH=CH_2$

l.

**8.** Draw structural formulas for the following.
a. 3-heptene
b. 2-methylnaphthalene
c. trichloromethane
d. 2-chloro-3-phenylhexane
e. 1,3-cyclopentadiene
f. toluene (methylbenzene)
g. 1,4-dibromobenzene
h. 2-bromo-3-methyl-2-butene

# 29:9  HYDROXY COMPOUNDS

The hydroxy compounds, or alcohols, have a **hydroxyl group,** —OH, attached to the alkyl group. They are named by dropping the -e of the alkane series and adding -ol. If the hydroxyl group is attached to an aromatic group, the compound is called a **phenol.** Consider the following examples.

$CH_3OH$          $CH_3CH_2OH$          $CH_3CH_2CH_2OH$
methanol          ethanol               1-propanol

$CH_3\overset{\overset{\displaystyle }{}}{\underset{\underset{\displaystyle OH}{|}}{C}}HCH_3$          $CH_3CH_2CH_2CH_2OH$          $CH_3\overset{\overset{\displaystyle }{}}{C}HCH_2CH_3$
2-propanol          1-butanol          $\overset{\displaystyle OH}{}$
                                        2-butanol

$CH_3\overset{\overset{\displaystyle }{}}{C}HCH_2OH$          $CH_3\overset{\overset{\displaystyle CH_3}{|}}{\underset{\underset{\displaystyle OH}{|}}{C}}CH_3$
$\overset{\displaystyle CH_3}{|}$
2-methyl-1-propanol          2-methyl-2-propanol

phenol                3-bromophenol            2-hydroxynaphthalene
                                                (2-naphthol)

## 29:10  CARBOXYLIC ACIDS

All organic acids have the functional group

$$-C\begin{matrix} \nearrow O \\ \searrow OH \end{matrix}$$

which is called the **carboxyl group.** The carboxylic acid group is usually written as —COOH. The carbon of this group is considered the first carbon of the chain in naming compounds. The -*e* in the chain name is dropped and -*oic* plus the word *acid* is added. The common names are given in parenthesis.

HCOOH              $CH_3COOH$           $(CH_3)_2CHCOOH$
methanoic acid      ethanoic acid        2-methylpropanoic acid
(formic acid)       (acetic acid)

benzoic acid            4-bromobenzoic acid        2-hydroxybenzoic acid

## 29:11  ALDEHYDES

The functional group characteristic of aldehydes is

$$-C\begin{matrix} \nearrow O \\ \searrow H \end{matrix}$$

These compounds are named by dropping the -e and adding -al to the chain name. The aldehyde carbon is given the number 1 in naming.

HCHO          CH₃CHO      CH₃CH₂CHO
methanal       ethanal        propanal
(formaldehyde)

CH₃CH₂CH₂CHO     (CH₃)₂CHCHO

butanal          2-methylpropanal       benzaldehyde

## 29:12   KETONES

Ketones contain the functional group

$$\diagdown\text{C}{=}\text{O}\diagup$$

These compounds have the ending -one. The functional group is given the lowest possible number.

propanone       2-butanone       3-pentanone
(acetone)

2-pentanone     3-methyl-2-butanone     1-phenylethanone

diphenylmethanone

## 29:13   ESTERS

Esters contain the group

and are formed from organic acids. The -ic of the acid name is dropped and the ending -ate is added. The alkyl group replacing the hydrogen atom in the carboxyl group is named first as a separate word.

$$CH_3CH_2 \overset{\overset{O}{\|}}{C} -OCH_2CH_3 \qquad CH_3 \overset{\overset{O}{\|}}{C} -OCH_2CH_3$$

ethyl propanoate               ethyl 2-methylpropanoate

$$CH_3CH_2 \overset{\overset{O}{\|}}{C} -O \overset{\overset{CH_3}{|}}{C} HCH_3 \qquad \overset{\overset{O}{\|}}{C} -OCH_3$$

2-methylethyl propanoate           methyl benzoate

## 29:14   ETHERS

Ethers have the general formula R—O—R in which an oxygen atom is joined to two separate hydrocarbon groups. Ethers are named as *oxy*-derivatives of hydrocarbons.

$$CH_3-O-CH_2CH_3 \qquad CH_3CH_2CH_2-O-CH_2CH_3 \qquad CH_3-O-C_6H_5$$

methoxyethane           1-ethoxypropane           methoxybenzene

**Table 29-3**

| Organic Compounds Containing Oxygen | | | |
|---|---|---|---|
| Compound | General Formula* | Characteristic Group | Ending |
| Alcohol | R—OH | —OH | -ol |
| Carboxylic Acid | $R-\overset{\overset{O}{/\!/}}{\underset{\backslash}{}}_{OH}$ | $-\overset{\overset{O}{/\!/}}{\underset{\backslash}{}}_{OH}$ | -oic acid |
| Aldehyde | $R-\overset{\overset{O}{/\!/}}{\underset{\backslash}{C}}_{H}$ | $-\overset{\overset{O}{/\!/}}{\underset{\backslash}{C}}_{H}$ | -al |
| Ketone | $R-\overset{\overset{O}{\|}}{C}-R$ | $-\overset{\overset{O}{\|}}{C}-$ | -one |
| Ester | $R-\overset{\overset{O}{\|}}{C}-O-R$ | $-\overset{\overset{O}{\|}}{C}-O-$ | -ate |
| Ether | R—O—R | —O— | -oxy- |
| *R represents any alkyl group such as -CH₃, methyl; -CH₃CH₂, ethyl; etc. | | | |

# 29:15   NITROGEN CONTAINING COMPOUNDS

Amines are organic compounds containing nitrogen. Amines are derivatives of ammonia. One, two, or three of the hydrogens in ammonia can be replaced with an alkyl group. General formulas for amines are

Nitrogen group substituted chains should be numbered so that the carbon attached to the nitrogen has the lowest possible number. The following table lists other classes of nitrogen containing organic compounds.

**Table 29-4**

| Organic Compounds Containing Nitrogen | | |
|---|---|---|
| **Compound** | **General Formula*** | **Example** |
| Amines | $R{-}NH_2$ | $CH_3CH_2NH_2$   ethylamine |
| Amides | $\overset{\displaystyle O}{\overset{\displaystyle \|}{R{-}C{-}NH_2}}$ | $CH_3CONH_2$   ethanamide |
| Amino acids | $\overset{\displaystyle NH_2}{\overset{\displaystyle \|}{G{-}CH{-}COOH}}$ | $CH_3CH(NH_2)COOH$   alanine (2-aminopropanoic acid) |
| Nitriles | $R{-}C{\equiv}N$ | $CH_3CH_2CH_2CN$   butanenitrile |
| Nitro compounds | $R{-}NO_2$ | $C_6H_5NO_2$   nitrobenzene |

*R represents any alkyl group such as —CH₃, methyl; CH₃CH₂—, ethyl and so on. G can represent a group made up of elements other than just carbon and hydrogen.

## CHAPTER REVIEW PROBLEMS

1. Write structural formulas for the following compounds.
   a. 2-chlorobutane
   b. 2-butene
   c. 2-ethyl-3-methyl-1-butanol
   d. 3,3-dimethylbutanoic acid
   e. 2,5,5-trimethyl-4-heptone
   f. 1,8-nonadiyne
   g. 1,3-diiodobenzene
   h. ethoxybenzene
   i. 1-butanol
   j. 3-methyl-2-pentene

**k.** 2-ethyl-4-methylpentanal
**l.** 3-ethyl-2,4-dimethyl-3-hexanol
**m.** 5-chloro-3-ethyl-2-methylheptanoic acid
**n.** 2-phenylbutane
**o.** 7-bromo-2-naphthol
**p.** 4-bromobenzoic acid

**2.** Name the following organic compounds.

**a.** $CH_3CH\!-\!CHCH_2CH_3$
    |   |
   $CH_3$ $OH$

**b.** $CH_3CH_2\overset{\displaystyle O}{\overset{\displaystyle \|}{C}}CHCH_3$
      |
     $CH_3$

**c.** $CH_3CHCH\!=\!CH_2$
    |
   $CH_3$

**d.** $CH_3CH_2CH_2C\overset{\displaystyle O}{\diagup}$
         $\diagdown$
          $H$

**e.** $CH_3\overset{\displaystyle CH_3}{\underset{\displaystyle CH_3}{C}}CH_2CH_2CH_2OH$

**f.** $CH_2\!=\!CHC\overset{\displaystyle CH_3}{\underset{\displaystyle OH}{C}}CH\!=\!CHCH_3$

**3.** Name the following organic compounds.

**a.** $CH_3CH_2CHCH_2Cl$
     |
    $CH_3$

**b.** $CH_3\overset{\displaystyle CH_3}{\underset{\displaystyle CH_3}{C}}\!-\!\overset{}{\underset{\displaystyle CH_3}{C}}HCH_2Br$

**c.** △—Br

**d.** $CH_3CH_2CHCH_2CH_3$
      |
     $Cl$

**e.** $CH_3\overset{\displaystyle CH_3}{\underset{\displaystyle OH}{C}}CH_2CH_3$

**f.** $CH_3CH_2C\!=\!CHCH_3$
     |
     $Br$

**g.** $CH_3(CH_2)_2CH_2NH_2$

**h.** $H_2N\!-\!\overset{}{\underset{\displaystyle O}{\overset{\displaystyle \|}{C}}}\!-\!CH_2CH_3$

**4.** Each of the following formulas can be written as two compounds with different functional groups. Write the structural formulas, name the compounds, and identify the functional groups.
 **a.** $C_2H_6O$       **b.** $C_3H_6O$       **c.** $C_5H_{10}$

**5.** Draw structural formulas for the following.

a. ethanal

b. 2-butanone

c. 2-methyl-2-propanol

d. ethanoic acid

e. trimethylamine

f. propene

g. 2-pentyne

h. cyclobutane

i. cyclohexylamine

j. 2-aminopentane

k. 1,4-nitrophenol

l. 1,3-nitrobenzoic acid

m. ethanenitrile

n. propenoic acid

# ORGANIC REACTIONS AND BIOCHEMISTRY 30

## 30:1 TYPES OF ORGANIC REACTIONS

In order to simplify your study of the thousands of organic reactions, a few main types are presented. By understanding these few reactions, you can predict the products of many organic reactions.

An **oxidation reaction** occurs when oxygen atoms are added to or hydrogen atoms are removed from a hydrocarbon molecule. Oxygen gas is a very strong oxidizer. When $O_2$ reacts with most hydrocarbons at high temperatures, $H_2O$ and $CO_2$ are produced.

### Example 1

Complete and balance. (Assume complete oxidation.)

$$C_4H_{10} + O_2 \rightarrow$$

**Solving Process:**
In a complete oxidation reaction, the products are $CO_2$ and $H_2O$. Add these to the product side and balance the equation.

$$2C_4H_{10} + 13O_2 \rightarrow 8CO_2 + 10H_2O$$

A **substitution reaction** occurs when a part of a reactant molecule is substituted for a hydrogen atom on a hydrocarbon molecule. All of the hydrogens of an alkane can be substituted. Thus, many unwanted products are formed in addition to the desired product. The hydrogen atoms of benzene, an aromatic, usually undergo substitution also.

### Example 2

Complete the following substitution reaction.

$+ Br_2 \rightarrow$

**Solving Process:**
Each angle of the benzene hexagon represents a hydrogen bonded to a carbon atom. The bromine molecule breaks into two atoms in the presence

**229**

of a catalyst. One Br atom is substituted for the hydrogen atom. The hydrogen combines with the other Br atom.

$$\text{benzene} + Br_2 \rightarrow \text{bromobenzene} + HBr$$

An **addition reaction** occurs when a reactant is added to each atom of a carbon-carbon multiple bond. Alkenes are more reactive than alkanes because of the double bond. Some reactants add to the double bond. Under certain conditions an alkene can add to another alkene to form chains called **polymers.** Alkynes can add to form polymers, also.

## Example 3

What is the product of the following addition reaction?

$$CH_3-C\equiv C-CH_3 + 2Cl_2 \rightarrow$$

**Solving Process:**
Chlorine will add to the triple bond.

$$CH_3-C\equiv C-CH_3 + 2Cl_2 \rightarrow CH_3-\underset{\underset{Cl}{|}}{\overset{\overset{Cl}{|}}{C}}-\underset{\underset{Cl}{|}}{\overset{\overset{Cl}{|}}{C}}-CH_3$$

In the previous example, atoms were added to the triple bond. It is also possible to remove certain atoms to form double or triple bonds in an **elimination reaction.** In one type of elimination reaction a hydrogen atom from one carbon atom and a hydroxyl group from an adjacent carbon atom are removed, a double bond is formed in the original molecule, and a water molecule is formed. The $H_2SO_4$ acts as a dehydrating agent.

$$\underset{\substack{\text{2-propanol} \\ \text{(isopropyl alcohol)}}}{H-\underset{\underset{H}{|}}{\overset{\overset{H}{|}}{C}}-\underset{\underset{OH}{|}}{\overset{\overset{H}{|}}{C}}-\underset{\underset{H}{|}}{\overset{\overset{H}{|}}{C}}-H} \xrightarrow{H_2SO_4} \underset{\text{propene}}{H-\underset{\underset{H}{|}}{\overset{\overset{H}{|}}{C}}-\overset{\overset{H}{|}}{C}=\overset{\overset{H}{|}}{C}-H} + \underset{\text{water}}{H_2O}$$

$H_2O$, HCl, and $HNO_2$ are often products of elimination reactions.

## Example 4

Predict the products that will be formed in this elimination reaction.

$$CH_3-\overset{\overset{\displaystyle Cl}{|}}{C}-\overset{\overset{\displaystyle H}{|}}{C}-CH_3 \rightarrow$$
$$\underset{CH_3}{|}\quad\underset{H}{|}$$

**Solving Process:**

On two adjacent carbon atoms there are hydrogen and chlorine atoms. These atoms are eliminated to form HCl. The products are

$$CH_3-\overset{\overset{\displaystyle Cl}{|}}{\underset{\underset{CH_3}{|}}{C}}-\overset{\overset{\displaystyle H}{|}}{\underset{\underset{H}{|}}{C}}-CH_3 \rightarrow HCl + CH_3-\overset{\overset{\displaystyle}{|}}{\underset{\underset{CH_3}{|}}{C}}=\overset{}{\underset{\underset{H}{|}}{C}}-CH_3$$

When a carboxylic acid is mixed with an alcohol and heated, an ester is formed. This type of reaction is an **esterification reaction.** Flavor enhancers and perfumes are mixtures of esters and other substances.

## Example 5

An apple scent can be produced by reacting methanol and butanoic acid. Complete the reaction.

$$CH_3-CH_2-CH_2-\overset{\overset{\displaystyle O}{\|}}{C}-OH + CH_3-OH \rightarrow$$

**Solving Process:**

The —OH from the carboxylic acid (R-COOH) will combine with the —H from the alcohol (R—OH) to form water. The two remaining parts of the molecules combine to form the ester

$$(R-\overset{\overset{\displaystyle O}{\|}}{C}-O-R')$$

$$CH_3CH_2CH_2\overset{\overset{\displaystyle O}{\|}}{C}-OH + CH_3-OH \rightarrow CH_3CH_2CH_2\overset{\overset{\displaystyle O}{\|}}{C}-O-CH_3 + H_2O$$

The reaction of a carboxylic acid and an alcohol is reversible. When an ester reacts with water to form a carboxylic acid and an alcohol, the process is called **hydrolysis.** The hydrolysis reaction will go to completion in the presence of a base. The products will be an alcohol and the metallic salt of the carboxylic acid (soap). **Saponification** (Latin for soap) is the hydrolysis of an ester in the presence of a base.

$$CH_2-O-\overset{\overset{\displaystyle O}{\|}}{C}-C_{17}H_{35} \qquad\qquad CH_2-OH$$

$$CH-O-\overset{\overset{\displaystyle O}{\|}}{C}-C_{17}H_{35} + 3NaOH \rightarrow CH-OH + 3C_{17}H_{35}COO^-Na^+$$

$$CH_2-O-\overset{\overset{\displaystyle O}{\|}}{C}-C_{17}H_{35} \qquad\qquad CH_2-OH$$

ester $\qquad$ + $\quad$ base $\quad \rightarrow \quad$ alcohol $+$ $\quad$ salt (soap)

## PROBLEMS

*Complete and balance the following equations.*

**1.** $C_3H_8 + O_2 \rightarrow$ (oxidation reaction)

**2.** $CH_2{=}CH_2 + Br_2 \rightarrow$ (addition reaction)

**3.** ⬡ $+ Cl_2 \rightarrow$ (substitution reaction)

**4.** $CH_3-CH_2-CH_2-\overset{\overset{\displaystyle OH}{|}}{CH}-CH_3 \rightarrow$ (elimination reaction)

**5.** $CH_3-CH_2-\overset{\overset{\displaystyle O}{\|}}{C}-OH + CH_3-CH_2-OH \rightarrow$ (esterification reaction)

## 30:2   BIOMOLECULES

Twenty-one chemical elements have been found in living systems. These elements combine to form four groups of biomolecules: proteins, carbohydrates, lipids, and nucleic acids.

**Proteins** are polymers made of **amino acids.** A protein may contain 30 to several thousand amino acid units linked together. The sequence of the amino acids composing the protein determines the properties. Five amino acids can be arranged in 120 possible sequences. The chemical properties of a protein also depend upon the way in which the polymer chain is folded and coiled. The polar and nonpolar side chains help determine the characteristic twists and folds.

Molecules that have the general formula $C_x(H_2O)_y$ are called **carbohydrates.** They are important to living systems because they are used to provide energy and raw materials for cellular activity. They are also used to provide structure to plants (cellulose) and insects (chitin).

Monosaccharides are simple sugars that can link together to form polymers called polysaccharides. Cellulose is a polysaccharide that has a molecular mass in the millions. Plants store sugars in the form of starch, while animals form the polysaccharide glycogen. Carbohydrate storage provides the organism's energy reserves.

A biological substance that is more soluble in nonpolar organic solvents than in water is a **lipid.** Fats, oils, steroid hormones, and some vitamins are lipids.

Vegetable oils contain unsaturated fatty acids. Unsaturated fats contain double bonds and are generally liquids at room temperature. Animal fats are saturated and are usually solids at room temperature.

Fats are esters formed from glycerol and three fatty acids. Fatty acids are long chain carboxylic acids having 12 to 20 carbon atoms in the chain.

**Nucleic acids** are vital to plants and animals. They control cell metabolism and transfer genetic information. Nucleic acids are polymers of **nucleotides.** A nucleotide has three parts: a nitrogen base, a sugar, and a phosphate group. The general structure of a nucleotide consists of a phosphate group bonded to a sugar (5 carbons) which is bonded to an organic base.

$$PO_4^{3-}-CH_2$$

a nucleotide

The five organic bases most often found in nucleotides are adenine, cytosine, guanine, thymine, and uracil.

Recall that the sequence of amino acids in a protein determines its properties. In the same way, the sequence of nucleotides determines the properties of the nucleic acid.

Two nucleic acids are present in the cells, ribonucleic acid (RNA) and deoxyribonucleic acid (DNA). Genetic information is transferred from one generation to the next by DNA. RNA aids in making chemicals such as enzymes.

## CHAPTER REVIEW PROBLEMS

1. Predict the product of the reaction between 2-butene and hydrogen iodide.

*Complete and balance the equation for the following four reactions.*

2. bromine + ethene
3. preparation of pentyl methanoate
4. complete oxidation of ethane
5. elimination of water from 1-pentanol

6. What is the principal function of DNA in the organism?
7. A nucleotide is composed of what three substances?
8. Soap is produced in what type of chemical reaction?
9. Proteins are polymers of what substances?
10. Why are carbohydrates important to living systems?
11. What is the difference between a saturated and an unsaturated fat?
12. What term is used to describe a lipid that contains double bonds?

# APPENDIX A

## DATA TABLES

### Table A-1

| SI Base Units | | |
|---|---|---|
| **Quantity** | **Name** | **Symbol** |
| Length | meter | m |
| Mass | kilogram | kg |
| Time | second | s |
| Electric current | ampere | A |
| Thermodynamic temperature | kelvin | K |
| Amount of substance | mole | mol |
| Luminous intensity | candela | cd |

### Table A-2

| SI Prefixes | | | | |
|---|---|---|---|---|
| **Prefix** | **Symbol** | **Meaning** | **Multiplier** (Numerical) | **Multiplier** (Exponential) |
| *Greater than 1* | | | | |
| tera | T | trillion | **1 000 000 000 000 | $10^{12}$ |
| giga | G | billion | 1 000 000 000 | $10^{9}$ |
| mega | M | million | 1 000 000 | $10^{6}$ |
| *kilo | k | thousand | 1 000 | $10^{3}$ |
| hecto | h | hundred | 100 | $10^{2}$ |
| deka | da | ten | 10 | $10^{1}$ |
| *Less than 1* | | | | |
| *deci | d | tenth | 0.1 | $10^{-1}$ |
| *centi | c | hundredth | 0.01 | $10^{-2}$ |
| *milli | m | thousandth | 0.001 | $10^{-3}$ |
| *micro | μ | millionth | 0.000 001 | $10^{-6}$ |
| *nano | n | billionth | 0.000 000 001 | $10^{-9}$ |
| pico | p | trillionth | 0.000 000 000 001 | $10^{-12}$ |
| femto | f | quadrillionth | 0.000 000 000 000 001 | $10^{-15}$ |
| atto | a | quintillionth | 0.000 000 000 000 000 001 | $10^{-18}$ |

*These prefixes are commonly used in this book and should be memorized.
**Spaces are used to group digits in long numbers. In some countries, a comma indicates a decimal point. Therefore, commas will not be used.

## Table A-3

| Greek Alphabet | | | | | |
|---|---|---|---|---|---|
| **Greek letter** | **Greek name** | **English equiv- alent** | **Greek letter** | **Greek name** | **English equiv- alent** |
| A α | alpha | ä | N ν | nu | n |
| B β | beta | b | Ξ ξ | xi | ks |
| Γ γ | gamma | g | O o | omicron | o |
| Δ δ | delta | d | Π π | pi | p |
| E ε | epsilon | e | P ρ | rho | r |
| Z ζ | zeta | z | Σ σ | sigma | s |
| H η | eta | ā | T τ | tau | t |
| Θ θ | theta | th | Υ υ | upsilon | ü,ōō |
| I ι | iota | ē | Φ φ | phi | f |
| K κ | kappa | k | X χ | chi | h |
| Λ λ | lambda | l | Ψ ψ | psi | ps |
| M μ | mu | m | Ω ω | omega | ō |

## Table A-4

| Common Physical Constants |
|---|
| Absolute Zero = $-273.15°C$ = 0 K |
| Atmospheric pressure (standard): 1 atm = 1.013 25 Pa = 760 mm Hg |
| Avogadro's number: $N_0$ = $6.022\ 17 \times 10^{23}$ per mole |
| Charge of the electron: $e$ = $-1.602\ 19 \times 10^{-19}$ coulomb |
| Faraday's constant: $F$ = 96 486.7 C/mol $e^-$ |
| Gas constant: $R$ = 8.314 30 J/mol·K |
| Enthalpy of fusion of ice: 334 J/g |
| Enthalpy of vaporization of water: 2260 J/g |
| Mass of electron: $m_e$ = $9.109\ 53 \times 10^{-31}$ kg = $5.49 \times 10^{-4}$ u |
| Mass of neutron: $m_n$ = $1.6754\ 95 \times 10^{-27}$ kg = 1.00867 u |
| Mass of proton: $m_p$ = $1.673\ 265 \times 10^{-27}$ kg = 1.00728 u |
| Molar volume: 22.4136 $dm^3$ |
| Planck's constant: $h$ = $6.626\ 20 \times 10^{-34}$ J/Hz (J·s) |
| Speed of light in vacuum: $c$ = $2.997\ 925 \times 10^8$ m/s |

## Table A-5

| Symbols and Abbreviations | |
|---|---|
| $\alpha$ = rays from radioactive materials, helium nuclei | $K_b$ = ionization constant (base) |
| $\beta$ = rays from radioactive materials, electrons | $K_{eq}$ = equilibrium constant |
| | $K_{sp}$ = solubility product constant |
| $\gamma$ = rays from radioactive materials, high-energy quanta | kg = kilogram |
| | $M$ = molarity |
| $\Delta$ = change in | $m$ = mass, molality |
| $\lambda$ = wavelength | m = meter (*length*) |
| $\nu$ = frequency | mol = mole (*amount*) |
| $\Pi$ = osmotic pressure | min = minute (*time*) |
| A = ampere (*electric current*) | N = newton (*force*) |
| °C = Celsius degree (*temperature*) | $N_A$ = Avogadro's number |
| C = coulomb (*quantity of electricity*) | $n$ = number of moles |
| $c$ = speed of light | $P$ = pressure, power |
| cd = candela (*luminous intensity*) | Pa = pascal (*pressure*) |
| $C_p$ = specific heat | $p$ = momentum |
| $D$ = density | $q$ = heat |
| $E$ = energy, electromotive force | $R$ = gas constant |
| $F$ = force, Faraday | $S$ = entropy |
| $G$ = free energy | s = second (*time*) |
| g = gram (*mass*) | $T$ = temperature |
| $H$ = enthalpy | $U$ = internal energy |
| Hz = hertz (*frequency*) | u = atomic mass unit |
| $h$ = Planck's constant | $V$ = volume |
| h = hour (*time*) | V = volt (*electromotive force*) |
| J = joule (*energy*) | $v$ = velocity |
| K = kelvin (*temperature*) | W = watt (*power*) |
| $K_a$ = ionization constant (acid) | $w$ = work |
| | $x$ = mole fraction |

## Table A-6

| Oxidation Numbers of Monatomic Ions | | |
|---|---|---|
| **1+** | **2+** | **3+** |
| cesium, $Cs^+$ | barium, $Ba^{2+}$ | aluminum, $Al^{3+}$ |
| copper(I), $Cu^+$ | beryllium, $Be^{2+}$ | antimony(III), $Sb^{3+}$ |
| hydrogen, $H^+$ | cadmium, $Cd^{2+}$ | bismuth(III), $Bi^{3+}$ |
| indium(I), $In^+$ | calcium, $Ca^{2+}$ | boron, $B^{3+}$ |
| lithium, $Li^+$ | chromium(II), $Cr^{2+}$ | cerium(III), $Ce^{3+}$ |
| potassium, $K^+$ | cobalt(II), $Co^{2+}$ | cobalt(III), $Co^{3+}$ |
| rubidium, $Rb^+$ | copper(II), $Cu^{2+}$ | chromium(III), $Cr^{3+}$ |
| silver, $Ag^+$ | iridium(II), $Ir^{2+}$ | gallium(III), $Ga^{3+}$ |
| sodium, $Na^+$ | iron(II), $Fe^{2+}$ | indium(III), $In^{3+}$ |
| thallium(I), $Tl^+$ | lead(II), $Pb^{2+}$ | iridium(III), $Ir^{3+}$ |
| | magnesium, $Mg^{2+}$ | iron(III), $Fe^{3+}$ |
| | manganese(II), $Mn^{2+}$ | phosphorus(III), $P^{3+}$ |
| | mercury(II), $Hg^{2+}$ | rhodium(III), $Rh^{3+}$ |
| | nickel(II), $Ni^{2+}$ | thallium(III), $Tl^{3+}$ |
| | platinum(II), $Pt^{2+}$ | titanium(III), $Ti^{3+}$ |
| | strontium, $Sr^{2+}$ | uranium(III), $U^{3+}$ |
| | tin(II), $Sn^{2+}$ | vanadium(III), $V^{3+}$ |
| | titanium(II), $Ti^{2+}$ | |
| | tungsten(II), $W^{2+}$ | |
| | vanadium(II), $V^{2+}$ | |
| | zinc, $Zn^{2+}$ | |
| | zirconium(II), $Zr^{2+}$ | |

| **4+** | | **5+** |
|---|---|---|
| cerium(IV), $Ce^{4+}$    titanium(IV), $Ti^{4+}$ | | antimony(V), $Sb^{5+}$ |
| germanium(IV), $Ge^{4+}$    tin(IV), $Sn^{4+}$ | | bismuth(V), $Bi^{5+}$ |
| iridium(IV), $Ir^{4+}$    tungsten(IV), $W^{4+}$ | | phosphorus(V), $P^{5+}$ |
| lead(IV), $Pb^{4+}$    uranium(IV), $U^{4+}$ | | tungsten(V), $W^{5+}$ |
| platinum(IV), $Pt^{4+}$    vanadium(IV), $V^{4+}$ | | uranium(V), $U^{5+}$ |
| thorium(IV), $Th^{4+}$    zirconium(IV), $Zr^{4+}$ | | vanadium(V), $V^{5+}$ |

| **1−** | **2−** | **3−** | **4−** |
|---|---|---|---|
| bromide, $Br^-$ | oxide, $O^{2-}$ | nitride, $N^{3-}$ | carbide, $C^{4-}$ |
| chloride, $Cl^-$ | selenide, $Se^{2-}$ | phosphide, $P^{3-}$ | |
| fluoride, $F^-$ | sulfide, $S^{2-}$ | | |
| hydride, $H^-$ | | | |
| iodide, $I^-$ | | | |

## Table A-7

| Charges of Common Polyatomic Ions | |
|---|---|
| **1+**<br>ammonium, $NH_4^+$ | **2+**<br>mercury(I), $Hg_2^{2+}$ |
| **1−**<br>acetate, $CH_3COO^-$<br>azide, $N_3^-$<br>benzoate, $C_6H_5COO^-$<br>bromate, $BrO_3^-$<br>chlorate, $ClO_3^-$<br>cyanide, $CN^-$<br>formate, $HCOO^-$<br>hydroxide, $OH^-$<br>hypochlorite, $ClO^-$<br>hypophosphite, $PH_2O_2^-$<br>iodate, $IO_3^-$<br>metaphosphate, $PO_3^-$<br>nitrate, $NO_3^-$<br>nitrite, $NO_2^-$<br>perchlorate, $ClO_4^-$<br>periodate, $IO_4^-$<br>permanganate, $MnO_4^-$<br>peroxyborate, $BO_3^-$<br>thiocyanate, $SCN^-$<br>vanadate, $VO_3^-$ | **2−**<br>carbonate, $CO_3^{2-}$<br>chromate, $CrO_4^{2-}$<br>dichromate, $Cr_2O_7^{2-}$<br>hexachloroplatinate(IV), $PtCl_6^{2-}$<br>hexafluorosilicate, $SiF_6^{2-}$<br>molybdate, $MoO_4^{2-}$<br>oxalate, $C_2O_4^{2-}$<br>peroxide, $O_2^{-2}$<br>peroxydisulfate, $S_2O_8^{2-}$<br>selenate, $SeO_4^{2-}$<br>silicate, $SiO_3^{2-}$<br>sulfate, $SO_4^{2-}$<br>sulfite, $SO_3^{2-}$<br>tartrate, $C_4H_4O_6^{2-}$<br>tellurate, $TeO_4^{2-}$<br>tetraborate, $B_4O_7^{2-}$<br>thiosulfate, $S_2O_3^{2-}$<br>tungstate, $WO_4^{2-}$ |
| | **3−**<br>arsenate, $AsO_4^{3-}$<br>citrate, $C_6H_5O_7^{3-}$<br>hexacyanoferrate(III), $Fe(CN)_6^{3-}$<br>phosphate, $PO_4^{3-}$ |
| | **4−**<br>hexacyanoferrate(II), $Fe(CN)_6^{4-}$<br>pyrophosphate, $P_2O_7^{4-}$ |

## Table A-8

| Heat Capacities (in $J/g \cdot C°$) | | | | | |
|---|---|---|---|---|---|
| **Substance** | $C_p$ | **Substance** | $C_p$ | **Substance** | $C_p$ |
| Al | 0.900 | $CH_3CH_2OH$ | 2.45 | $LiNO_3$ | 1.21 |
| $AlF_3$ | 0.987 | $CH_3COOH$ | 2.05 | $MgCO_3$ | 0.837 |
| As | 0.331 | Fe | 0.448 | $Mg(OH)_2$ | 1.31 |
| Au | 0.128 | glass | 0.753 | $MgSO_4$ | 0.929 |
| BeO | 1.05 | He | 5.19 | $Na_2CO_3$ | 1.41 |
| $CaC_2$ | 1.00 | HI | 0.235 | $PCl_3$ | 0.874 |
| $CaSO_4$ | 0.716 | $H_2O(cr)$ | 2.06 | SiC | 0.686 |
| $CCl_4$ | 0.856 | $H_2O(l)$ | 4.18 | $SiO_2$ | 0.749 |
| $C_6H_6$ | 1.74 | $H_2O(g)$ | 2.02 | Sn | 0.220 |
| $C_6H_{14}$ | 2.26 | ICl | 0.661 | steel(cr) | 0.448 |
| $C_6H_5Br$ | 0.989 | In(cr) | 0.235 | steel(l) | 0.719 |
| $C_6H_5CH_3$ | 1.80 | In(l) | 0.216 | Ti | 0.520 |
| $CCl_3CCl_3$ | 0.728 | $K_2CO_3$ | 0.904 | $TiCl_4$ | 0.803 |
| chalk | 0.920 | kerosene | 2.09 | ZnS | 0.469 |
| $CH_3COCH_3$ | 2.18 | | | | |

## Table A-9

## Electronegativities and First Ionization Energies

Legend (key element box):
↖ Ionization energy (kJ/mol)
↙ Electronegativity

Each cell below lists: Ionization energy (kJ/mol) / Symbol / Electronegativity.

| 1 | 2 | 3 | 4 | 5 | 6 | 7 | 8 | 9 | 10 | 11 | 12 | 13 | 14 | 15 | 16 | 17 | 18 |
|---|---|---|---|---|---|---|---|---|---|---|---|---|---|---|---|---|---|
| 1312 H 2.20 | | | | | | | | | | | | | | | | | 2373 He – |
| 520 Li 0.96 | 900 Be 1.50 | | | | | | | | | | | 801 B 2.02 | 1087 C 2.56 | 1402 N 2.81 | 1314 O 3.37 | 1681 F 4.00 | 2081 Ne – |
| 496 Na 0.96 | 738 Mg 1.29 | | | | | | | | | | | 578 Al 1.63 | 787 Si 1.94 | 1012 P 2.04 | 1000 S 2.46 | 1251 Cl 3.00 | 1521 Ar – |
| 419 K 0.84 | 590 Ca 1.02 | 631 Sc 1.28 | 658 Ti 1.44 | 650 V 1.54 | 653 Cr 1.61 | 717 Mn 1.57 | 759 Fe 1.74 | 758 Co 1.79 | 737 Ni 1.83 | 745 Cu 1.67 | 906 Zn 1.60 | 579 Ga 1.86 | 762 Ge 1.93 | 947 As 2.12 | 941 Se 2.45 | 1143 Br 2.82 | 1351 Kr – |
| 403 Rb 0.85 | 550 Sr 0.97 | 616 Y 1.16 | 659 Zr 1.27 | 664 Nb 1.23 | 685 Mo 1.73 | 702 Tc 1.36 | 711 Ru 1.42 | 720 Rh 1.87 | 805 Pd 1.78 | 731 Ag 1.57 | 868 Cd 1.52 | 558 In 1.69 | 708 Sn 1.84 | 834 Sb 1.83 | 869 Te 2.03 | 1009 I 2.48 | 1170 Xe – |
| 376 Cs 0.82 | 503 Ba 0.93 | 524 *Lu 1.20 | 675 Hf 1.23 | 761 Ta 1.33 | 733 W 1.88 | 760 Re 1.46 | 839 Os 1.52 | 888 Ir 1.88 | 868 Pt 1.86 | 890 Au 1.98 | 1006 Hg 1.72 | 589 Tl 1.74 | 716 Pb 1.87 | 703 Bi 1.76 | 812 Po 1.76 | 917 At 1.96 | 1037 Rn – |
| – Fr 0.86 | 509 Ra** 0.97 | 666 **Ac 1.00 | | | | | | | | | | | | | | | |

**Lanthanides (*):**

| 538 *La 1.09 | 565 Ce 1.09 | 556 Pr 1.10 | 530 Nd 1.10 | 536 Pm 1.07 | 543 Sm 1.12 | 547 Eu 1.01 | 592 Gd 1.15 | 564 Tb 1.10 | 572 Dy 1.16 | 581 Ho 1.16 | 589 Er 1.17 | 596 Tm 1.18 | 603 Yb 1.06 |
|---|---|---|---|---|---|---|---|---|---|---|---|---|---|

**Actinides (**):**

| 666 **Ac 1.00 | 671 Th 1.11 | – Pa 1.14 | 587 U 1.30 | – Np 1.29 | 560 Pu 1.25 | 579 Am 1.2 | – Cm | – Bk | – Cf | – Es | – Fm | – Md 1.2 |
|---|---|---|---|---|---|---|---|---|---|---|---|---|

←———— estimated ————→

## Table A-10

| Thermodynamic Properties (at standard states) | | | |
| --- | --- | --- | --- |
| $\Delta H_f^\circ$ in kJ/mol    $\Delta G_f^\circ$ in kJ/mol    $S^\circ$ in J/mol · K concentration of aqueous solutions is 1$M$ | | | |
| Substance | $\Delta H_f^\circ$ | $\Delta G_f^\circ$ | $S^\circ$ |
| Ag(cr) | 0 | 0 | 42.7 |
| $Ag_2SO_4$(aq) | −698 | −590 | 33.1 |
| Al(cr) | 0 | 0 | 28.3 |
| $Al_2O_3$(cr) | −1670 | −1580 | 51.0 |
| $Br_2$(g) | 30.9 | 3.1 | 245.4 |
| $Br_2$(l) | 0 | 0 | 152 |
| $CH_4$(g) | −74.8 | −50.8 | 186 |
| $C_2H_4$(g) | 52.3 | 68.1 | 219 |
| $C_2H_6$(g) | −84.7 | −32.9 | 229 |
| $C_4H_{10}$(g) | −125 | −15.7 | 310 |
| $CO_2$(g) | −393.5 | −394.4 | 214 |
| Ca(cr) | 0 | 0 | 41.6 |
| $CaCl_2$(aq) | −878 | −815 | 54.8 |
| CaO(cr) | −635 | −604 | 38.2 |
| $Ca(OH)_2$(cr) | −987 | −897 | 77.41 |
| $Cl_2$(g) | 0 | 0 | 223 |
| Cu(cr) | 0 | 0 | 33.1 |
| $Cu(NO_3)_2$(aq) | −350 | −157 | 193 |
| $CuSO_4$(aq) | −679 | −844 | 109 |
| Fe(cr) | 0 | 0 | 27.3 |
| $Fe_2O_3$(cr) | −822 | −741 | 90.0 |
| H(g) | 218 | 203 | 115 |
| $H_2$(g) | 0 | 0 | 131 |
| HBr(g) | −36.2 | −53.2 | 198 |
| HCl(g) | −92.3 | −95.3 | 187 |
| HCl(aq) | −167 | −131 | 56.5 |
| $HNO_2$(aq) | −119 | −55.6 | 46.1 |
| $HNO_3$(aq) | −207 | −111 | 53.3 |
| $H_2O$(l) | −286 | −237 | 70.0 |
| $H_2O$(g) | −242 | −229 | 189 |
| $H_2O_2$(l) | −186 | −118 | 110 |
| $H_3PO_4$(aq) | −1280 | −1120 | 110 |
| $H_2SO_4$(l) | −814 | −690 | 139 |
| $H_2SO_4$(aq) | −908 | −742 | 17.2 |
| KBr(cr) | −392 | −379 | 96.4 |
| $K_2SO_4$(aq) | −1409 | — | — |
| Mg(cr) | 0 | 0 | 32.5 |
| $Mg_3N_2$(cr) | −461 | −422 | 88 |
| $Mg(NO_3)_2$(aq) | −875 | −677 | 175 |
| $Mg(OH)_2$(cr) | −925 | −834 | 63.1 |
| (table continued on next page) | | | |

| Substance | $\Delta H_f°$ | $\Delta G_f°$ | $S°$ |
|---|---|---|---|
| $N_2(g)$ | 0 | 0 | 192 |
| $NH_3(g)$ | −46.2 | −16.6 | 193 |
| $NH_4Cl(aq)$ | −300 | −211 | 170 |
| $NH_4NO_3(cr)$ | −366 | −184 | 151 |
| $NO(g)$ | 90.4 | 86.4 | 211 |
| $NO_2(g)$ | +33.8 | 51.8 | 240 |
| $N_2O(g)$ | 82.1 | 104 | 220 |
| $NaCl(cr)$ | −411 | −384 | 72.4 |
| $NaCl(aq)$ | −446 | −372 | 207 |
| $NaNO_3(aq)$ | −447 | −373 | 205 |
| $NaOH(aq)$ | −427 | −379 | 64.5 |
| $Na_2SO_4(aq)$ | −1380 | −1270 | 149 |
| $O_2(g)$ | 0 | 0 | 205 |
| $P_4O_{10}(cr)$ | −2980 | −2700 | 229 |
| $Zn(cr)$ | 0 | 0 | 41.6 |
| $Zn(NO_3)_2(aq)$ | −569 | −370 | 181 |
| $Zn(OH)_2(cr)$ | −642 | −554 | 81.2 |

**Table A-11**

### Solubility Rules

You will be working with water solutions, and it is helpful to have a few rules concerning what substances are soluble in water. The more common rules are listed below.
1. All common salts of the Group IA elements and ammonium ion are soluble.
2. All common acetates and nitrates are soluble.
3. All binary compounds of Group VIIA elements (other than F) with metals are soluble except those of silver, mercury(I), and lead.
4. All sulfates are soluble except those of barium, strontium, lead, calcium, silver, and mercury(I).
5. Except for those in Rule 1, carbonates, hydroxides, oxides, and phosphates are insoluble.

## Table A-12

| Molal Freezing and Boiling Point Constants (in C°/mol/1000 g of solvent) | | | | |
|---|---|---|---|---|
| Substance | Freezing point (°C) | Molal freezing point constant | Boiling point (°C) | Molal boiling point constant |
| Acetic Acid | 16.604 | −3.90 | 117.9 | 3.07 |
| Benzene | 5.5 | −4.90 | 80.1 | 2.53 |
| Camphor | 179.8 | −37.7 | 204 | 5.95 |
| Cyclohexane | 6.55 | −20.0 | 80.74 | 2.79 |
| Nitrobenzene | 5.7 | −7.00 | 210.8 | 5.24 |
| Phenol | 43 | −7.40 | 181.75 | 3.56 |
| Water | 0.00 | −1.86 | 100.00 | 0.512 |

## Table A-13

| Ionization Constants | | | |
|---|---|---|---|
| Substance | Ionization Constant | Substance | Ionization Constant |
| $HCOOH$ | $1.69 \times 10^{-4}$ | $H_2O_2$ | $1.78 \times 10^{-12}$ |
| $CH_3COOH$ | $1.76 \times 10^{-5}$ | $H_3PO_4$ | $7.52 \times 10^{-3}$ |
| $CH_2ClCOOH$ | $1.40 \times 10^{-3}$ | $H_2PO_4^-$ | $6.23 \times 10^{-8}$ |
| $CHCl_2COOH$ | $3.32 \times 10^{-2}$ | $HPO_4^{2-}$ | $2.20 \times 10^{-13}$ |
| $CCl_3COOH$ | $2.00 \times 10^{-1}$ | $H_3PO_3$ | $1.00 \times 10^{-2}$ |
| $HOOCCOOH$ | $5.90 \times 10^{-2}$ | $H_2PO_3^-$ | $2.60 \times 10^{-7}$ |
| $HOOCCOO^-$ | $6.40 \times 10^{-5}$ | $H_3PO_2$ | $7.94 \times 10^{-2}$ |
| $CH_3CH_2COOH$ | $1.34 \times 10^{-5}$ | $H_2S$ | $1.32 \times 10^{-7}$ |
| $C_6H_5COOH$ | $6.46 \times 10^{-5}$ | $HS^-$ | $1.10 \times 10^{-13}$ |
| $(C_6H_5)_2CHCOOH$ | $1.15 \times 10^{-4}$ | $HSO_4^-$ | $1.20 \times 10^{-2}$ |
| $H_3AsO_4$ | $6.31 \times 10^{-3}$ | $H_2SO_3$ | $1.54 \times 10^{-2}$ |
| $H_2AsO_4^-$ | $1.05 \times 10^{-7}$ | $HSO_3^-$ | $1.02 \times 10^{-7}$ |
| $H_3BO_3$ | $7.30 \times 10^{-10}$ | $HSeO_4^-$ | $1.20 \times 10^{-2}$ |
| $H_2BO_3^-$ | $1.80 \times 10^{-13}$ | $H_2SeO_3$ | $3.50 \times 10^{-2}$ |
| $HBO_3^{-2}$ | $1.60 \times 10^{-14}$ | $HSeO_3^-$ | $4.80 \times 10^{-9}$ |
| $H_2CO_3$ | $4.30 \times 10^{-7}$ | $HBrO$ | $2.40 \times 10^{-9}$ |
| $HCO_3^-$ | $5.61 \times 10^{-11}$ | $HClO$ | $2.95 \times 10^{-5}$ |
| $HCN$ | $4.93 \times 10^{-10}$ | $HIO$ | $2.30 \times 10^{-11}$ |
| $H_2CrO_4$ | $1.82$ | $NH_3^*$ | $1.77 \times 10^{-5}$ |
| $HCrO_4^-$ | $1.26 \times 10^{-6}$ | $H_2NNH_2^*$ | $1.70 \times 10^{-6}$ |
| $HF$ | $3.53 \times 10^{-4}$ | $N_2NOH^*$ | $1.07 \times 10^{-8}$ |
| $HNO_2$ | $4.60 \times 10^{-4}$ | | |

## Table A-14

| Vapor Pressure of Water | | | |
|---|---|---|---|
| Temperature (°C) | Pressure (kPa) | Temperature (°C) | Pressure (kPa) |
| 0 | 0.6 | 26 | 3.4 |
| 5 | 0.9 | 27 | 3.6 |
| 8 | 1.1 | 28 | 3.8 |
| 10 | 1.2 | 29 | 4.0 |
| 12 | 1.4 | 30 | 4.2 |
| 14 | 1.6 | 35 | 5.6 |
| 16 | 1.8 | 40 | 7.4 |
| 18 | 2.1 | 50 | 12.3 |
| 20 | 2.3 | 60 | 19.9 |
| 21 | 2.5 | 70 | 31.2 |
| 22 | 2.6 | 80 | 47.3 |
| 23 | 2.8 | 90 | 70.1 |
| 24 | 3.0 | 100 | 101.3 |
| 25 | 3.2 | | |

## Table A-15

| Solubility Product Constants (at 25°C) | | | |
|---|---|---|---|
| Substance | $K_{sp}$ | Substance | $K_{sp}$ |
| AgBr | $7.70 \times 10^{-13}$ | CuS | $6.31 \times 10^{-36}$ |
| AgBrO$_3$ | $5.77 \times 10^{-5}$ | FeC$_2$O$_4$ | $2.10 \times 10^{-7}$ |
| Ag$_2$CO$_3$ | $6.15 \times 10^{-12}$ | Fe(OH)$_3$ | $3.98 \times 10^{-38}$ |
| AgCl | $1.56 \times 10^{-10}$ | FeS | $3.70 \times 10^{-19}$ |
| Ag$_2$CrO$_4$ | $9.00 \times 10^{-12}$ | Hg$_2$SO$_4$ | $7.41 \times 10^{-7}$ |
| Ag$_2$Cr$_2$O$_7$ | $2.00 \times 10^{-7}$ | Li$_2$CO$_3$ | $1.70 \times 10^{-2}$ |
| AgI | $1.50 \times 10^{-16}$ | MgCO$_3$ | $2.60 \times 10^{-5}$ |
| AgSCN | $1.16 \times 10^{-12}$ | MgC$_2$O$_4$ | $8.57 \times 10^{-5}$ |
| Al(OH)$_3$ | $1.26 \times 10^{-33}$ | MgF$_2$ | $6.46 \times 10^{-9}$ |
| Al$_2$S$_3$ | $2.00 \times 10^{-7}$ | MnCO$_3$ | $1.82 \times 10^{-11}$ |
| BaCO$_3$ | $8.10 \times 10^{-8}$ | NiCO$_3$ | $6.61 \times 10^{-9}$ |
| BaCrO$_4$ | $1.17 \times 10^{-10}$ | NiS | $3.16 \times 10^{-19}$ |
| BaF$_2$ | $1.05 \times 10^{-6}$ | PbCl$_2$ | $1.62 \times 10^{-5}$ |
| BaSO$_4$ | $1.08 \times 10^{-10}$ | PbI$_2$ | $1.39 \times 10^{-8}$ |
| CaCO$_3$ | $8.70 \times 10^{-9}$ | Pb(IO$_3$)$_2$ | $2.60 \times 10^{-13}$ |
| CaSO$_4$ | $9.12 \times 10^{-6}$ | SrCO$_3$ | $1.60 \times 10^{-9}$ |
| CdS | $3.60 \times 10^{-29}$ | TlBr | $3.39 \times 10^{-6}$ |
| Cu(IO$_3$)$_2$ | $1.40 \times 10^{-7}$ | ZnCO$_3$ | $1.45 \times 10^{-11}$ |
| CuC$_2$O$_4$ | $2.87 \times 10^{-8}$ | Zn(OH)$_2$ | $1.20 \times 10^{-17}$ |
| Cu(OH)$_2$ | $2.19 \times 10^{-20}$ | ZnS | $1.20 \times 10^{-23}$ |

## Table A-16

| Standard Reduction Potentials (at 25°C, 101.325 kPa, 1M) | |
| --- | --- |
| **Half-Reaction** | **E° (Volts)** |
| $Li^+ + e^- \rightarrow Li$ | −3.05 |
| $K^+ + e^- \rightarrow K$ | −2.93 |
| $Cs^+ + e^- \rightarrow Cs$ | −2.92 |
| $Ba^{2+} + 2e^- \rightarrow Ba$ | −2.90 |
| $Ca^{2+} + 2e^- \rightarrow Ca$ | −2.87 |
| $Na^+ + e^- \rightarrow Na$ | −2.71 |
| $Am^{3+} + 3e^- \rightarrow Am$ | −2.38 |
| $Mg^{2+} + 2e^- \rightarrow Mg$ | −2.36 |
| $Ce^{3+} + 3e^- \rightarrow Ce$ | −2.34 |
| $H_2 + 2e^- \rightarrow 2H^-$ | −2.25 |
| $Pu^{3+} + 3e^- \rightarrow Pu$ | −2.03 |
| $Be^{2+} + 2e^- \rightarrow Be$ | −1.85 |
| $Al^{3+} + 3e^- \rightarrow Al$ | −1.66 |
| $SiF_6^{2-} + 4e^- \rightarrow Si + 6F^-$ | −1.20 |
| $Mn^{2+} + 2e^- \rightarrow Mn$ | −1.18 |
| $OCN^- + H_2O + 2e^- \rightarrow CN^- + 2OH^-$ | −0.97 |
| $Cr^{2+} + 2e^- \rightarrow Cr$ | −0.91 |
| $2H_2O + 2e^- \rightarrow H_2 + 2OH^-$ | −0.83 |
| $Zn^{2+} + 2e^- \rightarrow Zn$ | −0.76 |
| $U^{4+} + e^- \rightarrow U^{3+}$ | −0.61 |
| $Ga^{3+} + 3e^- \rightarrow Ga$ | −0.56 |
| $H_3PO_3 + 2H^+ + 2e^- \rightarrow H_3PO_2 + H_2O$ | −0.50 |
| $2CO_2 + 2H^+ + 2e^- \rightarrow H_2C_2O_4$ | −0.49 |
| $NO_2^- + H_2O + e^- \rightarrow NO + 2OH^-$ | −0.46 |
| $Fe^{2+} + 2e^- \rightarrow Fe$ | −0.44 |
| $Eu^{3+} + 3e^- \rightarrow Eu$ | −0.43 |
| $Cr^{3+} + e^- \rightarrow Cr^{2+}$ | −0.41 |
| $2H^+(10^{-7}M) + 2e^- \rightarrow H_2$ | −0.41 |
| $Cd^{2+} + 2e^- \rightarrow Cd$ | −0.40 |
| $PbSO_4 + 2e^- \rightarrow Pb + SO_4^{2-}$ | −0.36 |
| $Co^{2+} + 2e^- \rightarrow Co$ | −0.28 |
| $Ni^{2+} + 2e^- \rightarrow Ni$ | −0.25 |
| $Sn^{2+} + 2e^- \rightarrow Sn$ | −0.14 |
| $Pb^{2+} + 2e^- \rightarrow Pb$ | −0.13 |
| $AgCN + e^- \rightarrow Ag + CN^-$ | −0.02 |
| $2H^+ + 2e^- \rightarrow H_2$ | 0.00 |
| $UO_2^{2+} + e^- \rightarrow UO_2^+$ | 0.06 |
| $S + 2H^+ + 2e^- \rightarrow H_2S$ | 0.14 |

Weak Oxidizing Agents/Strong Reducing Agents →

Strong Oxidizing Agents/Weak Reducing Agents →

(table continued on next page)

| Half-Reaction | E° (Volts) |
|---|---|
| $Sn^{4+} + 2e^- \rightarrow Sn^{2+}$ | 0.15 |
| $Cu^{2+} + e^- \rightarrow Cu^+$ | 0.15 |
| $SO_4{}^{2-} + 4H^+ + 2e^- \rightarrow SO_2(aq) + 2H_2O$ | 0.17 |
| $AgCl + e^- \rightarrow Ag + Cl^-$ | 0.22 |
| $Hg_2Cl_2 + 2e^- \rightarrow 2Hg + 2Cl^-$ | 0.27 |
| $UO_2{}^{2+} + 4H^+ + 2e^- \rightarrow U^{4+} + 2H_2O$ | 0.33 |
| $Cu^{2+} + 2e^- \rightarrow Cu$ | 0.34 |
| $Fe(CN)_6{}^{3-} + e^- \rightarrow Fe(CN)_6{}^{4-}$ | 0.36 |
| $Cu^+ + e^- \rightarrow Cu$ | 0.52 |
| $I_2 + 2e^- \rightarrow 2I^-$ | 0.53 |
| $Hg_2SO_4 + 2e^- \rightarrow 2Hg + SO_4{}^{2-}$ | 0.62 |
| $2HgCl_2 + 2e^- \rightarrow Hg_2Cl_2 + 2Cl^-$ | 0.63 |
| $O_2 + 2H^+ + 2e^- \rightarrow H_2O_2$ | 0.68 |
| $Fe^{3+} + e^- \rightarrow Fe^{2+}$ | 0.77 |
| $Hg_2{}^{2+} + 2e^- \rightarrow 2Hg$ | 0.79 |
| $Ag^+ + e^- \rightarrow Ag$ | 0.80 |
| $NO_3{}^- + 2H^+ + e^- \rightarrow NO_2 + H_2O$ | 0.80 |
| $O_2 + 4H^+(10^{-7}M) + 4e^- \rightarrow 2H_2O$ | 0.82 |
| $Hg^{2+} + 2e^- \rightarrow Hg$ | 0.85 |
| $ClO^- + H_2O + 2e^- \rightarrow Cl^- + 2OH^-$ | 0.90 |
| $2Hg^{2+} + 2e^- \rightarrow Hg_2{}^{2+}$ | 0.92 |
| $NO_3{}^- + 3H^+ + 2e^- \rightarrow HNO_2 + H_2O$ | 0.94 |
| $NO_3{}^- + 4H^+ + 3e^- \rightarrow NO(g) + 2H_2O$ | 0.96 |
| $Pd^{2+} + 2e^- \rightarrow Pd$ | 0.99 |
| $Br_2 + 2e^- \rightarrow 2Br^-$ | 1.07 |
| $MnO_2 + 4H^+ + 2e^- \rightarrow Mn^{2+} + 2H_2O$ | 1.23 |
| $O_2 + 4H^+ + 4e^- \rightarrow 2H_2O$ | 1.23 |
| $2HNO_2 + 4H^+ + 4e^- \rightarrow N_2O + 3H_2O$ | 1.27 |
| $Cr_2O_7{}^{2-} + 14H^+ + 6e^- \rightarrow 2Cr^{3+} + 7H_2O$ | 1.33 |
| $Cl_2 + 2e^- \rightarrow 2Cl^-$ | 1.36 |
| $Au^{3+} + 2e^- \rightarrow Au^+$ | 1.42 |
| $PbO_2 + 4H^+ + 2e^- \rightarrow Pb^{2+} + 2H_2O$ | 1.46 |
| $2ClO_3{}^- + 12H^+ + 10e^- \rightarrow Cl_2 + 6H_2O$ | 1.47 |
| $HClO + H^+ + 2e^- \rightarrow Cl^- + H_2O$ | 1.49 |
| $Au^{3+} + 3e^- \rightarrow Au$ | 1.50 |
| $MnO_4{}^- + 8H^+ + 5e^- \rightarrow Mn^{2+} + 4H_2O$ | 1.51 |
| $MnO_4{}^- + 4H^+ + 3e^- \rightarrow MnO_2 + 2H_2O$ | 1.70 |
| $H_2O_2 + 2H^+ + 2e^- \rightarrow 2H_2O$ | 1.78 |
| $Co^{3+} + e^- \rightarrow Co^{2+}$ | 1.81 |
| $S_2O_8{}^{2-} + 2e^- \rightarrow 2SO_4{}^{2-}$ | 2.01 |
| $O_3 + 2H^+ + 2e^- \rightarrow O_2 + H_2O$ | 2.07 |
| $F_2 + 2e^- \rightarrow 2F^-$ | 2.87 |
| $F_2 + 2H^+ + 2e^- \rightarrow 2HF$ | 3.03 |

(left margin, bottom-to-top) Weak Oxidizing Agents/Strong Reducing Agents

(right margin, top-to-bottom) Strong Oxidizing Agents/Weak Reducing Agents

# APPENDIX B

## LOGARITHMS

A logarithm or log is an exponent. We will work with exponents given in terms of base 10.

$$N = b^x$$

$$\text{number} = \text{base}^{\text{exponent or logarithm}}$$

$$100 = 10^{2.0000}$$

For the log 2.000, the part of the numeral to the left of the decimal point is the characteristic. The part to the right of the decimal point is the mantissa.

$$\text{Log } 100 = 2.000$$

characteristic     mantissa

### Example 1

Find the log of 657.

**Solving Process:**

(a) Write the number in scientific notation, $6.57 \times 10^2$.

(b) Look in the table under the column ($N$). Find the first two digits, (65).

(c) Look to the right and find the mantissa that is in the vertical column under the third digit of the number (7). It is .8176.

(d) From the scientific notation, write the power of ten as the characteristic, to the left of the decimal point.

(e) Write the four digits from the table as the mantissa to the right of the characteristic and the decimal point, 2.8176.

$$\text{Thus } 657 = 10^{2.8176} \text{ or log } 657 = 2.8176.$$

When given a logarithm and asked to find the number it represents, we use the table to find the first three digits for the number. We use the characteristic to determine where to locate the decimal point with respect to these digits.

### Example 2

Given the logarithm 2.8176, find the number it represents (antilog).

**Solving Process:**

(a) In the log table, find the mantissa that is closest to .8176.

**248**

**(b)** We find by looking under the column (N) that this mantissa corresponds to 65. The third digit is found at the top of the column in which the mantissa appears, 7. (657)

**(c)** Write the three digits (657) in scientific notation, $6.57 \times 10^x$.

**(d)** The characteristic will be the power of ten.

$$\text{antilog } 2.8176 = 6.57 \times 10^2 \text{ or } 657$$

## Example 3

Find the log 0.00657.

**Solving Process:**

**(a)** Write the number in scientific notation, $6.57 \times 10^{-3}$.

**(b)** Look in the table under the column N for the first two digits, 6.5, and to the right in the column under the third digit, 7, for the mantissa. Note that the mantissa is always a positive number, .8176.

**(c)** From the scientific notation, we get the negative characteristic, $-3$.

**(d)** Add the negative characteristic and the positive mantissa $(-3.0000) + (+.8176) = -2.1824$. This value is more commonly represented as 7.8176-10. However, the negative logarithm $-2.1824$ is more useful in pH calculations.

## Example 4

Find the antilog of $-2.1824$.

**Solving Process:**

**(a)** We ask ourselves what number would we add to the next, lesser integer, $-3.$, to get the log $-2.1824$. It would be 0.8176.

$$
\begin{array}{r}
-3.0000 \\
\text{subtract } \underline{-2.1824} \\
0.8176
\end{array}
$$

We know that logarithm tables do not give mantissas for negative numbers. So, we have changed the $-2.1824$ into the sum of a negative characteristic and a postive mantissa. The characteristic is always the next negative number. The positive mantissa was determined by asking ourselves what positive number would we add to the negative characteristic to get $-2.1824$.

$$-2.1824 = -3. + 0.8176$$

**(b)** Antilog $-2.1824$ = antilog $-3. \times$ antilog $0.8176$
We know the antilog of $-3.$ is $10^{-3}$. From the table, we find that the antilog $0.8176 = 6.57$. Therefore the antilog of $-2.1824 = 6.57 \times 10^{-3}$.

## Table B-1

| N | 0 | 1 | 2 | 3 | 4 | 5 | 6 | 7 | 8 | 9 |
|---|---|---|---|---|---|---|---|---|---|---|
| 10 | 0000 | 0043 | 0086 | 0128 | 0170 | 0212 | 0253 | 0294 | 0334 | 0374 |
| 11 | 0414 | 0453 | 0492 | 0531 | 0569 | 0607 | 0645 | 0682 | 0719 | 0775 |
| 12 | 0792 | 0828 | 0864 | 0899 | 0934 | 0969 | 1004 | 1038 | 1072 | 1106 |
| 13 | 1139 | 1173 | 1206 | 1239 | 1271 | 1303 | 1335 | 1367 | 1399 | 1430 |
| 14 | 1461 | 1492 | 1523 | 1553 | 1584 | 1614 | 1644 | 1673 | 1703 | 1732 |
| 15 | 1761 | 1790 | 1818 | 1847 | 1875 | 1903 | 1931 | 1959 | 1987 | 2014 |
| 16 | 2041 | 2068 | 2095 | 2122 | 2148 | 2175 | 2201 | 2227 | 2253 | 2279 |
| 17 | 2304 | 2330 | 2355 | 2380 | 2405 | 2430 | 2455 | 2480 | 2504 | 2529 |
| 18 | 2553 | 2577 | 2601 | 2625 | 2648 | 2672 | 2695 | 2718 | 2742 | 2765 |
| 19 | 2788 | 2810 | 2833 | 2856 | 2878 | 2900 | 2923 | 2945 | 2967 | 2989 |
| 20 | 3010 | 3032 | 3054 | 3075 | 3096 | 3118 | 3139 | 3160 | 3181 | 3201 |
| 21 | 3222 | 3243 | 3263 | 3284 | 3304 | 3324 | 3345 | 3365 | 3385 | 3404 |
| 22 | 3424 | 3444 | 3464 | 3483 | 3502 | 3522 | 3541 | 3560 | 3579 | 3598 |
| 23 | 3617 | 3636 | 3655 | 3674 | 3692 | 3711 | 3729 | 3747 | 3766 | 3784 |
| 24 | 3802 | 3820 | 3838 | 3856 | 3874 | 3892 | 3909 | 3927 | 3945 | 3962 |
| 25 | 3979 | 3997 | 4014 | 4031 | 4048 | 4065 | 4082 | 4099 | 4116 | 4133 |
| 26 | 4150 | 4166 | 4183 | 4200 | 4216 | 4232 | 4249 | 4265 | 4281 | 4298 |
| 27 | 4314 | 4330 | 4346 | 4362 | 4378 | 4393 | 4409 | 4425 | 4440 | 4456 |
| 28 | 4472 | 4487 | 4502 | 4518 | 4533 | 4548 | 4564 | 4579 | 4594 | 4606 |
| 29 | 4624 | 4639 | 4654 | 4669 | 4683 | 4698 | 4713 | 4728 | 4742 | 4757 |
| 30 | 4771 | 4786 | 4800 | 4814 | 4829 | 4843 | 4857 | 4871 | 4886 | 4900 |
| 31 | 4914 | 4928 | 4942 | 4955 | 4969 | 4983 | 4997 | 5011 | 5024 | 5038 |
| 32 | 5051 | 5065 | 5079 | 5092 | 5105 | 5119 | 5132 | 5145 | 5159 | 5172 |
| 33 | 5185 | 5198 | 5211 | 5224 | 5237 | 5250 | 5263 | 5276 | 5289 | 5302 |
| 34 | 5315 | 5328 | 5340 | 5353 | 5366 | 5378 | 5391 | 5403 | 5416 | 5428 |
| 35 | 5441 | 5453 | 5465 | 5478 | 5490 | 5502 | 5514 | 5527 | 5539 | 5551 |
| 36 | 5563 | 5575 | 5587 | 5599 | 5611 | 5623 | 5635 | 5647 | 5658 | 5670 |
| 37 | 5682 | 5694 | 5705 | 5717 | 5729 | 5740 | 5752 | 5763 | 5775 | 5786 |
| 38 | 5798 | 5809 | 5821 | 5832 | 5843 | 5855 | 5866 | 5877 | 5888 | 5899 |
| 39 | 5911 | 5922 | 5933 | 5944 | 5955 | 5966 | 5977 | 5988 | 5999 | 6010 |
| 40 | 6021 | 6031 | 6042 | 6053 | 6064 | 6075 | 6085 | 6096 | 6107 | 6117 |
| 41 | 6128 | 6138 | 6149 | 6160 | 6170 | 6180 | 6191 | 6201 | 6212 | 6222 |
| 42 | 6232 | 6243 | 6253 | 6263 | 6274 | 6284 | 6294 | 6304 | 6314 | 6325 |
| 43 | 6335 | 6345 | 6355 | 6365 | 6375 | 6385 | 6395 | 6405 | 6415 | 6425 |
| 44 | 6435 | 6444 | 6454 | 6464 | 6474 | 6484 | 6493 | 6503 | 6513 | 6522 |
| 45 | 6532 | 6542 | 6551 | 6561 | 6571 | 6580 | 6590 | 6599 | 6609 | 6618 |
| 46 | 6628 | 6637 | 6646 | 6656 | 6665 | 6675 | 6684 | 6693 | 6702 | 6712 |
| 47 | 6721 | 6730 | 6739 | 6749 | 6758 | 6767 | 6776 | 6785 | 6794 | 6803 |
| 48 | 6812 | 6821 | 6830 | 6839 | 6848 | 6857 | 6866 | 6875 | 6884 | 6893 |
| 49 | 6902 | 6911 | 6920 | 6928 | 6937 | 6946 | 6955 | 6964 | 6972 | 6981 |
| 50 | 6990 | 6998 | 7007 | 7016 | 7024 | 7033 | 7042 | 7050 | 7059 | 7067 |
| 51 | 7076 | 7084 | 7093 | 7101 | 7110 | 7118 | 7126 | 7135 | 7143 | 7152 |
| 52 | 7160 | 7168 | 7177 | 7185 | 7193 | 7202 | 7210 | 7218 | 7226 | 7235 |
| 53 | 7243 | 7251 | 7259 | 7267 | 7275 | 7284 | 7292 | 7300 | 7308 | 7316 |
| 54 | 7324 | 7332 | 7340 | 7348 | 7356 | 7364 | 7372 | 7380 | 7388 | 7396 |

| N | 0 | 1 | 2 | 3 | 4 | 5 | 6 | 7 | 8 | 9 |
|---|---|---|---|---|---|---|---|---|---|---|
| 55 | 7404 | 7412 | 7419 | 7427 | 7435 | 7443 | 7451 | 7459 | 7466 | 7474 |
| 56 | 7482 | 7490 | 7497 | 7505 | 7513 | 7520 | 7528 | 7536 | 7543 | 7551 |
| 57 | 7559 | 7566 | 7574 | 7582 | 7589 | 7597 | 7604 | 7612 | 7619 | 7627 |
| 58 | 7634 | 7642 | 7649 | 7657 | 7664 | 7672 | 7679 | 7686 | 7694 | 7701 |
| 59 | 7709 | 7716 | 7723 | 7731 | 7738 | 7745 | 7752 | 7760 | 7767 | 7774 |
| 60 | 7782 | 7789 | 7796 | 7803 | 7810 | 7818 | 7825 | 7832 | 7839 | 7846 |
| 61 | 7853 | 7860 | 7868 | 7875 | 7882 | 7889 | 7896 | 7903 | 7910 | 7917 |
| 62 | 7924 | 7931 | 7938 | 7945 | 7952 | 7959 | 7966 | 7973 | 7980 | 7987 |
| 63 | 7993 | 8000 | 8007 | 8014 | 8021 | 8028 | 8035 | 8041 | 8048 | 8055 |
| 64 | 8062 | 8069 | 8075 | 8082 | 8089 | 8096 | 8102 | 8109 | 8116 | 8122 |
| 65 | 8129 | 8136 | 8142 | 8149 | 8156 | 8162 | 8169 | 8176 | 8182 | 8189 |
| 66 | 8195 | 8202 | 8209 | 8215 | 8222 | 8228 | 8235 | 8241 | 8248 | 8254 |
| 67 | 8261 | 8267 | 8274 | 8280 | 8287 | 8293 | 8299 | 8306 | 8312 | 8319 |
| 68 | 8325 | 8331 | 8338 | 8344 | 8351 | 8357 | 8363 | 8370 | 8376 | 8382 |
| 69 | 8388 | 8395 | 8401 | 8407 | 8414 | 8420 | 8426 | 8432 | 8439 | 8445 |
| 70 | 8451 | 8457 | 8463 | 8470 | 8476 | 8482 | 8488 | 8494 | 8500 | 8506 |
| 71 | 8513 | 8519 | 8525 | 8531 | 8537 | 8543 | 8549 | 8555 | 8561 | 8567 |
| 72 | 8573 | 8579 | 8585 | 8591 | 8597 | 8603 | 8609 | 8615 | 8621 | 8627 |
| 73 | 8633 | 8639 | 8645 | 8651 | 8657 | 8663 | 8669 | 8675 | 8681 | 8686 |
| 74 | 8692 | 8698 | 8704 | 8710 | 8716 | 8722 | 8727 | 8733 | 8739 | 8745 |
| 75 | 8751 | 8756 | 8762 | 8768 | 8774 | 8779 | 8785 | 8791 | 8797 | 8802 |
| 76 | 8808 | 8814 | 8820 | 8825 | 8831 | 8837 | 8842 | 8848 | 8854 | 8859 |
| 77 | 8865 | 8871 | 8876 | 8882 | 8887 | 8893 | 8899 | 8904 | 8910 | 8915 |
| 78 | 8921 | 8927 | 8932 | 8938 | 8943 | 8949 | 8954 | 8960 | 8965 | 8971 |
| 79 | 8976 | 8982 | 8987 | 8993 | 8998 | 9004 | 9009 | 9015 | 9020 | 9025 |
| 80 | 9031 | 9036 | 9042 | 9047 | 9053 | 9058 | 9063 | 9069 | 9074 | 9079 |
| 81 | 9085 | 9090 | 9096 | 9101 | 9106 | 9112 | 9117 | 9122 | 9128 | 9133 |
| 82 | 9138 | 9143 | 9149 | 9154 | 9159 | 9165 | 9170 | 9175 | 9180 | 9186 |
| 83 | 9191 | 9196 | 9201 | 9206 | 9212 | 9217 | 9222 | 9227 | 9232 | 9238 |
| 84 | 9243 | 9248 | 9253 | 9258 | 9263 | 9269 | 9274 | 9279 | 9284 | 9289 |
| 85 | 9294 | 9299 | 9304 | 9309 | 9315 | 9320 | 9325 | 9330 | 9335 | 9340 |
| 86 | 9345 | 9350 | 9355 | 9360 | 9365 | 9370 | 9375 | 9380 | 9385 | 9390 |
| 87 | 9395 | 9400 | 9405 | 9410 | 9415 | 9420 | 9425 | 9430 | 9435 | 9440 |
| 88 | 9445 | 9450 | 9455 | 9460 | 9465 | 9469 | 9474 | 9479 | 9484 | 9489 |
| 89 | 9494 | 9499 | 9504 | 9509 | 9513 | 9518 | 9523 | 9528 | 9533 | 9538 |
| 90 | 9542 | 9547 | 9552 | 9557 | 9562 | 9566 | 9571 | 9576 | 9581 | 9586 |
| 91 | 9590 | 9595 | 9600 | 9605 | 9609 | 9614 | 9619 | 9624 | 9628 | 9633 |
| 92 | 9638 | 9643 | 9647 | 9652 | 9657 | 9661 | 9666 | 9671 | 9675 | 9680 |
| 93 | 9685 | 9689 | 9694 | 9699 | 9703 | 9708 | 9713 | 9717 | 9722 | 9727 |
| 94 | 9731 | 9736 | 9741 | 9745 | 9750 | 9754 | 9759 | 9763 | 9768 | 9773 |
| 95 | 9777 | 9782 | 9786 | 9791 | 9795 | 9800 | 9805 | 9809 | 9814 | 9818 |
| 96 | 9823 | 9827 | 9832 | 9836 | 9841 | 9845 | 9850 | 9854 | 9859 | 9863 |
| 97 | 9868 | 9872 | 9877 | 9881 | 9886 | 9890 | 9894 | 9899 | 9903 | 9908 |
| 98 | 9912 | 9917 | 9921 | 9926 | 9930 | 9934 | 9939 | 9943 | 9948 | 9952 |
| 99 | 9956 | 9961 | 9965 | 9969 | 9974 | 9978 | 9983 | 9987 | 9991 | 9996 |

# ANSWERS TO PROBLEMS

## CHAPTER 1 ⎯⎯⎯⎯⎯⎯⎯⎯⎯⎯⎯⎯⎯⎯⎯⎯⎯⎯

### PROBLEMS

1. d
2. c
3. a
4. b
5. c

6. a
7. a
8. b
9. b

### CHAPTER REVIEW PROBLEMS

1. a
2. c
3. b
4. c
5. d
6. a
7. a
8. the effects of temperature and pressure on the percent yield of $NH_3$

9. pressure
10. percent $NH_3$
11. kPa
12. 10
13. 25%
14. 98%
15. 63%
16. 300°C

## CHAPTER 2 ⎯⎯⎯⎯⎯⎯⎯⎯⎯⎯⎯⎯⎯⎯⎯⎯⎯⎯

### PROBLEMS

1. a. 4, ±0.001 g
   b. 3, ±0.001 kg
   c. 3, ±0.1 mL
   d. 2, ±100 m
   e. 2, ±0.001 g
   f. 4, ±0.01 g
   g. 3, ±0.001 cm
   h. 2, ±0.0001 g
   i. 3, ±0.0001 $cm^3$
   j. 5, ±0.001 cm
   k. 4, ±0.01 $cm^3$
   l. 4, ±0.0001 m
   m. 4, ±0.001 g
   n. 4, ±0.01 cm
   o. 7, ±1 g
2. a. 29 cm
   b. 32.9 g
   c. 7.16 m
   d. 0.181 g

3. a. 11.21 km
   b. 7.3 g
   c. 200 m
   d. 13.31 cm
4. a. 9.8 $cm^2$
   b. 2.4 $m^2$
   c. 0.0007 $m^2$
   d. 16 $km^2$
   e. 32 $dm^3$
   f. 64 $cm^3$
5. a. 56 cm
   b. 1.6
   c. 0.27 $dm^2$
   d. 8.08 m
   e. 2.32
   f. 30 $g/cm^3$

6. a. 750 000 mg
   b. 0.0015 km
   c. 86 400 s
   d. 520 m
   e. 0.065 kg
   f. 0.000 75 g
7. 800.0 g, $7.82
8. 523.1 km/hr
9. 0.915 m$^3$
10. 455 min.
11. 1.6 × 10$^{-5}$ light years
12. a. 3 × 10$^{-5}$ cm
    b. 8 × 10$^6$ g
    c. 5.5 × 10$^7$ m
    d. 2 × 10$^{-3}$ g
    e. 7 × 10$^{-6}$ m
    f. 6.5 × 10$^4$ km

13. a. 1.4 × 10$^{-6}$ cm$^2$
    b. 2.1 m$^2$
    c. 2.00 g/cm$^3$
    d. 4.61 × 10$^{-2}$ km
    e. 8.2 × 10$^5$ cm$^3$
    f. 3.0 × 10$^3$
    g. 3.0000 × 10$^4$ m/s
    h. 1 × 10$^6$ m$^3$
14. 1.40 g/cm$^3$
15. 11 g/cm$^3$
16. 1.40 g/dm$^3$
17. 22.0 cm$^3$
18. 120 g
19. 306.2 g

## CHAPTER REVIEW PROBLEMS

1. 1000 cm/s
2. a. 3.50 × 10$^2$ cm
   b. 0.065 kg
   c. 5.2 × 10$^5$ mm
   d. 8140 cm$^3$
3. (lab)(mess)
4. a. 2    f. 1
   b. 3    g. 5
   c. 4    h. 3
   d. 2    i. 7
   e. 3    j. 2

5. 3470 cm$^2$
6. 4.1 g/cm$^3$
7. 390 m$^3$
8. 4.6 × 10$^6$ cm$^3$
9. 20 m/s
10. 9000 cm$^3$
11. a. 25.8 cm$^3$
    b. 16.4 cm$^3$
    c. 24.0 cm$^3$
12. 445 g, iron heavier

# CHAPTER 3 _____

## PROBLEMS

1. a. solution
   b. element
   c. compound
   d. compound
   e. element
   f. compound
   g. solution
   h. heterogeneous mixture
   i. element
   j. heterogeneous mixture
   k. compound
   l. element

2. Properties
   a. chemical
   b. physical
   c. physical
   d. chemical
   e. physical
   f. physical
   g. physical
   h. chemical
   i. physical
   j. physical
   k. chemical
   l. physical

3. Changes
   a. physical
   b. chemical
   c. chemical
   d. physical
   e. chemical
   f. physical
   g. chemical
   h. physical

4. 93 300 J
5. 95 700 J
6. 2680 J
7. 15.5°C
8. 2.50 J/g·C°

## CHAPTER REVIEW PROBLEMS

1. 4360 J
2. $1.30 \times 10^3$ J
3. 54.8 J
4. 633 J

5. 1590 J
6. 17.58°C
7. 0.4823 J/g·C°
8. 322 000 J

# CHAPTER 4 ⸻

## PROBLEMS

1. a. Cu
   b. Bi
   c. Nb
   d. Mg
   e. Ta
   f. Al
2. a. copper
   b. potassium
   c. lithium
   d. calcium
   e. sodium
   f. magnesium
3. a. LiF
   b. LiCl
   c. LiBr
   d. LiI
   e. $Li_2O$
   f. $Li_2S$
   g. $CaF_2$
   h. $CaCl_2$
   i. $CaBr_2$
   j. $Ca(OH)_2$
   k. CaO
   l. CaS

4. a. NaCN
   b. NaOH
   c. $NaBrO_3$
   d. $NaCH_3COO$
   e. $Ba(CN)_2$
   f. $Ba(OH)_2$
   g. BaO
   h. $BaSO_4$
5. a. $Ba(N_3)_2$
   b. $ZnMoO_4$
   c. $CsClO_4$
   d. $Al_2(SiO_3)_3$
   e. BP
   f. $Ag_3N$
   g. $CdC_2O_4$
   h. KSCN
   i. $Ca_3(PO_2)_2$
   j. $Al_2(SiF_6)_3$
6. a. $CaSO_4$
   b. $NaNO_3$
   c. $KClO_4$
   d. $Al_2(SO_4)_3$
   e. $KClO_3$
   f. $MgSO_3$

g. $LiNO_2$
h. $NaClO_2$
i. $(NH_4)_2Cr_2O_7$
j. $NaNO_2$

7. a. sodium sulfide
   b. lithium oxide
   c. magnesium bromide
   d. aluminum nitride
   e. calcium fluoride
   f. potassium iodide
   g. magnesium sulfate
   h. calcium hypochlorite
   i. barium nitrite

8. a. magnesium hydroxide
   b. calcium oxide
   c. lithium acetate
   d. zinc chloride
   e. sodium phosphide
   f. potassium selenide
   g. ammonium magnesium phosphate
   h. potassium nitrite
   i. potassium sodium carbonate

9. a. sodium sulfate
   b. silver nitrate
   c. zinc dichromate
   d. ammonium acetate
   e. potassium perchlorate
   f. ammonium chlorate
   g. calcium oxalate
   h. barium carbonate
   i. sodium dihydrogen phosphate

10. a. $MnCl_3$
    b. $FeBr_3$
    c. $CrBr_3$
    d. $SnCl_4$
    e. $MnBr_2$
    f. $SnO_2$
    g. $Cr_2O_3$
    h. $PbO$
    i. $Mn_2O_7$
    j. $Hg_2O$

11. a. titanium(II) chloride
    b. titanium(IV) bromide
    c. copper(I) chloride
    d. lead(II) iodide
    e. tin(IV) chloride
    f. antimony(V) oxide
    g. chromium(VI) oxide
    h. manganese(II,III) oxide
    i. titanium(IV) oxide
    j. lead(II) oxide
    k. bismuth(V) fluoride
    l. nickel(II) bromide
    m. copper(II) bromide
    n. lead(II) chloride
    o. chromium(III) fluoride

12. a. iron(III) sulfate
    b. chromium(II) hydroxide
    c. mercury(I) chlorate
    d. iron(II) perchlorate
    e. manganese(II) sulfate
    f. mercury(II) iodate
    g. lead(II) chlorite
    h. copper(II) acetate
    i. copper(I) sulfate
    j. cobalt(II) sulfate

13. a. $Cu(ClO_3)_2$
    b. $Bi_2Te_3$
    c. $Mn_2(SO_4)_3$
    d. $Fe(NO_3)_3$
    e. $Sn(NO_3)_4$
    f. $Cr_2(SO_4)_3$
    g. $Fe(OH)_2$
    h. $Cu_3(PO_4)_2$
    i. $Hg_2(NO_2)_2$
    j. $Pb(NO_3)_2$

14. a. $Cl_2O$
    b. $ClO_2$
    c. $CS_2$
    d. $ClF_3$
    e. $Cl_2O_7$
    f. $SF_6$

15. a. carbon dioxide
    b. nitrogen dioxide
    c. sulfur trioxide
    d. phosphorus trichloride
    e. nitrogen monoxide
    f. diphosphorus pentoxide

16. a. CH
    b. CH
    c. $CH_2O$
    d. $C_2H_5$
    e. $P_2O_5$
    f. $SO_3$
    g. $NO_2$
    h. $NO_2$
    i. $AgC_2H_2O_3$
    j. $KS_2$

17. a. 5
    b. 1
    c. 6
    d. 1
    e. 2
    f. 12

18. a. 14H, 7O
    b. 6N, 24H, 2P, 8O
    c. 8Al, 12O
    d. 3Cu, 3S, 12O

## CHAPTER REVIEW PROBLEMS

1. a. $NaNO_2$
   b. $Na_2CO_3$
   c. $Na_2SO_4$
   d. KOH
   e. $KNO_3$
   f. $K_2SO_3$
   g. $K_3PO_4$
   h. $CdC_2O_4$
   i. $CdCO_3$
   j. $CdSO_4$
   k. $Cd_3(PO_4)_2$
   l. $AlBr_3$
   m. $Al(NO_3)_3$
   n. $Al_2S_3$
2. a. $Mg(NO_3)_2$
   b. $MgSO_4$
   c. $MgCO_3$
   d. $BaBr_2$
   e. $Ba(NO_3)_2$
   f. $BaSO_4$
   g. FeO
   h. $Fe(OH)_2$
   i. $FeCO_3$
   j. $FeSO_4$
   k. $FePO_4$
   l. $FeBr_3$
3. a. $SrCl_2$
   b. $Sr(OH)_2$
   c. $Sr(NO_3)_2$
   d. $SrSO_3$
   e. SrS
   f. $Fe_2(SO_4)_3$

   g. $FePO_4$
   h. $HgBr_2$
   i. $HgCO_3$
   j. HgS

4. a. sodium nitrate
   b. sodium sulfite
   c. sodium phosphate
   d. potassium nitrite
   e. potassium carbonate
   f. potassium sulfate
   g. cadmium bromide
   h. cadmium nitrate
   i. cadmium sulfite
   j. cadmium sulfide
   k. aluminum chloride
   l. aluminum hydroxide

5. a. magnesium nitrite
   b. magnesium sulfite
   c. magnesium phosphate
   d. barium nitrite
   e. barium sulfite
   f. barium carbonate
   g. aluminum sulfate
   h. aluminum phosphate
   i. iron(II) bromide
   j. iron(II) nitrate
   k. iron(II) sulfite
   l. iron(II) sulfide

6. a. barium phosphate
   b. strontium bromide
   c. strontium nitrate

d. strontium carbonate
e. strontium sulfate
f. strontium phosphate
g. iron(III) chloride
h. iron(III) nitrate
i. iron(III) sulfide
j. mercury(II) chloride
k. mercury(II) nitrate
l. mercury(II) sulfate

7. a. NaOH
   b. $HgSO_4$
   c. $Ca(ClO)_2$
   d. $Pb_3(PO_4)_2$
   e. $Al(ClO_3)_3$
   f. $(NH_4)_2S$
   g. $Cu_2CO_3$
   h. $Hg_2S$
   i. $Pb(CH_3COO)_2$
   j. $MnO_2$
   k. $MnSO_4$
   l. $Ag_2O$
   m. $Zn(NO_3)_2$
   n. $Cr_2(SO_3)_3$
   o. $(NH_4)_2Cr_2O_7$
   p. $Fe_2O_3$

8. a. sodium acetate
   b. nickel(II) nitrate
   c. mercury(I) chloride
   d. tin(II) phosphate
   e. chromium(II) hydroxide
   f. zinc chlorate
   g. magnesium bromide
   h. copper(I) azide
   i. calcium hydride
   j. barium nitrite
   k. manganese(II) sulfide
   l. tin(IV) nitrate
   m. ammonium sulfate
   n. lead(II) oxide
   o. potassium cyanide

9. a. $Mg(NO_3)_2$
   b. $AgCH_3COO$
   c. $Ba(ClO_4)_2$
   d. $KNO_2$

e. $(NH_4)_2SO_4$
f. $(NH_4)_2Cr_2O_7$
g. $BaMoO_4$
h. $Zn(SCN)_2$

10. a. iron(II) sulfate
    b. ammonium chlorate
    c. iron(II) acetate
    d. copper(II) chromate
    e. magnesium nitrate
    f. aluminum phosphate
    g. sodium sulfite
    h. calcium chlorite
    i. ammonium carbonate
    j. silver chromate
    k. barium phosphate
    l. potassium perchlorate

11. a. $ZnSiF_6$
    b. $Sb_2S_5$
    c. $Bi_2Te_3$
    d. $TiI_4$
    e. $NiF_2$
    f. $MnO_2$
    g. $PbO_2$
    h. $CaC_4H_4O_6$
    i. HgO
    j. $Co_2O_3$

12. a. zinc thiocyanate
    b. antimony(V) oxide
    c. titanium(II) oxide
    d. indium(III) phosphide
    e. manganese(III) oxide
    f. chromium(III) acetate

13. a. $C_3H_7$
    b. $CO_2$
    c. $NF_2$
    d. $C_3H_6Cl_2$
    e. $C_5H_{10}O_2$
    f. $PNCl_2$

14. a. 5
    b. 9
    c. 3
    d. 6
    e. 1
    f. 4

# CHAPTER 5

## PROBLEMS

1.  a. 98.1 u
    b. 40.0 u
    c. 80.0 u
    d. 233 u
    e. 131 u
    f. 213 u
    g. 1350 u
    h. 64.1 u
2.  180 u
3.  a. 6.02 g
    b. 69.0 g
    c. 137 g
    d. 209 g
4.  a. 2.02 mol
    b. 0.0992 mol
    c. 0.269 mol
    d. 0.150 mol
5.  a. $1.20 \times 10^{24}$ atoms
    b. $1.20 \times 10^{24}$ atoms
    c. $1.81 \times 10^{24}$ ions
    d. $1.20 \times 10^{24}$ molecules
6.  a. 23.0 g
    b. 61.0 g
    c. 87.7 g
    d. 5.73 g
7.  a. $1.00M$
    b. $0.250M$
    c. $1.21M$
8.  a. 41.6 g
    b. 421 g
    c. 71.0 g
9.  a. 1.00 dm$^3$
    b. 4.00 dm$^3$
    c. 0.737 dm$^3$
10. a. 30.0% O, 70% Fe
    b. 6.90% O, 93.1% Ag
    c. 7.37% O, 92.6% Hg
    d. 41.1% S, 58.9% Na

11. 32.4% Na
12. urea 46.7% N
    ammonia 82.4% N
13. a. 14.3% Na
    b. 9.97% S
    c. 69.6% O
    d. 55.9% $H_2O$
14. a. mono = 31.1% Ca
       di   = 27.3% Ca
       hexa = 18.3% Ca
    b. mono = 14.0% $H_2O$
       di   = 24.5% $H_2O$
       hexa = 49.3% $H_2O$
15. a. 15.3% $H_2O$ experimental
    b. 84.72% $BaCl_2$
    c. 3% error
16. a. FeS
    b. MnS
    c. $K_2Cr_2O_7$
17. a. $Na_2SO_4$
    b. $Na_2S_2O_3$
18. a. FeO
    b. $Fe_3O_4$
    c. $Fe_2O_3$
19. a. $P_2O_3$, $P_4O_6$
    b. $P_2O_5$, $P_4O_{10}$
20. $N_2O_4$
21. a. $CoCl_2 \cdot 6H_2O$
    b. $Pb(CH_3COO)_2 \cdot 3H_2O$
    c. $NiSO_4 \cdot 6H_2O$
    d. $CaSO_4 \cdot 2H_2O$
22. $MgHPO_4 \cdot 3H_2O$

## CHAPTER REVIEW PROBLEMS

1.  a. 256 u
    b. 381 u
    c. 198 u
    d. 666 u
    e. 108 u
    f. 149 u
    g. 106 u
    h. 129 u
    i. 58.5 u
2.  121 u
3.  132 u

4.  a. 204 g
    b. 108 g
    c. 221 g
    d. 911 g
    e. 778.7 g
    f. 131 g

5.  a. 2.875 mol
    b. 1.001 mol
    c. 5.246 mol
    d. 0.499 mol
    e. 0.128 mol
    f. 0.484 mol
6.  a. $3.00 \times 10^{23}$ Ca atoms
    b. $2.01 \times 10^{24}$ $CO_2$ molecules
    c. $1.20 \times 10^{24}$ $H_2S$ molecules
    d. $7.53 \times 10^{22}$ $Mg^{2+}$ ions
7.  a. 16.1 g S
    b. 72.1 g $H_2O$
8.  a. 1.00$M$
    b. 0.760$M$
9.  a. 134 g
    b. 49.0 g
10. a. 20.0 $dm^3$
    b. 0.177 $dm^3$
11. 11.2% Na, 41.0% C
12. 66.7% C
13. 51.2% $H_2O$
14. a. $K_2Cr_2O_7$
    b. $K_2CrO_4$
15. MgO
16. $C_{54}O_6H_{102}$
17. $C_6O_7H_8$

# CHAPTER 6

## PROBLEMS

1. $2Mg(cr) + O_2(g) \rightarrow 2MgO(cr)$
2. $4Fe(cr) + 3O_2(g) \rightarrow 2Fe_2O_3(cr)$
3. $H_2O(l) + N_2O_3(g) \rightarrow 2HNO_2(aq)$
4. $Na_2O(cr) + H_2O(l) \rightarrow 2NaOH(aq)$
5. $3Fe(cr) + 4H_2O(l) \rightarrow Fe_3O_4(cr) + 4H_2(g)$
6. $MgBr_2(aq) + Cl_2(g) \rightarrow MgCl_2(aq) + Br_2(g)$
7. $Cl_2(g) + 2NaI(cr) \rightarrow 2NaCl(cr) + I_2(g)$
8. $2KNO_3(cr) \rightarrow 2KNO_2(cr) + O_2(g)$
9. $Zn(cr) + 2HCl(aq) \rightarrow ZnCl_2(aq) + H_2(g)$
10. $CaO(cr) + 2HCl(aq) \rightarrow CaCl_2(aq) + H_2O(l)$
11. $2Al(cr) + 3Pb(NO_3)_2(aq) \rightarrow 2Al(NO_3)_3(aq) + 3Pb(cr)$
12. $Cu(cr) + 2AgNO_3(aq) \rightarrow Cu(NO_3)_2(aq) + 2Ag(cr)$
13. $2K(cr) + 2H_2O(l) \rightarrow 2KOH(aq) + H_2(g)$
14. $Cl_2(g) + 2LiI(aq) \rightarrow 2LiCl(aq) + I_2(g)$
15. $2Al(cr) + 6HCl(aq) \rightarrow 2AlCl_3(aq) + 3H_2(g)$
16. $Fe(cr) + CuSO_4(aq) \rightarrow FeSO_4(aq) + Cu(cr)$
17. $Zn(cr) + H_2SO_4(aq) \rightarrow ZnSO_4(aq) + H_2(g)$
18. $Cl_2(g) + MgI_2(aq) \rightarrow MgCl_2(aq) + I_2(g)$
19. $2Na(cr) + 2H_2O(l) \rightarrow 2NaOH(aq) + H_2(g)$
20. $Mg(cr) + 2HCl(aq) \rightarrow MgCl_2(aq) + H_2(g)$
21. $Ca(OH)_2(aq) + 2HCl(aq) \rightarrow CaCl_2(aq) + 2H_2O(l)$
22. $3KOH(aq) + H_3PO_4(aq) \rightarrow K_3PO_4(aq) + 3H_2O(l)$
23. $2Al(NO_3)_3(aq) + 3H_2SO_4(aq) \rightarrow Al_2(SO_4)_3(aq) + 6HNO_3(aq)$
24. $Na_2SO_3(aq) + 2HCl(aq) \rightarrow 2NaCl(aq) + H_2O(l) + SO_2(g)$
25. $3NaOH(aq) + H_3PO_4(aq) \rightarrow Na_3PO_4(aq) + 3H_2O(l)$
26. $(NH_4)_2SO_4(aq) + Ca(OH)_2(aq) \rightarrow 2NH_4OH(aq) + CaSO_4(cr)$
27. $AgNO_3(aq) + KCl(aq) \rightarrow KNO_3(aq) + AgCl(cr)$

28. $3Mg(OH)_2(aq) + 2H_3PO_4(aq) \rightarrow Mg_3(PO_4)_2(cr) + 6H_2O(l)$
29. $FeS(cr) + 2HCl(aq) \rightarrow FeCl_2(aq) + H_2S(g)$
30. $(NH_4)_2S(aq) + Fe(NO_3)_2(aq) \rightarrow 2NH_4NO_3(aq) + FeS(cr)$
31. $2KNO_3(cr) \rightarrow 2KNO_2(cr) + O_2(g)$
32. $2PbO_2(cr) \rightarrow 2PbO(cr) + O_2(g)$
33. $2NaOH(cr) \rightarrow Na_2O(cr) + H_2O(l)$
34. $MgCO_3(cr) \rightarrow MgO(cr) + CO_2(g)$
35. $H_2SO_3(aq) \rightarrow H_2O(l) + SO_2(g)$
36. $CaCO_3(cr) \rightarrow CaO(cr) + CO_2(g)$
37. $2Fe(OH)_3(cr) \rightarrow Fe_2O_3(cr) + 3H_2O(l)$
38. $2NaClO_3(cr) \rightarrow 2NaCl(cr) + 3O_2(g)$
39. $2Ag_2O(cr) \rightarrow 4Ag(cr) + O_2(g)$
40. $2H_2O(l) \overset{\text{electricity}}{\rightarrow} 2H_2(g) + O_2(g)$
41. $2Na(cr) + Cl_2 \rightarrow 2NaCl(cr)$
42. $Br_2(g) + 2H_2O(l) + SO_2(g) \rightarrow 2HBr(aq) + H_2SO_4(aq)$
43. $CaO(cr) + H_2O(l) \rightarrow Ca(OH)_2(aq)$
44. $P_2O_5(cr) + 3BaO(cr) \rightarrow Ba_3(PO_4)_2(cr)$
45. $BaO(cr) + H_2O(l) \rightarrow Ba(OH)_2(aq)$
46. $SO_2(g) + MgO(cr) \rightarrow MgSO_3(cr)$
47. $CO_2(g) + H_2O(l) \rightarrow H_2CO_3(aq)$
48. $2Mg(cr) + O_2(g) \rightarrow 2MgO(cr)$
49. $N_2O_3(g) + H_2O(l) \rightarrow 2HNO_2(aq)$
50. $4Fe(cr) + 3O_2(g) \rightarrow 2Fe_2O_3(cr)$
51. 78.4 g $MgCl_2$
52. 6.07 g $Cl_2$
53. 1.95 g $O_2$
54. 0.747 g Cu
55. 9.18 g $NH_3$
56. 18.7 g HCl
57. 8.36 g $Ag_3PO_4$
58. 20.4 g NaOH


## CHAPTER REVIEW PROBLEMS

1. $2HgO(cr) \rightarrow 2Hg(l) + O_2(g)$
2. $2H_2O(l) \rightarrow 2H_2(g) + O_2(g)$
3. $2Al(cr) + 3Pb(NO_3)_2(aq) \rightarrow 2Al(NO_3)_3(aq) + 3Pb(cr)$
4. $Cu(cr) + 2AgNO_3(aq) \rightarrow Cu(NO_3)_2(aq) + 2Ag(cr)$
5. $2K(cr) + 2H_2O(l) \rightarrow 2KOH(aq) + H_2(g)$
6. $MnO_2(cr) + 4HCl(aq) \rightarrow MnCl_2(aq) + Cl_2(g) + 2H_2O(l)$
7. $Cl_2(g) + 2LiI(aq) \rightarrow 2LiCl(aq) + I_2(g)$
8. $3F_2(g) + 3H_2O(l) \rightarrow 6HF(aq) + O_3(g)$
9. $2AgNO_3(aq) + K_2SO_4(aq) \rightarrow Ag_2SO_4(aq) + 2KNO_3(aq)$
10. $4NH_3(g) + 7O_2(g) \rightarrow 2N_2O_4(g) + 6H_2O(g)$
11. D.D. $Al(NO_3)_3(aq) + 3NaOH(aq) \rightarrow Al(OH)_3(cr) + 3NaNO_3(aq)$
12. D. $2SO_3(g) \rightarrow 2SO_2(g) + O_2(g)$

13. D.D. $2H_3PO_4(aq) + 3Mg(OH)_2(aq) \rightarrow Mg_3(PO_4)_2(cr) + 6H_2O(l)$
14. D. $NH_4NO_2(cr) \rightarrow N_2(g) + 2H_2O(l)$
15. D.D. $4NH_3(g) + 5O_2(g) \rightarrow 4NO(g) + 6H_2O(g)$
16. D.D. $BaCl_2(aq) + Na_2SO_4(aq) \rightarrow 2NaCl(aq) + BaSO_4(cr)$
17. D.D. $Fe_2O_3(cr) + 3CO(g) \rightarrow 2Fe(cr) + 3CO_2(g)$
18. D.D. $3Mg(OH)_2(aq) + 2(NH_4)_3PO_4(aq) \rightarrow Mg_3(PO_4)_2(cr) + 6NH_3(g) + 6H_2O(l)$
19. S.D. $2Al(cr) + 3CuCl_2(aq) \rightarrow 2AlCl_3(aq) + 3Cu$
20. S.D. $Fe(cr) + 2AgCH_3COO(aq) \rightarrow Fe(CH_3COO)_2(aq) + 2Ag(cr)$
21. $3Mg(OH)_2(aq) + 2H_3PO_4(aq) \rightarrow 6H_2O(l) + Mg_3(PO_4)_2(cr)$
22. $FeS(cr) + 2HCl(aq) \rightarrow FeCl_2(aq) + H_2S(g)$
23. $(NH_4)_2S(aq) + Fe(NO_3)_2 \rightarrow 2NH_4NO_3(aq) + FeS(cr)$
24. $H_2SO_4(aq) + 2KOH(aq) \rightarrow K_2SO_4(aq) + 2H_2O(l)$
25. $Al_2(SO_4)_3(aq) + Ca_3(PO_4)_2(cr) \rightarrow 3CaSO_4(cr) + 2AlPO_4(cr)$
26. $BaCO_3(cr) + 2HCl(aq) \rightarrow BaCl_2(aq) + H_2O(l) + CO_2(g)$
27. $2AgCH_3COO(aq) + K_2CrO_4(aq) \rightarrow 2KCH_3COO(aq) + Ag_2CrO_4(cr)$
28. $2(NH_4)_3PO_4(aq) + 3Ba(OH)_2(aq) \rightarrow Ba_3(PO_4)_2(cr) + 6NH_4OH(aq)$
29. $Cr_2(SO_3)_3(aq) + 3H_2SO_4(aq) \rightarrow Cr_2(SO_4)_3(cr) + 3H_2SO_3(aq)$
30. $Ca(OH)_2(aq) + 2HNO_3(aq) \rightarrow Ca(NO_3)_2(aq) + 2H_2O(l)$
31. a. $Cu(cr) + 4HNO_3(aq) \rightarrow Cu(NO_3)_2(aq) + 2NO_2(g) + 2H_2O(l)$
    b. $Cu(NO_3)_2(aq) + 2NaOH(aq) \rightarrow Cu(OH)_2(cr) + 2NaNO_3(aq)$
    c. $Cu(OH)_2(cr) \rightarrow CuO(cr) + H_2O(l)$
    d. $CuO(cr) + H_2SO_4(aq) \rightarrow CuSO_4(aq) + H_2O(l)$
    e. $CuSO_4(aq) + Zn(cr) \rightarrow ZnSO_4(aq) + Cu(cr)$
32. a. $Na_2CO_3(aq) + H_2SO_4(aq) \rightarrow Na_2SO_4(aq) + CO_2(g) + H_2O(l)$
    b. $2NaHCO_3(aq) + H_2SO_4(aq) \rightarrow Na_2SO_4(aq) + 2CO_2(g) + 2H_2O(l)$
    sodium hydrogen carbonate
33. $4FeS_2(cr) + 11O_2(g) \rightarrow 2Fe_2O_3(cr) + 8SO_2(g)$
34. $2NaHSO_3(aq) \rightarrow Na_2SO_3(aq) + SO_2(g) + H_2O(l)$
35. $Fe_2O_3(cr) + 3C(cr) \rightarrow 2Fe(l) + 3CO(g)$, 313 mol Fe
36. $2NH_3(g) + H_2SO_4(aq) \rightarrow (NH_4)_2SO_4(aq)$, 742.24 kg $H_2SO_4$
37. $2C(cr) + 2H_2O(l) \rightarrow CH_4(g) + CO_2(g)$, 667 kg $CH_4$
38. $2NO(g) + O_2(g) \rightarrow 2NO_2(g)$
    $2NO_2(g) + H_2O(l) \rightarrow HNO_2(aq) + HNO_3(aq)$
    $5.00 \times 10^2$ kg $HNO_3$/year
39. $6CO_2(g) + 6H_2O(l) \rightarrow C_6H_{12}O_6(l) + 6O_2(g)$, 18.0 g $H_2O$

# CHAPTER 7

## PROBLEMS

1. a. $^{50}_{24}Cr$ $24e^-$, $24p^+$, $26n$
   b. $^{37}_{17}Cl$ $17e^-$, $17p^+$, $20n$
   c. $^{26}_{12}Mg$ $12e^-$, $12p^+$, $14n$
   d. $^{193}_{77}Ir$ $77e^-$, $77p^+$, $116n$
   e. $^{29}_{14}Si$ $14e^-$, $14p^+$, $15n$
   f. $^{22}_{10}Ne$ $10e^-$, $10p^+$, $12n$

2. a. hydrogen
   b. beryllium
   c. oxygen
   d. magnesium
   e. calcium
   f. zinc

3. 24.31 u

4. 192.2 u

## CHAPTER REVIEW PROBLEMS

1. T
2. F Atoms of the same element are identical in mass.
3. F Millikan is credited with the "oil drop" experiment.
4. F The mass of an electron is not equal to the mass of a proton.
5. T
6. F Thompson devised an experiment to determine the electron's mass.
7. F The atomic number is represented by the symbol Z.
8. T
9. F The isotopic mass difference is due to neutrons.
10. T
11. 51.996 u
12. a. 92     c. 2
    b. 34     d. 107
13. a. 24     c. 18
    b. 8     d. 36

14.

|      | Z  | A   | p  | n   | e  |
|------|----|-----|----|-----|----|
| Ca   | 20 | 43  | 20 | 23  | 20 |
| Pb   | 82 | 211 | 82 | 129 | 82 |
| Pu   | 94 | 242 | 94 | 148 | 94 |
| Cr   | 24 | 50  | 24 | 26  | 24 |

# CHAPTER 8

## PROBLEMS

1.

| n | l | m | s | total capacity |
|---|---|---|---|----------------|
| 4 | 3 | 3−, 2−, 1−, 0, 1+, 2+, 3+ | ±1/2 | $4f^{14}$  32 electrons |
|   | 2 | 2−, 1−, 0, 1+, 2+ | ±1/2 | $4d^{10}$ |
|   | 1 | 1−, 0, 1+ | ±1/2 | $4p^6$ |
|   | 0 | 0 | ±1/2 | $4s^2$ |

2. 32 electrons

3.

|       | s | p | d | f |
|-------|---|---|---|---|
| $l =$ | 0 | 1 | 2 | 3 |

4. three
5. two of opposite spin

6.

| $n$ | 2 | 3 | 4 | 4 | 5 |
|---|---|---|---|---|---|
| $l$ | 0 | 2 | 1 | 3 | 0 |
| sublevel | $2s$ | $3d$ | $4p$ | $4f$ | $5s$ |

7. $l = 0, 1, 2, 3, 4$
8. $m = 2-, 1-, 0, 1+, 2+$
9. a, b, d are correct
10. a. fluorine
    b. magnesium
    c. gallium
    d. sulfur
11. a. Al $1s^2 2s^2 2p^6 3s^2 3p^1$
    b. Fe $1s^2 2s^2 2p^6 3s^2 3p^6 4s^2 3d^6$
    c. Cd $1s^2 2s^2 2p^6 3s^2 3p^6 4s^2 3d^{10} 4p^6 5s^2 4d^{10}$
    d. C $1s^2 2s^2 2p^2$
    e. Ba $1s^2 2s^2 2p^6 3s^2 3p^6 4s^2 3d^{10} 4p^6 5s^2 4d^{10} 5p^6 6s^2$
    f. Hf $1s^2 2s^2 2p^6 3s^2 3p^6 4s^2 3d^{10} 4p^6 5s^2 4d^{10} 5p^6 6s^2 4f^{14} 5d^2$
12. a. $1s^2 2s^1$      e. $1s^2 2s^2 2p^1$
    b. $1s^2 2s^2 2p^3$   f. $1s^2 2s^2 2p^5$
    c. $1s^2 2s^2$       g. $1s^2 2s^2 2p^2$
    d. $1s^2 2s^2 2p^4$   h. $1s^2 2s^2 2p^6$

13.

| | $2s$ | $2p$ | | |
|---|---|---|---|---|
| a. | ↑ | | | |
| b. | ↑↓ | ↑ | ↑ | ↑ |
| c. | ↑↓ | | | |
| d. | ↑↓ | ↑↓ | ↑ | ↑ |
| e. | ↑↓ | ↑ | | |
| f. | ↑↓ | ↑↓ | ↑↓ | ↑ |
| g. | ↑↓ | ↑ | ↑ | |
| h. | ↑↓ | ↑↓ | ↑↓ | ↑↓ |

14. a. Li·
    b. ·Ṅ:
    c. Be:
    d. ·Ö:
    e. Ḃ:
    f. :Ḟ:
    g. ·Ċ:
    h. :Ṅe:

## CHAPTER REVIEW PROBLEMS

1. position, speed
2. four
3. $n$
4. $s, p, d, f$
5. two of opposite spin
6. Pauli Exclusion Principle
7. outer energy level electrons
8. electron configuration of an atom
9. three
10. seven
11. ten
12. $p$
13. opposite spin
14. a. Li· $\quad 1s^22s^1$
    b. Ra: $\quad 1s^22s^22p^63s^23p^64s^23d^{10}4p^65s^24d^{10}5p^66s^24f^{14}5d^{10}6p^67s^2$
    c. Na· $\quad 1s^22s^22p^63s^1$
    d. Hg: $\quad 1s^22s^22p^63s^23p^64s^23d^{10}4p^65s^24d^{10}5p^66s^24f^{14}5d^{10}$
    e. ·S̈n: $\quad 1s^22s^22p^63s^23p^64s^23d^{10}4p^65s^24d^{10}5p^2$
    f. :K̈r: $\quad 1s^22s^22p^63s^23p^64s^23d^{10}4p^6$

15. a. Ti: $\quad 4s^23d^3$    ↑↓   ☐ ☐ ☐

    b. Na· $\quad 3s^1$    ↑   ☐ ☐ ☐

    c. A̍l: $\quad 3s^23p^1$    ↑↓   ↑ ☐ ☐

    d. ·P̈: $\quad 3s^23p^3$    ↑↓   ↑ ↑ ↑

16. See Problems 14 and 15.

# CHAPTER 9 

## PROBLEMS

1. a. IIIA, 13
   b. IIA, 2
   c. VIIA, 17
   d. VIA, 16
   e. VB, 5
   f. IIB, 12

2. a. boron
   b. beryllium
   c. chlorine
   d. sulfur
   e. vanadium
   f. zinc

3.  a. $1s^22s^22p^63s^23p^64s^1$
    b. $1s^22s^22p^63s^23p^64s^23d^{10}4p^65s^24d^{10}5p^66s^24f^{14}5d^{10}$
    c. $1s^22s^1$
    d. $1s^22s^22p^63s^23p^3$
    e. $1s^22s^22p^63s^23p^64s^2$
    f. $1s^22s^22p^63s^23p^64s^23d^{10}4p^65s^24d^{10}5p^1$
4. period 5
5. chromium ($Z = 24$),
   copper ($Z = 29$)
6.  a. metal
    b. nonmetal
    c. metal
    d. metalloid
    e. metal
    f. metalloid
7. metals
8. C
9. D
10. A
11. B
12. F
13. G
14. H
15. E

# CHAPTER REVIEW PROBLEMS

1. nonmetals
2. metal
3. Dmitri Mendeleev
4. alkali metals
5. noble gases
6. principal quantum number, $n$
7. $(n - 1)$ $d$ sublevel
8. four pairs
9. $(n - 2)$ $f$ sublevel
10. a. $1s^22s^22p^63s^23p^2$
    b. $1s^22s^22p^63s^23p^64s^23d^{10}4p^6$
    c. $1s^22s^22p^63s^23p^64s^13d^{10}$
    d. $1s^22s^22p^63s^23p^64s^23d^{10}4p^65s^24d^{10}5p^66s^1$
11. a. titanium ($Z = 22$)
    b. neon ($Z = 10$)
    c. chromium ($Z = 24$)
    d. plutonium ($Z = 94$)
    e. bromine ($Z = 35$)
    f. sodium ($Z = 11$)
12. a. $1s^22s^22p^63s^23p^64s^23d^{10}4p^65s^24d^{10}5p^5$
    b. $1s^22s^22p^4$
    c. $1s^22s^22p^63s^23p^64s^23d^8$
    d. $1s^22s^22p^63s^23p^64s^23d^{10}4p^65s^2$
13. a. nonmetal
    b. metal
    c. metal
    d. metalloid
    e. metal
    f. metal

# CHAPTER 10

## PROBLEMS

1. a. Sr
   b. I
   c. Rb
   d. Mg
   e. P
   f. Ac
   g. Al
   h. Ba
2. a. Ca
   b. $Cl^-$
   c. $As^{3-}$
   d. Pb
   e. $Mg^{2+}$
   f. $Te^{2-}$
   g. $C^{4-}$
   h. Ag
3. a. 3+
   b. 3−
   c. 1−
   d. 2+
   e. 2+

f. 2−, 4+, 6+
g. 1+
h. 2+, 7+ (also 4+, 6+)

4. a. $4s$
   b. $2p$
   c. $2 - 4s, 1 - 4p$
   d. $3p$
   e. $2 - 5s, 2 - 5p$
   f. $4p$
   g. $4s$
   h. $2 - 4s, 1 - 3d$
5. a. O
   b. Sn
   c. F
   d. Ge
   e. I
   f. Ca
   g. Sb
   h. Al
   i. S

## CHAPTER REVIEW PROBLEMS

1. increase
2. decrease
3. a. Na
   b. K
   c. Al
   d. Br
   e. N
   f. Ar
4. a. $Fe^{3+}$
   b. S
   c. $U^{3+}$
   d. $Br^-$
   e. $Mo^{6+}$
   f. As
5. a. 1+
   b. 2+
   c. 3+
   d. 4+ or 4−
   e. 3−, 3+, 5+
   f. 2−

g. 1−
h. 0
i. 1+
6. a. 1+
   b. 2+, 3+
   c. 3+, 4+, 6+
   d. 3+, 5+
   e. 2+, 3+, 4+, 5+
   f. 2+
7. decrease
8. increase
9. metals
10. a. more
    b. less
    c. more
    d. less
11. decrease
12. decrease
13. increase

# CHAPTER 11 _____

## CHAPTER REVIEW PROBLEMS
1. false; . . . alkaline earth metals.
2. false; . . . allotropes of carbon.
3. false; . . . electrons are in $4f$ sublevels.
4. true
5. true
6. false; When hydrogen loses one electron . . .
7. true
8. false; . . . is called the noble gases.
9. true
10. false; . . . are in Groups IA (1) and VIIA (17).


# CHAPTER 12 _____

## PROBLEMS
1. a. ionic      d. ionic
   b. covalent    e. covalent
   c. covalent    f. covalent
2. a. 55% covalent    d. 97% covalent
   b. 85% covalent    e. 90% ionic
   c. 60% ionic      f. 93% covalent
3. a. bond length
   b. nonbonded distance
   c. ionic radius
   d. internuclear distance in the crystal
   e. internuclear distance in the crystal
   f. internuclear distance in the crystal
   g. ionic radius
4. covalent
5. ionic

## CHAPTER REVIEW PROBLEMS
1. a. ionic
   b. covalent
   c. covalent
   d. ionic
2. a. increases
   b. decreases
   c. increases
3. a. ionic
   b. metallic
   c. covalent

# CHAPTER 13

## PROBLEMS

1.  a. $\ddot{O}::C::\ddot{O}$     16 electrons, linear

    b. $:\ddot{C}l:$ B $:\ddot{C}l:$    24 electrons, trigonal planar
         $:\ddot{C}l:$

    c.
    $$\left[\begin{array}{c} :\ddot{O} \quad \ddot{O}: \\ N \\ :\ddot{O}: \end{array}\right]^{1-} \leftrightarrow \left[\begin{array}{c} :\ddot{O} \quad \ddot{O}: \\ N \\ :\ddot{O}: \end{array}\right]^{1-} \leftrightarrow \left[\begin{array}{c} :\ddot{O} \quad \ddot{O}: \\ N \\ :\ddot{O}: \end{array}\right]$$
    24 electrons trigonal planar

    d.   $:\ddot{O}:$
        H$:\ddot{O}:$P$:\ddot{O}:$H    32 electrons, tetrahedral
           $:\ddot{O}:$
           H

2.  a.   H$:\ddot{S}:$    8 electrons
         H

    b.
    $$\left[\begin{array}{c} H \\ H:\ddot{N}:H \\ H \end{array}\right]^{1+}$$
        8 electrons

    c.
    $$\left[\begin{array}{c} :\ddot{O} \quad \ddot{O}: \\ N \\ :\ddot{O}: \end{array}\right]^{1-} \leftrightarrow \left[\begin{array}{c} :\ddot{O} \quad \ddot{O}: \\ N \\ :\ddot{O}: \end{array}\right]^{1-} \leftrightarrow \left[\begin{array}{c} :\ddot{O} \quad \ddot{O}: \\ N \\ .\ddot{O}. \end{array}\right]^{1-}$$
    24 electrons.

    d. $:C:::O:$    10 electrons

    e.   $:\ddot{C}l:$
        $:\ddot{C}l:C:\ddot{C}l:$    32 electrons
        $:\ddot{C}l:$

    f.   $:\ddot{O}:$
        H$:C:\ddot{O}:$H    18 electrons
          $:\ddot{O}:$

3.  $NO_3^-$

4.  a. $(\sigma_{1s})^2$   $(\sigma_{1s}^*)^2$   $(\sigma_{2s})^2$,   B.O. $= 1$
    b. $(\sigma_{1s})^2$   $(\sigma_{1s}^*)^2$   $(\sigma_{2s})^2$,   $(\sigma_{2s}^*)^2$   B.O. $= 0$
    c. $(\sigma_{2s})^2$   $(\sigma_{1s}^*)^2$   $(\sigma_{2s})^2$   $(\sigma_{2s}^*)^2$   $(\pi_{2py})^2$   $(\pi_{2pz})^2$, B.O. $= 2$

# CHAPTER REVIEW PROBLEMS

1.  a. 24 electrons
    b. 10 electrons
    c. 26 electrons
    d. 16 electrons
    e. 32 electrons
    f. 34 electrons

2.  a. H:$\overset{\cdot\cdot}{\underset{H}{P}}$:H     8 electrons

    b. :$\overset{\cdot\cdot}{S}$::C::$\overset{\cdot\cdot}{S}$:     16 electrons

    c. $\left[:\overset{\cdot\cdot}{\underset{\cdot\cdot}{O}}:H\right]^{1-}$     8 electrons

    d. [:N:::O:]$^{1+}$     10 electrons

    e. $\left[\overset{:\overset{\cdot\cdot}{O}\quad\overset{\cdot\cdot}{O}:}{\underset{:\overset{\cdot\cdot}{O}:}{C}}\right]^{2-} \leftrightarrow \left[\overset{:\overset{\cdot\cdot}{O}\quad\overset{\cdot\cdot}{O}:}{\underset{:\overset{\cdot\cdot}{O}:}{C}}\right]^{2-} \leftrightarrow \left[\overset{:\overset{\cdot\cdot}{O}\quad\overset{\cdot\cdot}{O}:}{\underset{:\overset{\cdot\cdot}{O}:}{C}}\right]^{2-}$

       24 electrons

    f. H:C:::N:     10 electrons

    g. H:$\overset{\cdot\cdot}{\underset{H}{N}}$:H     8 electrons

    h. :$\overset{\cdot\cdot}{\underset{\cdot\cdot}{Cl}}$:$\overset{\cdot\cdot}{\underset{\cdot\cdot}{O}}$:$\overset{\cdot\cdot}{\underset{\cdot\cdot}{S}}$:$\overset{\cdot\cdot}{\underset{\cdot\cdot}{Cl}}$:     26 electrons

    i. trigonal bipyramid     40 electrons

$$\begin{array}{c} :\overset{\cdot\cdot}{Cl}: \\ :\overset{\cdot\cdot}{\underset{\cdot\cdot}{Cl}}:\overset{}{P}:\overset{\cdot\cdot}{\underset{\cdot\cdot}{Cl}}: \\ :\overset{\cdot\cdot}{\underset{\cdot\cdot}{Cl}}: \quad :\overset{\cdot\cdot}{\underset{\cdot\cdot}{Cl}}: \end{array}$$

3. $CO_2$ bonds are shorter than $CO_3^{2-}$
4. Bond angle, 107°, in $NH_3$ is less because of one unshared pair of electrons in nitrogen.
5. C $1s^2 2s^2 2p^2$. One $2s$ electron is promoted to occupy the empty $p$ orbital. The half-filled $s$ and three half-filled $p$ orbitals hybridize to produce four $sp^3$ hybrid orbitals, each with 1 electron.
6. $\sigma$ bond occurs when $s - s$, $s - p$, and end to end $p - p$ orbital overlap occurs.
   $\pi$ bond occurs when the $p - p$ overlap is between $p$ orbitals having parallel axes.

7. a. trigonal planar
   b. linear
   c. angular or bent
   d. tetrahedral
   e. tetrahedral
   f. octahedral
8. a. Construct a diagram similar to Figure 13-1 using the molecular orbital configuration.
   b. zero
   c. $(\sigma_{1s})^2 \quad (\sigma_{1s}^*)^2$
   d. no
9. a. See 8a.
   b. two
   c. $(\sigma_{1s})^2 \quad (\sigma_{1s}^*)^2 \quad (\sigma_{2s})^2 \quad (\sigma_{2s}^*)^2 \quad (\pi_{2py})^2 \quad (\pi_{2pz})^2$
   d. yes

# CHAPTER 14 _____

## PROBLEMS

1. As—Br is most polar
   a. I
   b. I
   c. Br
   d. N

2. a. :Ö—S̈=Ö: nonpolar-resonance structures, linear

   b. :C̈l—Äs—C̈l: polar-pyramidal structure
      |
      :C̈l:

   c. H—S̈e: polar-angular structure
      |
      H

   d.   :O:
        ‖
        S       nonpolar-resonance structures, trigonal planar
       ╱ ╲
   :Ö:   :Ö:

3. Pyramidal $NH_3$ is polar and has stronger intermolecular forces than symmetrical $CH_4$.
4. $F_2$, $Cl_2$, $Br_2$, $I_2$
5. a. tetrachloroaurate(III) ion
   b. chlorotriamminechromium(III) ion

c. tetraamminecopper(II) ion
d. tetraiodomercurate(II) ion
6. a. $Cr(H_2O)_6^{3+}$
   b. $Co(NH_3)_6^{3+}$

## CHAPTER REVIEW PROBLEMS

1. H—H, H → S, H ← Ga, H → Br, H → Cl, H → O
2. a. polar C → O

   b. nonpolar

   c. polar

   d. polar
3. a. $CH_3Cl$
   b. $N_2$
   c. $AsCl_3$
   d. $SO_3$
   e. $H_2S$
   f. $CCl_4$
4. polar molecule, negative ion
5. Shared pair of electrons is more strongly attracted by one atom in polar covalent bond.
6. complex ion
7. polar molecules
8. polar
9. a. tetrahydroxozincate ion
   b. dithiosulfatoargentate ion
   c. tetrachloroplumbate(II) ion
   d. hexaamminenickel(II) ion
10. a. $Fe(NH_3)_4^{2+}$, square planar or tetrahedral
    b. $Cu(H_2O)_6^{2+}$, octahedral
    c. $Ag(NH_3)_2^{+}$, linear
    d. $Sn(OH)_6^{2-}$, octahedral
11. hexacyanoferrate(II) ion
12. tetrachlorocuprate(II) ion
    tetraaquocopper(II) ion

# CHAPTER 15

## PROBLEMS

1. 75 kPa
2. 111 kPa
3. 96.1 kPa
4. 15.46 kPa
5. a. 302 K
   b. 217 K
   c. 617 K
   d. 235 K
   e. 373 K
   f. 298 K
6. a. $-105°C$
   b. $-18°C$
   c. $273°C$
   d. $27°C$
   e. $-220°C$
   f. $0°C$

## CHAPTER REVIEW PROBLEMS

1. manometer
2. kinetic theory
3. barometer
4. absolute zero
5. 101.325 kPa
6. pressure
7. lighter molecule
8. 107 kPa
9. same
10. 84.8 kPa
11. 48.3 kPa
12. a. $243°C$
    b. 428 K
    c. 299 K
    d. $-259°C$
    e. 694 K
    f. $100°C$
13. $SO_2$

# CHAPTER 16

## PROBLEMS

1. a. magnesium carbonate
   b. magnesium carbonate trihydrate
   c. magnesium carbonate pentahydrate
   d. neodymium(III) acetate monohydrate
   e. nickel(II) cyanide tetrahydrate
   f. praseodymium(III) carbonate octahydrate
2. a. $CaC_2O_4 \cdot H_2O$
   b. $Ce(BrO_3)_3 \cdot 9H_2O$
   c. $HBr \cdot 6H_2O$
   d. $FeC_2H_2O_4 \cdot 2H_2O$
   e. $Fe_2(C_2O_4)_3 \cdot 5H_2O$
   f. $LiI \cdot 3H_2O$

## CHAPTER REVIEW PROBLEMS

1. Crystals are rigid bodies that have flat faces meeting at definite angles and having sharp melting points.
2. unit cell
3. space lattice
4. twelve

5. HCP, CCP(FCC), BCC
6. no
7. doped
8. polymorphous
9. hydrates
10. anhydrous
11. hygroscopic
12. deliquescent
13. efflorescent
14. There is no regular arrangement.
15. glass, paraffin
16. a. nickel(II) chloride hexahydrate
    b. magnesium perchlorate hexahydrate
    c. magnesium phosphate tetrahydrate
    d. calcium nitrate trihydrate
17. a. $CoCl_2 \cdot 6H_2O$
    b. $Ba(OH)_2 \cdot 8H_2O$
    c. $Ga_2O_3 \cdot H_2O$
    d. $MgHAsO_4 \cdot 7H_2O$

# CHAPTER 17 _____

## PROBLEMS

1. Your answers need to have only 2 significant digits.
   a. $-124°C$
   b. 5000 kPa
   c. $-217°C$
   d. $-183°C$
2. a. solid
   b. gas
   c. liquid
   d. gas
3. a. solid changes to liquid
   b. gas condenses to liquid
   c. liquid changes to solid

   d. no change
4. a. 21.9 kJ
   b. 32.1 kJ
   c. 21.1 kJ
   d. 10.6 kJ
   e. 4.96 kJ
5. a. 4360 J
   b. 958 J
   c. 153 J
   d. 813 J
   e. 2550 J

## CHAPTER REVIEW PROBLEMS

1. no
2. no
3. no
4. yes
5. weak
6. lower temperature, raise pressure
7. a. 10°C
   b. 20°C

   c. 35°C
   d. 285 kPa
   e. C.
   f. A.
8. 2090 J
9. 155 J
10. 546 kJ
11. 25.9g ice

# CHAPTER 18

## PROBLEMS

1. a. 106 cm$^3$ O$_2$
   b. 48.2 cm$^3$ H$_2$
   c. 472 cm$^3$ SO$_2$
   d. 126.6 cm$^3$ N$_2$
   e. 2.90 m$^3$ N$_2$
   f. 0.982 dm$^3$ Ne
2. 125 kPa
3. 266 cm$^3$
4. a. 25.0 m$^3$
   b. 16.7 m$^3$
   c. 1.00 × 10$^2$ m$^3$
5. 2.03 dm$^3$
6. 211.1 kPa
7. 94.9 kPa
8. 53.6 kPa
9. 75.3 cm$^3$
10. a. 47.4 cm$^3$
    b. 69.9 cm$^3$
    c. 128 cm$^3$
    d. 2.20 × 10$^2$ cm$^3$
11. a. 20.0 m$^3$
    b. 5.00 m$^3$

12. a. 294 cm$^3$
    b. 67.3 cm$^3$
    c. 91.0 cm$^3$
    d. 324 cm$^3$
    e. 2.64 dm$^3$
    f. 11 cm$^3$
13. 8.0°C
14. a. 550 cm$^3$
    b. 210 cm$^3$
    c. 111 cm$^3$
    d. 180 cm$^3$
15. a. 173 cm$^3$
    b. 109 cm$^3$
    c. 42.8 cm$^3$
    d. 2.80 × 10$^2$ cm$^3$
16. 548 cm$^3$
17. 42 cm$^3$
18. 221 kPa
19. 1.0 × 10$^1$ m$^3$
20. 2.93 g/dm$^3$
21. 2.96 g/dm$^3$
22. 312 K or 39.3°C
23. 3.16/1
24. 0.0431 m/s

## CHAPTER REVIEW PROBLEMS

1. a. 34.1 cm$^3$
   b. 295 cm$^3$
   c. 83.7 cm$^3$
   d. 150 cm$^3$
   e. 114 cm$^3$
   f. 1.31 dm$^3$
   g. 275 cm$^3$
   h. 237 cm$^3$
2. a. 1.67 g/dm$^3$
   b. 1.64 g/dm$^3$

3. 1.88 g/dm$^3$
4. 2.74 g/dm$^3$
5. 50 cm$^3$
6. 45.0 kPa
7. a. 1.0 × 10$^3$ dm$^3$
   b. 760 dm$^3$
   c. pressure
8. 546 K or 273°C
9. 8.0 × 10$^2$ K or 527°C
10. 1.04/1

# CHAPTER 19

## PROBLEMS

1. a. 2.23 mol
   b. 0.0446 mol
   c. 0.29 mol

   d. 0.67 mol
   e. 0.11 mol
   f. 0.0893 mol

2.  a. 14 300 g
    b. 4.7482 g
    c. 0.250 g
    d. 589 g
    e. 3800 g
    f. 5.3253 g
3.  a. $9.0 \times 10^1$ dm$^3$ Br$_2$
    b. 131 dm$^3$ H$_2$S
    c. 8.91 dm$^3$ SO$_2$
    d. 189.6 dm$^3$ Cl$_2$
    e. 56.0 dm$^3$ NH$_3$
    f. 24.3 dm$^3$ NO$_2$
    g. 157 dm$^3$ O$_2$
    h. 6.14 dm$^3$ HCl
4.  63.8 g/mol SO$_2$
5.  128 g/mol HI
6.  16.0 g/mol CH$_4$
7.  a. 0.0298 mol O$_2$
    b. 0.144 mol CO$_2$
8.  a. 73.7 dm$^3$ H$_2$
    b. 46.5 dm$^3$ Cl$_2$
9.  87.3 g/mol PF$_3$

10. 1370 cm$^3$ H$_2$
11. 1880 cm$^3$ Br$_2$
12. 35.5 g CuO
13. 3110 cm$^3$ O$_2$
14. 8.04 g Al
15. $1.50 \times 10^2$ cm$^3$ H$_2$
16. 30.0 cm$^3$ O$_3$
17. 90.0 dm$^3$ H$_2$, 30.0 dm$^3$ N$_2$
18. 25.0 cm$^3$ Cl$_2$
19. a. 2.97 g KClO$_3$
    b. 1.16 g O$_2$
    c. 811 cm$^3$
20. NaOH, 0.25 mol Na$_2$SO$_4$
21. AgNO$_3$, 0.118 mol Ag
22. NaBr, 0.121 mol Br$_2$
23. 5.09 dm$^3$ NH$_3$
24. MgSO$_4$, 13.7 g Mg(CH$_3$COO)$_2$
25. 2.06 dm$^3$ O$_2$
26. 13.2 dm$^3$ Cl$_2$
27. 32.0 dm$^3$ N$_2$
28. 16.6 g Fe

## CHAPTER REVIEW PROBLEMS

1.  22.40 dm$^3$/mol
2.  93.2 g/mol
3.  a. 0.0893 mol NH$_3$, 1.52 g
    b. 0.205 mol SO$_2$, 19.7 g
4.  a. 128 dm$^3$
    b. 267 dm$^3$
5.  46.6 g/mol
6.  365 cm$^3$ H$_2$

7.  0.542 g Mg
8.  30.0 dm$^3$ O$_2$
9.  84.75 dm$^3$ CO
10. 17.5 dm$^3$ C$_2$H$_2$
11. 200.0 cm$^3$ H$_2$O (g),
        50.0 cm$^3$ O$_2$ remain
12. 16.7 g NaHCO$_3$
13. 4.45 dm$^3$ H$_2$

# CHAPTER 20 ⸻

## PROBLEMS

1.  a. +117 kJ
    b. $-6.90 \times 10^2$ kJ
    c. $-124$ kJ
2.  a. +181 J/K
    b. $-451$ J/K
    c. +167 J/K
3.  a. $-3.2$ kJ, spontaneous
    b. $-2.6$ kJ, not spontaneous
    c. $-68$ kJ, not spontaneous

4.  a. $-456$ kJ, spontaneous
    b. $-140$ kJ, spontaneous
    c. $-245$ kJ, spontaneous
5.  189 J/mol·K
6.  $-742$ kJ/mol
7.  $-137$ kJ

## CHAPTER REVIEW PROBLEMS

1. a. −422 kJ, spontaneous
   b. −358 kJ, spontaneous
2. a. −248 kJ
   b. −1317 kJ
3. a. −553 J/K
   b. +128 J/K

4. a. −42.9 kJ, spontaneous
   b. −192 kJ, spontaneous
5. +70. kJ
6. −1360 kJ
7. −635 kJ/mol
8. −124 kJ/mol

# CHAPTER 21 ──────────────

## PROBLEMS

1. a. 0.606$M$
   b. 0.244$M$
   c. 1.21$M$
2. a. 1.00 dm$^3$
   b. 4.00 dm$^3$
   c. 0.333 dm$^3$
3. a. 41.6 g CaCl$_2$
   b. 421 g KOH
   c. 71.0 g Na$_2$SO$_4$

4. a. 2.00$m$
   b. 2.40$m$
   c. 1.67$m$
5. a. 252 g KOH
   b. 22.5 g CH$_3$COOH
6. 684 g H$_2$O
7. 0.0807 CH$_3$CH$_2$OH, 0.919 H$_2$O
8. 0.183 C$_6$H$_5$CH$_3$, 0.817 C$_6$H$_6$

## CHAPTER REVIEW PROBLEMS

1. a. 1.00$M$
   b. 0.800$M$
   c. 0.500$M$
2. a. 134 g Na$_2$SO$_4$·7H$_2$O
   b. 49.0 g KH$_2$PO$_4$
   c. 6.30 × 10$^2$ g HNO$_3$
3. a. 20.0 dm$^3$
   b. 0.200 dm$^3$
   c. 12.8 dm$^3$
4. 7.85 g Pb(CH$_3$COO)$_2$, 0.0483$M$

5. a. 1.30$m$
   b. 0.111$m$
   c. 1.33$m$
6. a. 9.00 × 10$^2$ g C$_6$H$_{12}$O$_6$
   b. 18.3 g NaCl
7. 621 g C$_2$H$_4$(OH)$_2$
8. 0.500 CH$_3$OH
9. 5.79 g Pb(NO$_3$)$_2$
10. 58.4 g FeSO$_4$·7H$_2$O

# CHAPTER 22 ──────────────

## PROBLEMS

1. −5.43°C, 2 ions
2. −1.86°C
3. a. 100.886°C, 3 ions
   b. 100.590°C, 2 ions
   5. 100.723°C, 2 ions
4. 43.0 g NaCl, 2 ions

5. 1990 g C$_2$H$_4$(OH)$_2$
6. 180 g/mol
7. 85.0 g/mol, 2 ions
8. 46.0 g/mol
9. 6940 kPa
10. 45.9 kPa

## CHAPTER REVIEW PROBLEMS

1. $-2.14°C$, $84.0°C$
2. $-2.85°C$, $100.785°C$, 2 ions
3. $1.60 \times 10^2$ g
4. $2.60 \times 10^2$ g
5. 105 g/mol

6. 43.6 g/mol
7. 624 kPa
8. 142 kPa
9. 132 g/mol, $C_8H_{10}O_2$
10. 218 g/mol, $C_{10}H_6N_2O_4$

# CHAPTER 23 _____

## PROBLEMS

1. $R = k[NO_2][O_2]$
2. $1.1$ dm$^3$/mol · s
3. $R = 9.9 \times 10^{-4}$ mol/dm$^3$ · s
4. a. right
   b. left
   c. left
   d. no change
   e. right
   f. left
   g. right
   h. left
   i. right
   j. left
   k. right
   l. no change
   m. left
   n. no change

5. 217
6. $0.0313M$
7. a. $K_{eq} = \dfrac{[CH_3OH]}{[CO][H_2]^2}$

   b. $K_{eq} = \dfrac{[CH_4][H_2O]}{[CO][H_2]^3}$

   c. $K_{eq} = \dfrac{[N_2]^2[H_2O]^6}{[NH_3]^4[O_2]^3}$

   d. $K_{eq} = \dfrac{[CO_2]^2}{[CO]^2[O_2]}$

8. 0.113
9. $4.52 \times 10^{-3}M$
10. $G = 26.4$ kJ
11. $K_{eq} = 0.461$

## CHAPTER REVIEW PROBLEMS

1. a. $K_{eq} = \dfrac{[N_2O_4]}{[NO_2]^2}$

   b. $K_{eq} = \dfrac{[CH_3OH]}{[H_2]^2[CO]}$

   c. $K_{eq} = \dfrac{[O_2]^5[NH_3]^4}{[NO]^4[H_2O]^6}$

   d. $K_{eq} = \dfrac{[H_2]^4[CS_2]}{[H_2S]^2[CH_4]}$

2. $R = k[A]^2$
3. $4.5 \times 10^{-4}$ mol/dm$^3$ · s

4. a. $R = k[C_2H_4O]$
   b. $0.024\ 44$ s$^{-1}$
5. a. right
   b. right
   c. left
   d. no change
6. $0.4999M$
7. 35.9
8. $8.00 \times 10^{24}$
9. $+95.0$ kJ

# CHAPTER 24 _____

## PROBLEMS

1. a. HCN, acid
   $SO_4^{2-}$, base
   $HSO_4^-$, conjugate acid
   $CN^-$, conjugate base

   b. $CH_3COO^-$, base
   $H_2S$, acid
   $CH_3COOH$, conjugate acid
   $HS^-$, conjugate base

2. a. $Al^{3+}$ Lewis acid
   $H_2O$ Lewis base

   b. $NH_3$ Lewis base
   $Ag^+$ Lewis acid

3. a. hydrochloric acid    g. nitrous acid
   b. nitric acid    h. hypochlorous acid
   c. sulfuric acid    i. sulfurous acid
   d. phosphoric acid    j. carbonic acid
   e. chloric acid    k. chlorous acid
   f. acetic acid    l. perchloric acid

4. a. sodium chlorate, chloric acid
   b. iron(II) perchlorate, perchloric acid
   c. ammonium bromate, bromic acid
   d. magnesium iodate, iodic acid
   e. manganese(II) iodide, hydroiodic acid
   f. barium nitrate, nitric acid
   g. lead(II) chloride, hydrochloric acid
   h. mercury(II) bromate, bromic acid
   i. zinc sulfate, sulfuric acid
   j. calcium hypochlorite, hypochlorous acid

5. a. $(NH_4)_2SO_4$, $H_2SO_4$    e. $Hg_2(BrO_3)_2$, $HBrO_3$
   b. $Ba(ClO)_2$, $HClO$    f. $Cr(NO_3)_3$, $HNO_3$
   c. $LiClO_3$, $HClO_3$    g. $MgCl_2$, $HCl$
   d. $CoSO_3$, $H_2SO_3$    h. $KClO_4$, $HClO_4$

6. a. $2Na + H_2O \rightarrow 2Na^+ + H_2 + 2OH^-$
   b. $6H^+ + 2PO_4^{3-} + 3Mg^{2+} + 6OH^- \rightarrow Mg_3(PO_4)_2 + 6H_2O$
   c. $Ba^{2+} + SO_4^{2-} \rightarrow BaSO_4$
   d. $3Mg^{2+} + 6OH^- + 6NH_4^+ + 2PO_4^{3-} \rightarrow Mg_3(PO_4)_2 + 3NH_3 + 6H_2O$
   e. $2Fe^{3+} + 3S^{2-} \rightarrow Fe_2S_3$

7. a. $1.85 \times 10^{-5}$
   b. $1.80 \times 10^{-5}$
   c. $6.16 \times 10^{-10}$

8. $[H_3O^+] = 4.20 \times 10^{-3}M$
   $[CH_3COO^-] = 4.20 \times 10^{-3}M$
   $[CH_3COOH] = 0.996M$
9. a. $7.90 \times 10^{-4}$      c. $1.85 \times 10^{-5}$
   b. $1.80 \times 10^{-4}$      d. $6.05 \times 10^{-10}$
10. 19.8% (using quadratic)
11. 0.001 36%
12. $4.69 \times 10^{-5}M$
13. $0.0352M$
14. a. $0.0346M$
    b. $0.0292M$

## CHAPTER REVIEW PROBLEMS

1. a. produces $H^+$ ($H_3O^+$) ions in water solution
   b. proton donor
   c. electron-pair acceptor
2. a. hydrobromic acid      g. hydroiodic acid
   b. nitrous acid      h. acetic acid
   c. sulfuric acid      i. arsenic acid
   d. hydrosulfuric acid      j. iodic acid
   e. phosphorous acid      k. silicic acid
   f. chloric acid      l. carbonic acid
3. a. $Mg(OH)_2$, base      d. $H_2SO_3$, acid
   b. HCl, acid      e. NaClO, salt
   c. $Zn(NO_3)_2$, salt      f. KOH, base
4. a. $HSO_4^-$, acid      b. $OH^-$, base
      $Cl^-$, base            $CH_3COOH$, acid
      $SO_4^{2-}$, conjugate base    $CH_3COO^-$, conjugate base
      HCl, conjugate acid       $H_2O$, conjugate acid
5. $Ni^{2+}$ Lewis acid
   $H_2O$ Lewis base
6. a. $H^+(aq) + OH^-(aq) \rightarrow H_2O(l)$
   b. $2K(cr) + 2H_2O(l) \rightarrow 2K^+(aq) + 2OH^-(aq) + H_2(g)$
   c. $Ag^+(aq) + Cl^-(aq) \rightarrow AgCl(cr)$
7. $3.57 \times 10^{-5}M = [H_3O^+]$
   $3.57 \times 10^{-5}M = [H_2BO_3^-]$
   $1.750M = [H_3BO_3]$
8. $1.02 \times 10^{-6}M$ (Simplified answer because the $[H_3O^+]$ from water is significant for such a weak acid.)
9. $1.77 \times 10^{-5}$
10. $4.32 \times 10^{-7}$
11. $3.03 \times 10^{-5}$
12. 0.008 12%
13. $3.96 \times 10^{-5}M$
14. $0.0317M$

# CHAPTER 25

## PROBLEMS

1. $1.50 \times 10^{-16}$
2. $4.90 \times 10^{-9}$
3. $4.14 \times 10^{-11}$
4. $2.96 \times 10^{-16}$
5. $3.63 \times 10^{-9}$
6. $2.82 \times 10^{-13}$
7. $2.51 \times 10^{-18}M$
8. $3.97 \times 10^{-4}M$
9. $2.61 \times 10^{-9}M$
10. $1.51 \times 10^{-3}M$
11. $0.0699$ g $SrC_2O_4/dm^3$, $0.696$ g $PbI_2/dm^3$
12. no, $1.08 \times 10^{-30} < 4.07 \times 10^{-28}$
13. no, $2.50 \times 10^{-7} < 1.05 \times 10^{-6}$
14. yes, $2.3 \times 10^{-11} > 9.00 \times 10^{-12}$
15. a. pH 4.0, pOH 10
    b. pH 12.3, pOH 1.74
    c. pH 9.21, pOH 4.79
    d. pH 1.39, pOH 12.6
16. a. $1.91 \times 10^{-4}M$
    b. $2.24 \times 10^{-7}M$
    c. $1.00 \times 10^{-2}M$
    d. $6.3 \times 10^{-9}M$
17. a. $1.00 \times 10^{-11}M$
    b. $1.78 \times 10^{-10}M$
    c. $3.2 \times 10^{-9}M$
    d. $7.9 \times 10^{-12}M$
18. a. pH 11.4, pOH 2.6      d. pH 1.3, pOH 12.7
    b. pH 2.3, pOH 11.7      e. pH 12.5, pOH 1.5
    c. pH 0.82, pOH 13.2     f. pH 10.2, pOH 3.8
19. $4.0 \times 10^{-8}M$
20. $6.3 \times 10^{-5}M$
21. pH $= 4.96$
22. pH $= 7.64$
23. a. $0.300M$ NaOH        c. $2.50M$ $HNO_3$
    b. $15.0$ cm$^3$ acid      d. $17.5$ cm$^3$ base
24. $4.80M$ NaOH
25. $21.4$ cm$^3$ acid
26. $2.01M$ $NH_3(aq)$
27. $0.600N$ $H_3PO_4$, $0.200M$ $H_3PO_4$
28. a. trial 1 $0.880N$, b. $52.8$ g/dm$^3$
       trial 2 $0.930N$,     $55.8$ g/dm$^3$
       trial 3 $0.908N$,     $54.5$ g/dm$^3$

# CHAPTER REVIEW PROBLEMS

1.  a. $1.53 \times 10^{-72}$
    b. $1.00 \times 10^{-25}$
2.  a. $2.51 \times 10^{-17}M$
    b. $1.41 \times 10^{-5}M$
3.  1.47 g $CaF_2$/100.0 $dm^3$
4.  yes, $4.38 \times 10^{-4} > 9.00 \times 10^{-12}$
5.  AgI precipitates first, $1.50 \times 10^{-13} < 1.56 \times 10^{-8}$

6.

| | pOH | $[H_3O^+]$ | $[OH^-]$ |
|---|---|---|---|
| a. | 11.1 | $1.3 \times 10^{-3}M$ | $7.9 \times 10^{-12}M$ |
| b. | 10.5 | $3.2 \times 10^{-4}M$ | $3.2 \times 10^{-11}M$ |
| c. | 7.8 | $6.3 \times 10^{-7}M$ | $1.6 \times 10^{-8}M$ |
| d. | 5.5 | $3.2 \times 10^{-9}M$ | $3.2 \times 10^{-6}M$ |
| e. | 11.0 | $1.0 \times 10^{-3}M$ | $1.0 \times 10^{-11}M$ |
| f. | 9.8 | $6.3 \times 10^{-5}M$ | $1.6 \times 10^{-10}M$ |
| g. | 6.2 | $1.6 \times 10^{-8}M$ | $6.3 \times 10^{-7}M$ |
| h. | 3.5 | $3.2 \times 10^{-11}M$ | $3.2 \times 10^{-4}M$ |

7.

| | pOH | $[H_3O^+]$ | $[OH^-]$ |
|---|---|---|---|
| a. | 13.0 | $1.00 \times 10^{-1}M$ | $1.00 \times 10^{-13}M$ |
| b. | 11.1 | $1.26 \times 10^{-3}M$ | $7.94 \times 10^{-12}M$ |
| c. | 2.90 | $7.94 \times 10^{-12}M$ | $1.26 \times 10^{-3}M$ |
| d. | 12.8 | $0.0631M$ | $1.58 \times 10^{-13}M$ |
| e. | 5.60 | $3.98 \times 10^{-9}M$ | $2.51 \times 10^{-6}M$ |
| f. | 1.00 | $1.00 \times 10^{-13}M$ | $1.00 \times 10^{-1}M$ |

8.  4.84
9.  a. 6.00 $cm^3$
    b. 20.0 $cm^3$
    c. 8.80 $cm^3$
    d. 54.0 $cm^3$
10. $0.157M$
11. 5.69 $cm^3$
12. 6.00 $cm^3$
13. $0.667N$, $0.333M$
14. $0.980N$
15. 0.76 $g/dm^3$

# CHAPTER 26

## PROBLEMS

1.  a. 3+       e. 3+
    b. 2+       f. 6+
    c. 7+       g. 4+
    d. 5+       h. 5+
2.  $2Cr(cr) + 3Sn^{4+}(aq) \rightarrow 2Cr^{3+}(aq) + 3Sn^{2+}(aq)$
3.  $2Al(cr) + 6H^+(aq) \rightarrow 2Al^{3+}(aq) + 3H_2(g)$

4. $Zn(cr) + 2Ag^+(aq) \rightarrow Zn^{2+}(aq) + 2Ag(cr)$
5. $6NO_3^-(aq) + S(cr) + 6H^+(aq) \rightarrow 6NO_2(g) + H_2SO_4(aq) + 2H_2O(l)$
6. $Br_2(l) + SO_3^{2-}(aq) + 2OH^-(aq) \rightarrow 2Br^-(aq) + SO_4^{2-}(aq) + H_2O(l)$
7. $5Fe^{2+}(aq) + MnO_4^-(aq) + 8H^+(aq) \rightarrow Mn^{2+}(aq) + 5Fe^{3+}(aq) + 4H_2O(l)$
8. $Cu(cr) + SO_4^{2-}(aq) + 4H^+(aq) \rightarrow Cu^{2+}(aq) + SO_2(g) + 2H_2O(l)$
9. $3Cu(cr) + 2NO_3^-(aq) + 8H^+(aq) \rightarrow 3Cu^{2+}(aq) + 2NO(g) + 4H_2O(l)$
10. $2MnO_4^-(aq) + 5S^{2-}(aq) + 16H^+(aq) \rightarrow 2Mn^{2+}(aq) + 5S(cr) + 8H_2O(l)$
11. $CuS(cr) + 2NO_3^-(aq) + 4H^+(aq) \rightarrow Cu^{2+}(aq) + S(cr) + 2NO_2(g) + 2H_2O(l)$
12. $2NO_2(g) + ClO^-(aq) + 2OH^-(aq) \rightarrow 2NO_3^-(aq) + Cl^-(aq) + H_2O(l)$
13. $6Fe^{2+}(aq) + Cr_2O_7^{2-}(aq) + 14H^+(aq) \rightarrow 6Fe^{3+}(aq) + 2Cr^{3+}(aq) + 7H_2O(l)$
14. $2MnO_4(aq) + 10Cl^-(aq) + 16H^+(aq) \rightarrow 2Mn^{2+}(aq) + 5Cl_2(g) + 8H_2O(l)$
15. $6IO_3^-(aq) + 5H_2S(g) + 4OH^-(aq) \rightarrow 3I_2(g) + 5SO_3^{2-}(aq) + 7H_2O(l)$
16. $H_2SeO_3(aq) + 4Br^-(aq) + 4H^+(aq) \rightarrow Se(cr) + 2Br_2(g) + 3H_2O(l)$
17. $BrO_3^-(aq) + 2MnO_2(cr) + 2OH^-(aq) \rightarrow Br^-(aq) + 2MnO_4^-(aq) + H_2O(l)$
18. $3H_2S(g) + 2NO_3^-(aq) + 2H^+(aq) \rightarrow 3S(cr) + 2NO(g) + 4H_2O(l)$

## CHAPTER REVIEW PROBLEMS

1.  a. 4+
    b. 3+
    c. 1+
    d. 5+
    e. 5+
    f. 5+
2. $3AsH_3(g) + 4ClO_3^-(aq) \rightarrow 3H_3AsO_4(aq) + 4Cl^-(aq)$
3. $2HNO_2(aq) + 2I^-(aq) + 2H^+ \rightarrow 2NO(g) + I_2(g) + 2H_2O(l)$
4. $2MnO_4^-(aq) + 5H_2O_2(aq) + 16H^+(aq) \rightarrow 2Mn^{2+}(aq) + 5O_2(g) + 8H_2O(l)$
5. $2MnO_2(cr) + ClO_3^-(aq) + 2OH^-(aq) \rightarrow 2MnO_4^-(aq) + Cl^-(aq) + H_2O(l)$
6. $6Br_2(l) + 12OH^-(aq) \rightarrow 10Br^-(aq) + 2BrO_3^-(aq) + 6H_2O(l)$
7. $3N_2O_4(aq) + Br^-(aq) + 6OH^-(aq) \rightarrow 6NO_2^-(aq) + BrO_3^-(aq) + 3H_2O(l)$
8. $3H_2PO_2^-(aq) + 2SbO_2^-(aq) + OH^-(aq) \rightarrow 3HPO_3^{2-}(aq) + 2Sb(cr) + 2H_2O(l)$
9. $2CrO_2^-(aq) + 3ClO^-(aq) + 2OH^-(aq) \rightarrow 2CrO_4^{2-}(aq) + 3Cl^-(aq) + H_2O(l)$
10. $2Cu(OH)_2(cr) + HPO_3^{2-}(aq) \rightarrow Cu_2O(cr) + PO_4^{3-}(aq) + 2H_2O(l) + H^+(aq)$
11. $3HS^-(aq) + IO_3^-(aq) + 3H^+(aq) \rightarrow I^-(aq) + 3S(cr) + 3H_2O(l)$
12. $N_2O(g) + 2ClO^-(aq) + 2OH^-(aq) \rightarrow 2Cl^-(aq) + 2NO_2^-(aq) + H_2O(l)$
13. $H_2SO_3(aq) + MnO_2(cr) \rightarrow SO_4^{2-}(aq) + Mn^{2+}(aq) + H_2O(l)$
14. $IO_4^-(aq) + 7I^-(aq) + 8H^+(aq) \rightarrow 4I_2(g) + 4H_2O(l)$
15. $2CrO_4^{2-}(aq) + 6I^-(aq) + 16H^+(aq) \rightarrow 2Cr^{3+}(aq) + 3I_2(g) + 8H_2O(l)$

# CHAPTER 27 ⎯⎯⎯⎯⎯⎯⎯⎯⎯⎯⎯⎯⎯⎯⎯⎯⎯⎯⎯

## PROBLEMS

1.  a. +0.66 V
    b. +1.66 V
    c. +0.54 V
    d. +0.74 V
    e. +1.21 V
    f. +0.13 V
2.  a. Zn
    b. Pb
    c. Zn
    d. Pb
    e. $Pb^{2+}$(aq)
    f. $Zn(cr) \rightarrow Zn^{2+}(aq) + 2e^-$
    g. +0.63 V

3.  a. Au
    b. Al
    c. Al
    d. Au
    e. Al(cr)
    f. $Au^{3+}$(aq) + $3e^- \rightarrow$ Au(cr)
    g. +3.16 V
4.  846 s
5.  0.726 A
6.  6.70 A
7.  223 g

## CHAPTER REVIEW PROBLEMS

1.  a. +0.59 V, will occur
    b. −0.29 V, will not as written
    c. −0.34 V, will not as written
    d. +0.90 V, will occur
    e. −0.63 V, will not as written
2.  +0.74 V
3.  $Cr(cr) \rightarrow Cr^{2+}(aq) + 2e^-$
4.  0.373 mol $e^-$

5.  $2.90 \times 10^4$ s
6.  3.29 g Cu
7.  164 g Zn
8.  $1.40 \times 10^2$ g Cd
9.  216 g
10. 5.97 mol Na
11. 268 s
12. 0.721 A

# CHAPTER 28 ⎯⎯⎯⎯⎯⎯⎯⎯⎯⎯⎯⎯⎯⎯⎯⎯⎯⎯⎯

## PROBLEMS

1.  a. $^{208}_{82}Pb$
    b. $^{210}_{82}Pb$
    c. $^{235}_{92}U$
    d. $^{14}_{6}C$
    e. $^{5}_{2}He$
    f. $^{40}_{19}K$
    g. $^{8}_{3}Li$
    h. $^{238}_{92}U$
2.  a. $^{7}_{3}Li + ^{2}_{1}H \rightarrow 2^{4}_{2}He$
    b. $^{3}_{1}H + ^{2}_{1}H \rightarrow ^{4}_{2}He + ^{1}_{0}n$
    c. $^{14}_{6}C \rightarrow ^{14}_{7}N + ^{0}_{-1}e$

d. $^{9}_{4}Be + ^{4}_{2}He \rightarrow ^{12}_{6}C + ^{1}_{0}n$
e. $^{14}_{7}N + ^{4}_{2}He \rightarrow ^{18}_{8}O + ^{0}_{+1}e$
f. $^{26}_{12}Mg + ^{1}_{0}n \rightarrow ^{27}_{11}Na + ^{0}_{+1}e$
g. $^{59}_{27}Co + ^{2}_{1}H \rightarrow ^{61}_{27}Co + ^{0}_{+1}e$
3.  a. $^{214}_{82}Pb \rightarrow ^{214}_{83}Bi + ^{0}_{-1}e$
    $^{214}_{83}Bi \rightarrow ^{214}_{84}Po + ^{0}_{-1}e$
    $^{214}_{84}Po \rightarrow ^{210}_{82}Pb + ^{4}_{2}He$
4.  9.6 minutes
5.  $7.3 \times 10^{22}$ atoms
6.  80.7 days

## CHAPTER REVIEW PROBLEMS

1. a. $^{22}_{11}Na \rightarrow ^{22}_{12}Mg + ^{0}_{-1}e$, beta
   b. $^{66}_{29}Cu \rightarrow ^{66}_{30}Zn + ^{0}_{-1}e$, beta
   c. $^{208}_{84}Po \rightarrow ^{204}_{82}Pb + ^{4}_{2}He$, alpha
   d. $^{27}_{14}Si \rightarrow ^{27}_{13}Al + ^{0}_{+1}e$, positron
2. a. $^{27}_{13}Al + ^{2}_{1}H \rightarrow ^{25}_{12}Mg + ^{4}_{2}He$
   b. $^{45}_{21}Sc + ^{1}_{0}n \rightarrow ^{42}_{19}K + ^{4}_{2}He$
   c. $^{63}_{29}Cu + ^{1}_{1}H \rightarrow ^{63}_{30}Zn + ^{1}_{0}n$
   d. $^{1}_{0}n + ^{235}_{92}U \rightarrow ^{136}_{53}I + ^{96}_{39}Y + 4^{1}_{0}n$

3. 244 years
4. 4860 years
5. $6.08 \times 10^{22}$ atoms

# CHAPTER 29

## PROBLEMS

1. a. 3,4-dimethylhexane
   b. 2,2,3-trimethylpentane
   c. 2,2-dimethylbutane
   d. 3,3-diethylhexane
   e. 2,3,4-trimethylhexane
   f. 3,4,5-trimethylheptane
   g. 3,4,5-trimethylheptane
   h. 2,3,4-trimethylhexane
2. a. 2-methylpentane
   b. 2-methylbutane
   c. 2,3-dimethylpentane
   d. 3-ethylpentane
   e. 2,4-dimethylpentane
   f. 2,3-dimethylpentane
   g. 3-methylpentane
   h. 2,3-dimethylpentane
3. a. heptane
   b. 2,4-dimethylpentane
   c. 2,2,3-trimethylbutane
   d. 
$$\begin{array}{c} CH_3 \quad CH_3 \\ | \quad\quad | \\ CH_3CH-CHCH_2CH_3 \end{array}$$
   e. 
$$\begin{array}{c} CH_3 \\ | \\ CH_3CH_2CCH_2CH_3 \\ | \\ CH_3 \end{array}$$
   f. 3-methylhexane
   g. 2,2-dimethylpentane
   h. 
$$\begin{array}{c} CH_3 \\ | \\ CH_3CHCH_2CH_2CH_2CH_3 \end{array}$$

   i. 
$$\begin{array}{c} CH_2CH_3 \\ | \\ CH_3CH_2CHCH_2CH_3 \end{array}$$
4. a. 2-pentene
   b. 1,2-dimethylbenzene
   c. cyclohexane
   d. phenylethyne
   e. cyclobutene
   f. 1-propyne
5. a. $CH_3CH_2C{\equiv}CCH_2CH_2CH_3$
   b. 
$$\begin{array}{c} CH \\ /\!\!/ \; \backslash \\ CH \quad CH_2 \\ | \quad\quad | \\ CH_2 - CH_2 \end{array}$$
   c. 
$$\begin{array}{c} CH_3 \\ | \\ CH_3-C-\!\!-\!\!-CHCH_2CH_2CH_3 \\ | \\ CH_3 \end{array}$$
   d. $CH_2{=}CHCH{=}CH_2$
   e. 
   f. 
$$\begin{array}{c} CH_3 \\ | \\ CH_3C{=}CHCHCH_3 \\ | \\ CH_3 \end{array}$$

6.  a. 1-chloropentane
    b. 1-chloro-3-methylbutane

    c.
$$CH_3\overset{\overset{\displaystyle Cl}{|}}{C}HCH_2CH_2CH_3$$

    d.
$$CH_3\overset{\overset{\displaystyle Cl}{|}}{\underset{\underset{\displaystyle CH_3}{|}}{C}}CH_2CH_3$$

    e. 3-chloropentane
    f. 2-chloro-3-methylbutane

    g.
$$ClCH_2\overset{\overset{\displaystyle CH_3}{|}}{C}HCH_2CH_3$$

    h.
$$ClCH_2\overset{\overset{\displaystyle CH_3}{|}}{\underset{\underset{\displaystyle CH_3}{|}}{C}}CH_3$$

7.  a. 1-bromo-3-ethyl-3-methylpentane
    b. 3-methyl-1, 4-pentadiene
    c. 3,3-dimethyl-1-butene
    d. chlorobenzene
    e. 2-pentene
    f. 2-methyl-2-butene
    g. 1-butene
    h. 4-methyl-2-pentene
    i. 2,3-dimethyl-2-pentene
    j. 2,4-dimethyl-1, 4-pentadiene
    k. 2,3,3-trimethyl-1, 4-hexadiene
    l. 1,4-dibromonaphthalene

8.  a. $CH_3CH_2CH{=}CHCH_2CH_2CH_3$

    b.

c. $HCCl_3$

    d.
$$CH_3\overset{\overset{\displaystyle Cl}{|}}{C}HCHCH_2CH_2CH_3$$

    e.
$$\begin{array}{c} CH \\ \diagup \diagdown\!\!\!= \\ CH_2 \quad CH \\ | \qquad | \\ CH = CH \end{array}$$

    f.

    g.

    h.
$$\underset{\underset{\displaystyle Br \quad CH_3}{|\qquad |}}{CH_3C{=}CCH_3}$$

# CHAPTER REVIEW PROBLEMS

1.  a.
$$CH_3CH_2\overset{\overset{\displaystyle Cl}{|}}{C}HCH_3$$

    b. $CH_3CH{=}CHCH_3$

    c.
$$CH_3\overset{\overset{\displaystyle CH_3}{|}}{C}H{-}\overset{\overset{\displaystyle CH_2CH_3}{|}}{C}HCH_2OH$$

    d.
$$CH_3\overset{\overset{\displaystyle CH_3}{|}}{\underset{\underset{\displaystyle CH_3}{|}}{C}}CH_2C\overset{\displaystyle O}{\diagup\!\!\diagup} \diagdown OH$$

e. 
$$CH_3CHCH_2 \overset{\overset{\displaystyle CH_3}{|}}{C}\overset{\overset{\displaystyle O}{\|}}{-}\overset{\overset{\displaystyle CH_3}{|}}{C}CH_2CH_3$$
$$\underset{\underset{\displaystyle CH_3}{|}}{}$$

m. 
$$CH_3CH_2\overset{\overset{\displaystyle Cl}{|}}{C}HCH_2\overset{\overset{\displaystyle CH_2CH_3}{|}}{C}H\overset{\overset{\displaystyle CH_3}{|}}{-}CH\overset{\overset{\displaystyle O}{\|}}{C}\overset{\diagdown}{OH}$$

f. $CH{\equiv}C(CH_2)_5C{\equiv}CH$

g. 

n. $CH_3CHCH_2CH_3$

h. $CH_3CH_2-O-$

i. $CH_3CH_2CH_2CH_2OH$

j. 
$$CH_3CH{=}\overset{\overset{\displaystyle CH_3}{|}}{C}CH_2CH_3$$

k. 
$$CH_3\overset{\overset{\displaystyle CH_3}{|}}{C}HCH_2\overset{\overset{\displaystyle O}{\|}}{C}HCH$$

o. Br— —OH

p. 
COOH
Br

l. 
$$CH_3CH\overset{\overset{\displaystyle CH_2CH_3}{|}}{-}C\overset{\overset{\displaystyle CH_2CH_3}{|}}{-}CHCH_2CH_3$$
$$\underset{\underset{\displaystyle CH_3}{|}\ \underset{\displaystyle OH}{|}\ \underset{\displaystyle CH_3}{|}}{}$$

2. a. 2-methyl-3-pentanol
   b. 2-methyl-3-pentanone
   c. 3-methyl-1-butene
   d. butanal
   e. 4,4-dimethyl-1-pentanol
   f. 3-methyl-1, 4-hexadiene-3-ol
3. a. 1-chloro-2-methylbutane
   b. 2,3,3-trimethyl-1-bromobutane
   c. bromocyclopropane
   d. 3-chloropentane
   e. 2-methyl-2-butanol
   f. 3-bromo-2-pentene
   g. butylamine
   h. propanamide
4. a. $CH_3CH_2OH$, ethanol; alcohol
      $CH_3OCH_3$, methoxymethane; ether

b. $CH_3CH_2CHO$, propanal; aldehyde

oxacyclobutane; ether

methyloxacyclopropane, ether

$$\overset{O}{\underset{\|}{}}$$
$CH_3CCH_3$, propanone; ketone

c. cyclopentane; cycloalkane

$CH_3CH{=}CHCH_2CH_3$, 2-pentene; alkene (and other isomers)

5. a. $CH_3C\overset{O}{\diagdown}H$

b. $CH_3\overset{O}{\underset{\|}{C}}CH_2CH_3$

c. $CH_3\overset{OH}{\underset{|}{C}}CH_3$ with $CH_3$ below

d. $CH_3C\overset{O}{\diagup}\diagdown OH$

e. $\overset{Ch_3}{\underset{|}{CH_3NCH_3}}$

f. $CH_2{=}CHCH_3$

g. $CH_3C{\equiv}CCH_2CH_3$

h. cyclobutane $H_2C-CH_2 \mid \mid H_2C-CH_2$

i. $NH_2{-}CH$ ... $CH_2{-}CH_2 / CH_2 \backslash CH_2{-}CH_2$

j. $\overset{NH_2}{\underset{|}{CH_3CHCH_2CH_2CH_3}}$

k. phenol with OH and NO2

l. COOH benzene with NO2

m. $CH_3C{\equiv}N$

n. $CH_2{=}CHC\overset{O}{\diagup}\diagdown OH$

# CHAPTER 30 _____

## PROBLEMS

1. $C_3H_8 + 5O_2 \rightarrow 3CO_2 + 4H_2O$

2. $CH_2CH_2 + Br_2 \rightarrow CH_2-CH_2$
   with $Br$ and $Br$ below the two carbons

3. $+ Cl_2 \rightarrow$ $-Cl + HCl$

4.
$$\underset{\phantom{CH_3CH_2CH_2}}{CH_3CH_2CH_2\overset{\displaystyle OH}{\underset{|}{C}}HCH_3} \rightarrow CH_3CH_2CH{=}CHCH_3 + H_2O$$

5.
$$CH_3CH_2\overset{\displaystyle O}{\overset{\|}{C}}-OH + CH_3CH_2-OH \rightarrow CH_3CH_2\overset{\displaystyle O}{\overset{\|}{C}}-O-CH_2CH_3 + H_2O$$

## CHAPTER REVIEW PROBLEMS

1.
$$CH_3CH{=}CHCH_3 + HI \rightarrow CH_3CH_2\overset{\displaystyle I}{\underset{|}{C}}HCH_3$$

2.
$$Br_2 + CH_2{=}CH_2 \rightarrow \overset{Br\quad Br}{\underset{|\quad\;\;|}{CH_2-CH_2}}$$

3.
$$CH_3CH_2CH_2CH_2CH_2-OH + H\overset{\displaystyle O}{\overset{\|}{C}}-OH \rightarrow$$
$$CH_3CH_2CH_2CH_2CH_2-O-\overset{\displaystyle O}{\overset{\|}{C}}H + H_2O$$

4. $2CH_3CH_3 + 7O_2 \rightarrow 4CO_2 + 6H_2O$

5. $CH_3CH_2CH_2CH_2CH_2-OH \rightarrow H_2O + CH_3CH_2CH_2CH{=}CH_2$

6. DNA is used to transfer genetic information to the next generation.

7. A nucleotide contains a nitrogen base, a sugar, and a phosphate group.

8. saponification

9. amino acids

10. Carbohydrates provide energy and raw materials for cellular activity.

11. Saturated fats contain only single C—C bonds and are usually solids at room temperature. Unsaturated fats contain at least one multiple C—C bond.

12. unsaturated

# INDEX

## A

**Acid,** 163–176, carboxylic, 223; nomenclature, 28, 164–165; polyprotic, 173–175; strength, 166, 180–184; theories, 163–164
**Actinides,** 69, 77
**Addition reaction,** 230
**Aldehyde,** 223
**Alkali metals,** 68, 75
**Alkaline earth metals,** 68, 76
**Alkanes,** 213–214
**Alkenes,** 218
**Alkynes,** 218
**Allotrope,** 76
**Alpha particles,** 207
**Amines,** 226
**Amino acid,** 232
**Amphoteric oxide,** 76
**Anhydrous substance,** 103
**Arrhenius theory,** 163
**Atomic mass,** 33; average, 59
**Atomic mass scale,** 33
**Atomic number,** 57–58
**Atomic orbital,** 61; filling diagrams, 64
**Atomic radius,** 71
**Atomic theories,** 57
**Average atomic mass,** 59
**Avogadro's number,** 34–35, 123–124

## B

**Barometer,** 97, 111
**Base,** 163–176; strength, 166, 180–184; theories, 163–164
**Battery,** 200–202
**Beta particles,** 207
**Binary compounds,** 23, 26–28

**Biomolecules,** 232–233
**Boiling point,** 107, 149, 150–151
**Bond,** 79–82; coordinate covalent, 93; covalent, 79; ionic, 79; length, 80–81; polar, 91–92
**Boyle's law,** 111–113
**Brønsted-Lowry theory,** 163
**Buffer,** 184–185

## C

**Carbohydrate,** 232
**Carboxyl group,** 223
**Carboxylic acids,** 223
**Catenation,** 76
**Chalcogen family,** 68
**Charles' law,** 115–116
**Chemical bonding,** see Bond
**Chemical change,** 20, 47, 49–52
**Chemical equations,** 47–52; balanced, 47–49; nuclear, 208–209
**Chemical formulas,** 23–32
**Chemical property,** 20
**Chemical reaction,** see Reaction
**Chemical symbol,** 23
**Coefficient,** 30
**Colligative properties,** 145, 149–154
**Combined gas law,** 117–119
**Compound,** 19; binary, 23, 26–28; naming, 26-29; organic, 76, 213–227; saturated, 213; unsaturated, 213
**Condensing point,** 107
**Conduction band,** 81
**Conversion factors,** 11
**Covalent bond,** 79
**Crystal,** 101–103
**Cycloalkanes,** 217

Physical change, 20
Physical property, 20
Polymer, 230
Pressure, 97–98, 106, 111–114; osmotic, 152–153; standard, 117
Principal quantum number, 61
Protein, 232

## Q

Quantum mechanics, 61
Quantum numbers, 61–63; principal, 61

## R

Radiation, types of, 207–208
Radioactive decay, 207
Reactant, limiting, 129–131
Reaction, 47–56; decomposition, 51; double displacement, 50; endothermic, 135; exothermic, 135; organic, 229–232; rate, 156–157; redox, 194–197; reversible, 155; single displacement, 49; spontaneous, 137–139
Reduction, 194
Resonance, 84–85
RNA, 233

## S

Salts, 165
Saponification, 231–232
Scientific notation, 13–16
Shielding effect, 73
SI, 7
Significant digits, 7–9
Single displacement reactions, 49
Skeleton equations, 47

Solid, amorphous, 101; polymorphous, 102
Solubility product constant, 177–180
Solute, 19, 143; moles of, 149
Solution, 19, 143–154; of electrolytes, 177–192; normality of, 189; standard, 143, 186
Solvent, 19, 143
Specific heat, 21, 108
Specific rate constant, 156
State, changes of, 106–110
Stoichiometry, 52
STP, 117, 131
Substance, 19
Substitution reaction, 229

## T

Temperature, 7, 107–108; Kelvin, 114–115; standard, 117
Titration, 186–191
Transition element, 69, 76–77
Transmutation, 209

## U

Unit cell, 101

## V

Van der Waals forces, 92
Variables, 4
Voltaic cell, 200–202
Volume, 126–129, 131–133

## W

Water of hydration, 39, 103
Weight, 7

# International Atomic Masses

| Element | Symbol | Atomic number | Atomic mass | Element | Symbol | Atomic number | Atomic mass |
|---|---|---|---|---|---|---|---|
| Actinium | Ac | 89 | 227.0278* | Neon | Ne | 10 | 20.179 |
| Aluminum | Al | 13 | 26.98154 | Neptunium | Np | 93 | 237.0482 |
| Americium | Am | 95 | 243.0614* | Nickel | Ni | 28 | 58.69 |
| Antimony | Sb | 51 | 121.75 | Niobium | Nb | 41 | 92.9064 |
| Argon | Ar | 18 | 39.948 | Nitrogen | N | 7 | 14.0067 |
| Arsenic | As | 33 | 74.9216 | Nobelium | No | 102 | 259.1009* |
| Astatine | At | 85 | 209.9871* | Osmium | Os | 76 | 190.2 |
| Barium | Ba | 56 | 137.33 | Oxygen | O | 8 | 15.9994 |
| Berkelium | Bk | 97 | 247.0703* | Palladium | Pd | 46 | 106.42 |
| Beryllium | Be | 4 | 9.01218 | Phosphorus | P | 15 | 30.97376 |
| Bismuth | Bi | 83 | 208.9804 | Platinum | Pt | 78 | 195.08 |
| Boron | B | 5 | 10.811 | Plutonium | Pu | 94 | 244.0642* |
| Bromine | Br | 35 | 79.904 | Polonium | Po | 84 | 208.9824* |
| Cadmium | Cd | 48 | 112.41 | Potassium | K | 19 | 39.0983 |
| Calcium | Ca | 20 | 40.078 | Praseodymium | Pr | 59 | 140.9077 |
| Californium | Cf | 98 | 251.0796* | Promethium | Pm | 61 | 144.9128* |
| Carbon | C | 6 | 12.011 | Protactinium | Pa | 91 | 231.0359* |
| Cerium | Ce | 58 | 140.12 | Radium | Ra | 88 | 226.0254 |
| Cesium | Cs | 55 | 132.9054 | Radon | Rn | 86 | 222.0176* |
| Chlorine | Cl | 17 | 35.453 | Rhenium | Re | 75 | 186.207 |
| Chromium | Cr | 24 | 51.9961 | Rhodium | Rh | 45 | 102.9055 |
| Cobalt | Co | 27 | 58.9332 | Rubidium | Rb | 37 | 85.4678 |
| Copper | Cu | 29 | 63.546 | Ruthenium | Ru | 44 | 101.07 |
| Curium | Cm | 96 | 247.0703* | Samarium | Sm | 62 | 150.36 |
| Dysprosium | Dy | 66 | 162.50 | Scandium | Sc | 21 | 44.95591 |
| Einsteinium | Es | 99 | 252.0828* | Selenium | Se | 34 | 78.96 |
| Erbium | Er | 68 | 167.26 | Silicon | Si | 14 | 28.0855 |
| Europium | Eu | 63 | 151.96 | Silver | Ag | 47 | 107.8682 |
| Fermium | Fm | 100 | 257.0951* | Sodium | Na | 11 | 22.98977 |
| Fluorine | F | 9 | 18.998403 | Strontium | Sr | 38 | 87.62 |
| Francium | Fr | 87 | 223.0197* | Sulfur | S | 16 | 32.066 |
| Gadolinium | Gd | 64 | 157.25 | Tantalum | Ta | 73 | 180.9479 |
| Gallium | Ga | 31 | 69.723 | Technetium | Tc | 43 | 97.9072* |
| Germanium | Ge | 32 | 72.59 | Tellurium | Te | 52 | 127.60 |
| Gold | Au | 79 | 196.9665 | Terbium | Tb | 65 | 158.9254 |
| Hafnium | Hf | 72 | 178.49 | Thallium | Tl | 81 | 204.383 |
| Helium | He | 2 | 4.002602 | Thorium | Th | 90 | 232.0381 |
| Holmium | Ho | 67 | 164.9304 | Thulium | Tm | 69 | 168.9342 |
| Hydrogen | H | 1 | 1.00794 | Tin | Sn | 50 | 118.710 |
| Indium | In | 49 | 114.82 | Titanium | Ti | 22 | 47.88 |
| Iodine | I | 53 | 126.9045 | Tungsten | W | 74 | 183.85 |
| Iridium | Ir | 77 | 192.22 | Unnilennium† | Une | 109 | 266* |
| Iron | Fe | 26 | 55.847 | Unnilhexium† | Unh | 106 | 263* |
| Krypton | Kr | 36 | 83.80 | Unniloctium† | Uno | 108 | 265* |
| Lanthanum | La | 57 | 138.9055 | Unnilpentium† | Unp | 105 | 262* |
| Lawrencium | Lr | 103 | 260.1054* | Unnilquadium† | Unq | 104 | 261* |
| Lead | Pb | 82 | 207.2 | Unnilseptium† | Uns | 107 | 262* |
| Lithium | Li | 3 | 6.941 | Uranium | U | 92 | 238.0289 |
| Lutetium | Lu | 71 | 174.967 | Vanadium | V | 23 | 50.9415 |
| Magnesium | Mg | 12 | 24.305 | Xenon | Xe | 54 | 131.29 |
| Manganese | Mn | 25 | 54.9380 | Ytterbium | Yb | 70 | 173.04 |
| Mendelevium | Md | 101 | 258.0986* | Yttrium | Y | 39 | 88.9059 |
| Mercury | Hg | 80 | 200.59 | Zinc | Zn | 30 | 65.39 |
| Molybdenum | Mo | 42 | 95.94 | Zirconium | Zr | 40 | 91.224 |
| Neodymium | Nd | 60 | 144.24 | | | | |

*The mass of the isotope with the longest known half-life.

†Names for elements 104-109 have been approved for temporary use by the IUPAC. The USSR has proposed Kurchatovium (Ku) for element 104, and Bohrium (Bh) for element 105. The United States has proposed Rutherfordium (Rf) for element 104, and Hahnium (Ha) for element 105.